HANDBOOK OF

INDUSTRIAL METROLOGY

A PUBLICATION IN THE A.S.T.M.E.
MANUFACTURING ENGINEERING SERIES

PRENTICE-HALL INTERNATIONAL, INC. *London*
PRENTICE-HALL OF AUSTRALIA, PTY. LTD. *Sydney*
PRENTICE-HALL OF CANADA, LTD. *Toronto*
PRENTICE-HALL OF INDIA (PRIVATE) LTD. *New Delhi*
PRENTICE-HALL OF JAPAN, INC. *Tokyo*

HANDBOOK OF

INDUSTRIAL METROLOGY

A REFERENCE BOOK ON PRINCIPLES, TECHNIQUES, AND INSTRU-
MENTATION DESIGN AND APPLICATION FOR PHYSICAL MEASURE-
MENTS IN THE MANUFACTURING INDUSTRIES

Prepared Under Policy Supervision of

PUBLICATIONS COMMITTEE

AMERICAN SOCIETY OF TOOL AND MANUFACTURING ENGINEERS

John W. Greve
Editor Text and Handbooks

Frank W. Wilson
Senior Staff Editor

PRENTICE-HALL, INC.
Englewood Cliffs, New Jersey

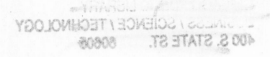

Library of Congress Catalog Card Number: 67–12084
C–37850

Current Printing (last digit):
10 9 8 7 6 5 4 3 2 1

MEMBERS OF THE
ASTME PUBLICATIONS COMMITTEE
(For the Society Year 1966–1967)

LIST OF CONTRIBUTORS

CHARLES O. BADGETT, Technical Programs Manager,
Industrial Nucleonics Corporation

CORTLAND A. BASSETT, General Sales Manager,
The L. S. Starrett Company

C. E. BLANCHARD, Superintendent-Gages
Pratt & Whitney Company, Inc.

JOHN E. BOBBIN, Manager, Applied Research, Ultrasonics Testing Division
Branson Instruments, Inc.

HENRY L. BOPPEL, Works Manager
The Sheffield Corporation

THEODORE N. BUSCH, Vice President
Dundick Corporation

HENRY R. CHOPE, Executive Vice President
Industrial Nucleonics Corporation

HUGH G. COLLINS, Divisional Sales Engineer, Webber Gage Division
The L. S. Starrett Company

WILLIAM J. DARMODY, Technical Consultant
The Sheffield Corporation

CHARLES H. GOOD, Sales Manager, Micrometrical Division
The Bendix Corporation

EUGENE V. GRUMMAN, Chief Experimental Engineer
The Bullard Company

L. O. HEINOLD, JR., Manager-Sales Engineering
Federal Products Corporation

RUSSELL F. HOLMES, Technical Assistant to the Director
Engineering Standards, Engineering Staff, Technical Center
General Motors Corporation

PHILIP KISSAM, Professor of Civil Engineering,
School of Engineering and Applied Science
Princeton University

HARRY H. KU, Mathematical Statistician, Statistical Engineering Laboratory
Institute for Basic Standards
National Bureau of Standards

CASIMIR S. KOPEC, Mechanical Engineer, Metrology Division
Institute for Basic Standards
National Bureau of Standards

MAURICE K. LAUFER, Physical Standards Division
Sandia Corporation

ERWIN G. LOEWEN, Head, Metrology Research and Development
Bausch & Lamb, Incorporated

ALVIN G. MCNISH, Chief, Metrology Division
    Institute for Basic Standards
    National Bureau of Standards

JULIAN C. MOODY, Physical Standards Division
    Sandia Corporation

STUART L. NISBETT, Assistant Professor, Process Engineering Department
    General Motors Institute

WAYNE G. NORTON, Vice President and General Manager
    Optical Gaging Products, Inc.

W. RICHARD STRUWIN, Senior Specialist, Scientific Facilities
    General Motors Institute

JAY E. WATSON, Chief Engineer, Conventional Gages
    Pratt & Whitney Company, Inc.

THEODORE R. YOUNG, Chief, Length Section, Metrology Division
    Institute for Basic Standards
    National Bureau of Standards

PREFACE

Thinking for this book started to crystallize with a conference at the National Bureau of Standards three years ago. We had able assistance from Irvin Fullmer and Alvin McNish of the Bureau, plus several educators from George Washington University, which then, so far as known, was the only American graduate school with a full metrology course. The meeting minutes state these desirable objectives:

"The group consensus seemed to focus upon a reference book or treatise that would, in an orderly and systematic manner, present the theory and principles of measurement by mechanical, electrical or electronic, optical and any and all other significant means. Data would be characterized by established research findings, typically presented in the form of equations, graphs, and tables. Textual treatment should be within the scope of the average engineer's (not specialist's) comprehension."

We believe the contributors to this book have accomplished those objectives ably. They have done more. They have added breadth to the depth of the original concept, and joined both with the cohesive bond of practical application.

The first four chapters set the groundwork for truly understanding metrology, by defining its nature, its principles, and the mathematical concepts and standards that govern it.

The next eleven chapters cover, with minor exceptions, the entire range of instruments, tools, and machines used in making measurements by all physical means. The emphasis is upon proper and efficient application. There is little concern with manipulations; suppliers' instruction books take care of that.

The last chapter of the book does a critically necessary job. Measurements made in the manufacturing industries, however precise and accurate, however "scientific" or ingenious, are not an end in themselves. Speaking of all the preceding book chapters, the author says, "All this impressive array of data on the principles and tools of measurement, for effective use, needs to be *tied together* and utilized by sound operational management of the techniques used in inspection, quality control, and testing." Then, the author proceeds to do just that.

In an ASTME paper, *Understanding the Language of Metrology*, Arnold Young says:

> "The language common to all that ties a product together is the language of the metrologist. Not too long ago this was relatively simple: Thousandth of an inch, minute of arc, polished or good ground surface, degrees of temperature, mass, hardness. All these were easily and completely expressed by the draftsman on his print, and understood by the machine operator and inspection department—maybe not as the designer meant them to be understood, but by perfect agreement arrived at among the shop personnel . . . with a little juggling to meet the print specifications, the products were built."

It's all changed now. Along with higher-precision automatically controlled machine tools, new instrumentation and finer measurement capabilities have collaterally developed. To utilize these developments effectively, engineers must learn and use a new language, that of metrology, which cannot tolerate ambiguity. May this be their textbook!

Most sincere thanks of the Society and staff are extended to all the contributors, whose voluntary work in hard-to-spare time has resulted in this book, a major offering from an engineering society whose charter goal is to disseminate reliable data "out of the knowhow of all for the benefit of all."

FRANK W. WILSON
Dearborn, Michigan

CONTENTS

HANDBOOK OF

INDUSTRIAL METROLOGY

1

GENERAL MEASUREMENT

CONCEPTS

Over a hundred years ago, Lord Kelvin made a classic statement concerning metrology:

> "When you can measure what you are speaking about and express
> it in numbers, you know something about it; and when you cannot
> measure it, when you cannot express it in numbers, your knowledge
> is of a meagre and unsatisfactory kind. It may be the beginning of
> knowledge, but you have scarcely in your thought advanced to the
> stage of a science."

The two sections of this chapter—*The Nature of Measurement* and
Elements of a Generalized Measuring System—lay the scientific groundwork
of metrology, so essential to understanding measurement terms, procedures,
and applications.

THE NATURE OF MEASUREMENT*

A unit is the magnitude of a quantity in terms of which magnitudes of other quantities of the same kind are expressed. Laying a board beside a carpenter's scale and deciding by visual inspection whether the board is longer or shorter than the scale is making a measurement. The length of the board is the quantity we wish to measure and the carpenter's scale is the standard for length. Humanly, there is reluctance to use the word "standard" to describe a carpenter's scale, or any similar device; this high-sounding name tends to be reserved for the material objects kept at the National Bureau of Standards and other standardizing laboratories. Nevertheless these devices in a strict sense are standards; they are replicas, though sometimes faulty and imperfect, of the exalted ones.

If one asserts only that the board is longer or shorter than the scale, he has not supplied all the information that is obtainable in the measuring process. He should also state *how much* longer or shorter it is. This requires that he select some unit in terms of which the measurement is expressed, be it an inch, a meter, or a cubit.

A unit is a quantity expressed in a magnitude that is comparable with the magnitudes of other quantities of the same kind. A standard is the physical embodiment of a unit. Thus, for every kind of quantity measured, there must be a unit to express the result of the measurement and a standard to permit making the measurement.

Frequently, the magnitude of a quantity such as area is of concern. Strictly speaking, area usually is not measured. What is measured are the lengths of the sides, say, of a piece of land, and the angles which the sides make with each other. Then the area is computed from geometric formulas. Such a process is called a *determination*.

If the area of an irregularly shaped figure is to be measured, say, the area under a curve on a chart, the outline of that area could be traced with the stylus of a planimeter. If the planimeter is calibrated by running the stylus around the perimeter of a regular figure with measured sides whose area can be calculated, then a measurement has been made, since an unknown quantity has been compared with a standard for that quantity. The standard is the figure of measured dimensions, even though we constructed it ourselves, and the planimeter is a comparator.

Suppose that we did not calibrate the planimeter ourselves, that we merely read the dials. Did we then perform a measurement? If the manufacturer calibrated the planimeter before supplying it, then we performed part of a measurement, the manufacturer having performed the other part.

*By Alvin G. McNish, Chief, Metrology Division, Institute for Basic Standards, National Bureau of Standards.

But if no calibration had been performed, if we relied completely on the accuracy of the manufacturing process for the accuracy of our assignment of area, then no measurement was performed, even though the number of area units we assigned to the unknown area may have been very close to the true area.

Principles for Achieving Accuracy

The simple example above serves to illustrate many important aspects of the measuring process. To achieve accuracy in measurements with a planimeter, the standard of area which was constructed should be as much like the unknown area as feasible in both shape and size, because *the more alike two things are, the more accurately they may be compared.*

The reasons for this should be obvious. The registration of the planimeter may depend on the configuration of its arms during the tracing operation, and this should be kept the same when tracing the standard as when tracing the unknown area. Numerous illustrations of this principle will be encountered in later chapters. For example, in calibrating working gage blocks by comparison with a set of reference standards, the reference and working blocks should be as much alike as possible. Then their thermal expansion will be the same and less control of temperature is necessary. If they are compared in length by a mechanical comparator, the indentation of the stylus will be the same. Often, requirements of the measuring process do not permit fulfillment of optimum conditions and one is forced into some compromises.

In tracing the standard area and the unknown area, established procedures should be followed. The standard and the unknown should be placed in the same position on the tracing surface. If the standard is traced in a clockwise direction, the unknown should be similarly traced so that errors due to direction of tracing will be the same in both cases. This is a very general principle of metrology: *The operations performed on the standard and on the unknown must be as identical as feasible.*

This principle is very often ignored in precise metrology, with consequent impairment of accuracy. If the first precept on alikeness of the unknown and the standard is adhered to, both the unknown and the standard will respond to environment in the same way. If, also, the procedures followed in the measuring process are the same when applied to the unknown as when applied to the standard, the systematic errors will be small, perhaps negligible, and the numerical value assigned to the unknown in terms of the unit embodied in the standard will be close to what we call its true value.

The gist of the measurement problem is this: Not only must the magnitude of the unknown quantity be known, but also some knowledge about the *correctness* of the measurement, i.e., whether or not the result is given with sufficient correctness for the particular need.

Methods for Estimating Accuracy and Precision

The planimeter experiment affords an excellent demonstration of how one can attack this problem of determining the correctness of the result. Suppose that the outlines of the standard area S and of the unknown area U are alternately traced. From each such pair of tracings an individual measurement of the unknown area can be obtained. (Of course, the procedure may be altered, such as: S-U-U-S-S-U-U-S, etc.) It is highly unlikely that the results from all such pairs will be in agreement. If they are, it is because not enough care has been taken in estimating the fractions of divisions in reading the dials of the planimeter. If this is the case, the ultimate in the measuring process has not been achieved.

Assuming that the results are in disagreement, the mean, or average, may be calculated, also the standard deviation of a single measurement, and of the mean, as described in a subsequent chapter. This yields information about the *repeatability* or *precision* of the measuring process.

Now, in doing this, the question arises: Have the uncertainties in the measurement procedures been fully explored? If the outlines of the unknown and of the standard were always traced in a clockwise direction, would the same results have been obtained by tracing them in a counterclockwise direction? Let us try this. It is likely that the results from the two procedures, clockwise and counterclockwise, will be different. But, are they significantly different? There are statistical tests which help to decide this question. If the axiom of alikeness between the standard and the unknown has been adhered to, perhaps it could not be achieved completely. As a check, the shapes of the areas can be varied. If the unknown area is roughly rectangular in shape, the standard area can be made triangular. Are the measurements now the same, or significantly different, as determined by statistical tests? This will show how closely the principle of alikeness must be adhered to, in order to achieve the accuracy desired in measuring the unknown area in terms of the constructed standards.

If it is desired to achieve an area measurement accurate to one percent in terms of the standard, a procedure must be selected which yields a standard deviation for a series of measurements somewhat smaller than this for minor variations in the conditions such as clockwise vs. counterclockwise direction, and sizes and shapes of the standards as compared with the unknown. If large variations in these conditions do not yield appreciably different standard deviations or mean values from one series of measurements to another, considerable confidence may be had in the trustworthiness of the procedures; but if they do, a careful study of the procedures is necessary to reveal systematic errors.

Precision and Accuracy

So far, distinction has not been made between two very significant concepts of measurement, *precision* and *accuracy*. This distinction is very important because it bears on the purpose for which a measurement is performed.

Meaning of Precision. Precision is the repeatability of a measuring process, or simply, how well identically performed measurements agree with each other. This concept applies to a process or a set of measurements, not to a single measurement, for in any set of measurements the individual results will scatter about the mean. Since the means of the results from groups of measurements tend to scatter less about the overall mean than individual results, reference is commonly made to the precision of a single measurement as contrasted with the precision of groups of measurements, but this is a misuse of the term. What is really meant is the precision of *a set* of single measurements or the precision of *a set of groups* of measurements.

Meaning of Accuracy. Accuracy is the agreement of the result of a measurement with the true value of the measured quantity. The difference between the measured value and the true value is the error of the measurement. Since the true value can never be known, the best that can be done is to estimate by various means the magnitude of the error. This is called the *uncertainty*.

Estimate can be made of the uncertainty of a measuring process or of a single measurement obtained from the process. This estimate must include contributions to the uncertainty due to scatter of the results about the mean, and those due to systematic and constant errors of the process. Contributions to the uncertainty arising from scattering of results about the mean may be estimated with considerable confidence. Since most measurement processes approximate the normal error law, one would expect that about two-thirds of the individual measurements would have an uncertainty due to scatter no greater than one standard deviation of the measurement process, and 399 out of 400 no greater than three standard deviations.

Systematic Errors. Assessment of uncertainty due to systematic errors is more difficult. What is meant here by systematic errors is those due to the measuring procedure. In the previously-cited planimeter experiment, repeated sets of measurements of the same unknown area can be made, using different-sized and different-shaped standards for each set, and tracing the standards and the unknown in both clockwise and counterclockwise directions. If all of the means from the several sets fall within the range $\pm\Delta A$, it may be assumed with considerable confidence that the uncertainty due to systematic errors is no greater than ΔA. Also, the means of the sets may be arranged according to the size or according to the shape of the standard used. If there is a trend in the magnitude of the unknown area, or a trend in the scatter of individual measurements in the sets when so arranged, more is known about the systematic error. Suppose the means for all sets in which clockwise tracings were made of both the unknown and the standards average significantly higher than those for the counter-clockwise tracings. Which procedure then, if either, has the lesser systematic error? Is the systematic error due to the direction of tracing of opposite sign in the two procedures? One might be inclined to answer this last question affirmatively, but this is a risky inclination. Since no difference was expected in results depending on direction of tracing, this difference suggests that a systematic error of unknown origin is present in the procedure, and that error must be rooted out.

Constant Errors. A constant error is one which affects all measurements in a measurement process by the same amount, or by an amount propor-tional to the magnitude of the quantity being measured, such as might be caused by a measuring stick which had worn off at one end (for the former case) or one which had stretched or shrunk uniformly (for the latter case). A constant error may occur in planimeter measurements because of an error in the scale used to construct the standard, or because an incorrect conversion factor was used in converting between the units embodied by the scale and the units in which the result of the measurements were expressed.

It is therefore necessary for accuracy in measurement that any standard used be traceable to the defining standard for that quantity. This means that it must have been compared with the defining standard or with some standard in a chain of standards which leads back to the defining standard. The longer this chain is, the less well-known is the value of a standard at the far end of the chain.

It is not necessary for a standard to be compared directly with the defining standard for its value to be well-known. For example, if a standard has been compared n times with another standard which in turn has been compared n times with the defining standard, its uncertainty is no greater than would be obtained from a single direct comparison, if $n = 2$. This is also true if it is compared with n different standards, each of which has been compared once with the defining standard. (It is assumed, of course, that the measuring process is the same in all cases.) A larger value of n leads to a smaller uncertainty, so that multiple comparisons through inter-mediate standards may result in a smaller uncertainty than a small number of direct comparisons.

Sensitivity and Readability

The terms "sensitivity" and "readability" are often used in discussing measurement, and sometimes the concepts they involve are confused with accuracy and precision. Sensitivity and readability are primarily associated with equipment while accuracy and precision are associated with the measuring process. The most sensitive or the most readable equipment may not always lead to the most precise or the most accurate results.

By *sensitivity* is meant the ability of a measuring device to detect small differences in a quantity being measured. For instance, if a very small change in voltage applied to two voltmeters results in a perceptible change in the indication of one instrument and not in the other, the former is the more sensitive instrument. It is possible that the more sensitive instrument may be subject to drifts due to thermal or other effects, so that its indications may be less repeatable than those of the instrument of lower sensitivity.

By *readability* is meant the susceptibility of a measuring device to having its indications converted to a meaningful number. A vernier on a micrometer makes that instrument more readable. Fine and closely spaced graduation lines ordinarily improve the readability. Very finely spaced lines may make a scale more readable when a microscope is used, but will impair its readability for the unaided eye.

Needs for Accuracy and Precision

Accuracy is usually sought for in a measurement process, when often only precision is required. This is fortunate because it is easier to achieve great precision than great accuracy, and much cheaper.

In most planimeter measurements it is only precision that is needed. The chief concern is with comparing areas relative to each other, and it is of no concern whether the area unit, call it a square inch or a square centimeter, is even approximately what it is called. All that is needed is *internal* agreement of the measurements. But if the planimeter is used to obtain land areas from an accurate aerial photograph, the chief concern is with accuracy, i.e., not only with the factors which affect the planimeter measurements but also with the accuracy of map reduction itself. This differentiation of requirements appears in all measurement situations.

If a carpenter is going to cut a board to fit a shelf into a cupboard, it does not matter whether his scale is accurate or not, provided he uses the same scale to measure the board that he used to measure the cupboard. But if he is going to order a pre-cut piece from a lumber yard, his situation requires that he have confidence that the scale used by the lumber yard is in reasonable agreement with his. One way to achieve this is to have both scales accurate, that is, reasonably good embodiments of the unit of measurement employed.

With our highly complicated industrial system, where parts are made in different plants and subsequently assembled in another, the simplest way to maintain compatibility of parts is for the measuring processes of all plants to be accurate. When the accuracy requirements are excessive, mating parts are better made in a single plant where internal measuring precision can more easily achieve the desired goals.

Nomenclature for Standards and Traceability

In order to maintain accuracy, standards in a vast industrial complex must be traceable to a single source, usually the national standards of the country. Since the national laboratories of well developed countries maintain close connections with the International Bureau of Weights and Measures, there is assurance that items manufactured to identical dimensions in different countries will be compatible.

Application of precise measurement has increased so much during the past few years that it is no longer practicable for a single national laboratory to perform directly all the calibrations and standardizations required by a large country with a high technical development. This has led to the establishment of a considerable number of standardizing laboratories in industry and in various branches of the state and national governments (see Fig. 1-1). In order that results of calibrations be uniform, the standardizing laboratories must maintain close rapport with the national laboratory. This is facilitated by use of uniform terminology in discussing standards.

The expansion of precision measurement in industry and various branches

Fig. 1-1. Classification of standards in orders.

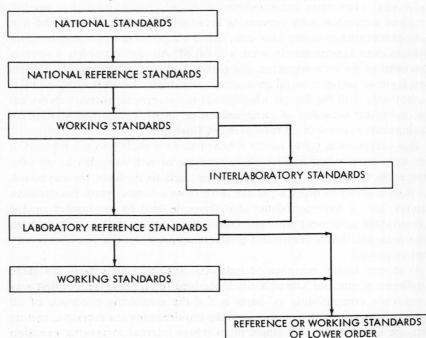

of the government has been a natural growth to fill a present need. It is not surprising that terminology used in describing and specifying types and classes of standards varies among the organizations involved, particularly when one observes that terminology varies even among the various disciplines in national laboratories.

Many adjectives are commonly used to describe standards. Various individuals attach different specific meanings to these words. Many words, selected for their primitive meanings to describe types of standards, possess other meanings in ordinary usage. This gives rise to incorrect ideas regarding the nature of the standards they describe. Some terms are so ingrained in the literature and jargon that the changing of them appears hopeless and perhaps undesirable. Some appear even in the laws establishing the legal units of measurement for the United States.

Words like "basic," "fundamental," "absolute," etc., are avoided in standards terminology. Similarly, the words "primary" and "secondary" should not be used because they will be applied freely by many users of standards to denote relative accuracy, importance, or line of derivation without regard to the meanings which may be formally assigned to them.

Standards for different quantities may be subject to uncertainties of greatly different magnitudes. Even different standards for the same quantity may vary greatly in the fidelity with which they embody the unit they represent.

Clearly, there is a degradation of accuracy in passing from the defining standards to the standards in use. The accuracy of a particular standard depends on a combination of the number of times it has been compared with a standard in a higher echelon, the recentness of such comparisons, the care with which it was done, and the stability of the particular standard itself. Clearly, if a standard has high stability, the time since its last comparison and the number of comparisons are of little importance, provided the number has been sufficient to establish its value. This is not true for a standard of low stability.

The rank of the standard with which a particular standard has been compared is ordinarily taken as an index of the accuracy of that standard, but this is not a good criterion. Some standards, such as banks of standard cells for voltage measurement, are so susceptible to damage during transit that a better standard can be maintained by keeping them under constant conditions and never comparing them directly with the standards of other laboratories, but effecting such comparison by means of go-between standards. By this means, such standards will acquire a reliability greater than that exhibited by the standards shipped about to effect the intercomparisons.

It is possible to establish hierarchies for standards to which names can be attached which will indicate both the use and supposed reliability of the standard. The wavelength of krypton 86 is the defining standard for length both nationally and internationally. It is backed up by several meter bars of platinum-iridium whose lengths are well known in terms of this wavelength. Their highly national character suggests the name "national" for this order of standards. In cases where any ambiguity may be involved, the adjective equivalent "United States" may be prefixed or substituted for "national."

Since frequent use may impair the accuracy of any standard, direct comparisons with the national standards are seldom performed. Also, it is desirable to have other standards which are comparable to the national standards in case some accident should befall the latter. These represent a slightly lower order of standards which are called "national reference standards."

Some standards belong in a third order which are called "working standards," and which are ordinarily used in calibration work. They are compared as frequently as necessary with the reference standards, and sometimes even with the national standards. When such standards are maintained by a national laboratory, they might be called "national working standards," but this additional adjective seems a bit superfluous.

There is nothing specified in these three orders of standards about their relative or absolute accuracy, although some degradation of accuracy is implied as one proceeds from the wavelength of light to working standards. For that matter, the accuracy of an individual standard is not an invariant; it is a function of many things. It depends on the history of intercomparisons, the quality of the standard itself, and the circumstances under which it is used in performing calibration. The important requirement is that the standard be accurate enough to assure that the errors involved in using it do not exceed the allowable limits specified for the calibration to be performed.

It is not the practice of the National Bureau of Standards to state in detail how an individual calibration has been performed, nor to state with what particular standard or standards a calibrated item has been compared. This is left entirely to the discretion of the staff members responsible for the test. Their knowledge of the accuracy of various reference and working standards at the time of the calibration is a better guide than a fixed rule. But when a report is supplied, the correction is given in terms of the national standard, and the limits of the stated uncertainty include the accrued errors in referring back to the national standard.

The above statements on calibration procedures and accuracy have been made to show the impossibility of devising any uniform nomenclature to specify the accuracy of a standard which would apply to all standards. The classification and nomenclature can indicate accuracy only as an *intensive* quantity; to express it as an *extensive* quantity it is necessary to assign a number to each and every standard.

Nomenclature for Calibration Laboratories

The classification and nomenclature for national standards can be applied with slight modification for the many laboratories which are tied in with the national standards. These laboratories include the rather extensive system in the Department of Defense, including those operated directly by that department and those maintained by its contractors, as well as the standardizing laboratories of various manufacturing companies which deal directly with the Bureau. Some of these commercial laboratories, particularly those maintained by manufacturers of precise instruments, do just as excellent a job in calibrating as the Bureau, and they maintain some standards which are of as good quality as the national standards. Depending upon the work of each laboratory, each will maintain standards of various sorts inherently subject to a wide range in accuracy.

Consistent with this system, only one laboratory in a country could have an order of standards called "national standards." This distinguished order is reserved for the laboratory which is responsible for establishing the standards of measurement on a national basis. The highest ranking for any other laboratory should be called the laboratory reference standard. Where further distinction is necessary, the name of the laboratory could be included for a particular standard, thus: "the John Doe Laboratory reference standard." The values for the laboratory reference standards would be obtained by comparison with the standards at the National Bureau of Standards or with the standards at some other standardizing laboratory. It may at some times be advisable to have this procedure flexible. Certain types of standards at a particular standardizing laboratory may best fulfill their needs by always using the Bureau for intercomparisons, while others will depend on intercomparisons with another standardizing laboratory. The important requirement is that the accuracy of the standard be sufficient for its purpose.

Good practice at standardizing laboratories is to minimize use of reference standards. Therefore, working standards should be used for most calibration work, reference standards being employed only for calibration of the working standards or for performing calibrations requiring extreme accuracy or confidence.

Laboratories at lower echelons and manufacturing establishments requiring standardization of their product might be supplied with working standards alone. Such establishments would not be responsible for maintenance of standards, but would depend upon a laboratory with reference standards.

Since it is inadvisable to ship some kinds of standards from one laboratory to another because of possible injury in transit, intercomparison of some reference standards of various laboratories is better and more safely effected by "interlaboratory standards" as is the case for standard cells. Interlaboratory standards are not inherently inferior in quality to reference standards except that the act of shipping may make them so.

These several orders adequately provide for the classification of standards maintained at a standardizing laboratory. One may consider the desirability of considering an even lower order to include the measuring devices used in shops and laboratories, the gages, graduated scales, etc., which are often of fine quality, and call such things "shop standards." To do this would derogate from the concept of standards. It seems better to reserve the use of the word "standard" for such things as are employed primarily for the calibration of measuring devices, and not apply it to devices in general measuring use.

Objections may be raised that these orders do not possess sufficiently fine structure to permit adequate specification of how accurately an individual calibration has been performed by a standardizing laboratory, that they do not serve to show with which standard a particular device has been compared. But as has been pointed out, the National Bureau of Standards in calibrating a device does not ordinarily state exactly how the calibration is effected nor with what standards it was compared. It does state the value of the tested standard in terms of the national standards, or states that it does not have an error greater than a specified amount relative to the national standards. The same procedure might well be followed by all standardizing laboratories. Each laboratory would decide on the method of test for a given type of device, and the standards to be used in order that the required accuracy be achieved.

Results of all such tests should be given in terms of the national standard to avoid any uncertainty in the values involved. This places considerable responsibility on each laboratory to assure that its standards are adequate to meet these requirements of accuracy. All laboratories, of course, might not be qualified to calibrate to the same accuracy. The science of measurement is now so well developed that the limits of surety can be assigned with considerable confidence.

Summary

It has not been possible in the brief space allotted to cover completely all of the philosophy of measurement and measurement systems. The nature of some of the problems of measurement and the general technique of their solutions have been pointed out. In each particular measurement situation particular problems arise. Many of these cases will be discussed in the other chapters of this book. But the solutions for all problems will not be found in the pages of this book or any other. In measurement as in all other fields of human endeavor there is no substitute for intelligence. This the metrologist himself must bring to bear on each problem before him.

ELEMENTS OF A GENERALIZED MEASURING SYSTEM*

The objective of a measuring system should be to provide accuracy capabilities that will assure the attainment of accuracy goals. In general, the elements of such a system include the instrumentation, the calibration standards, environmental influences, person or human operator limitations, and the features of the workpiece or object being measured. Each of these elements may involve detailed studies of extended scope. The design of measuring systems involves proper analysis of cost-to-accuracy considerations. A general approach to this analysis can be expressed by the equation

$$y = f(x)^{-a}$$

where y represents cost, x represents accuracy goals, and $-a$ is an exponent determining the shape of the curve. This general characteristic curve is portrayed graphically in Fig. 1-2.

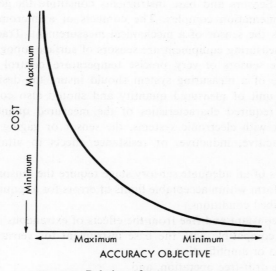

Fig. 1-2. Relation of accuracy to cost.

It should be noted that very demanding accuracy objectives—usually near the measuring limitations of modern instrumentation—can result in an asymptotic (exponential) rise in costs. If the measured quantity relates to a tolerance (i.e., the permissible variation in the measured quantity), the accuracy objective may be ten percent or less of the tolerance. There are no standards or regulations that require rigid adherence to any specified accuracy ratio, and the desired ratio of accuracy to tolerance is normally

*By William J. Darmody, Technical Consultant, The Sheffield Corporation.

arrived at by balancing the cost of measurement against the quality and reliability criteria of the product in question.

Functional Design of Systems

The functional design of measuring systems can include consideration of many approaches and employment of a variety of physical phenomena useful in establishing parametric variables from the measured quantity. In linear measuring systems, the basic function may be mechanical, optical, pneumatic, electronic, radiological, or combinations of these.

Transducers. The transducer is a basic element of many measuring instrument concepts. These are devices that respond to a phenomenon by producing a signal which is related to one or more variables of the phenomenon. Such devices vary from the delicate and reliable transducers of space vehicle telemetry systems to the simple air gages for measuring cylinder bores.

Sensors. Sensors and base instruments constitute the general elements of an instrumentation complex. The contacts of a micrometer might be considered as the sensor of a mechanical measurement. Tracers of surface roughness measuring equipment are sensors of surface topography. Thermistors are the sensors of very precise temperature control systems. The sensory stage of a measuring system should insure the desired change of readout per unit of measured quantity and should also completely comprehend all required characteristics of the measured quantity. In length measurement with electronic systems, the sensor or gaging cartridge may employ capacitive, inductive, or resistance effects to attain the desired sensitivity.

Objectives of an adequate sensory stage require the sensor:

1. to perform within acceptable limits of errors for a required time under prescribed conditions,
2. to be constant and free from the effects of extraneous influences,
3. to be compatible with the base instrument for versatility in magnification or amplification,
4. to give drift-free operation, and
5. to yield characteristics repeatable within specified limits.

Signal modification and amplification requirements in the sensory stage vary with the measured quantity. Telemetry measurements in missile technology are very sophisticated in such signal modification and amplification. The requirements for cutoff and tracing speed in surface roughness measurements constitute one of the few applications of the need for these characteristics in linear measurement instrumentation.

A new and developing field for direct use of the sensor signal without complex modification is that of fluid amplifiers, devices which enable the direct application of the sensor signal to an actuating force. They combine the desirable feature of a pneumatic system's high reliability with a minimum need for mechanical or electrical components in the measuring system. The inductive or capacitive types of sensors for linear measurement usually require modification of the input frequency in order to attain desired stability and also to minimize the size of the differential transformer elements. Simplicity often triumphs over sophistication in successful measuring systems; therefore, the necessity for signal modification and amplification should be carefully weighed.

Readout. Readout, whether indicating, digital, or recording, is a major function of the base instrument section of the measuring system. The distance from the sensor to the required location of the readout is a factor in the selection of the type of readout. Modern machine tools are using long-range linear transducers with digital readout located for convenient operation. Numerical control for precise tolerances demands long-range transducers with a signal that can be applied to the feedback loop of the system.

Adequate resolution is the degree to which small increments of the measured quantity can be discriminated in the instrument output. It is an important element of the measuring system. Frequently, an operator mistakenly will prefer a limited resolution in the belief that it represents a gain in repeatability. This is a mistaken concept, not to be followed. The resolution utilized should always be one digit greater than the least significant digit of the accuracy objective. Whether the readout be analog or digital, it should be compatible with the observer's ability to distinguish between two nearly equal quantities.

The question whether to have recorder or indicating readout is related to the complexity and scope of the measured quantity, and to the need for a history of values over a period of time. The techniques for measuring radial roundness are illustrative of the necessity for recorder readout to obtain a complete picture of a geometrical configuration. Measurement of process variables usually employs simultaneous use of both indicating and recorder readout.

Damping. Damping in measurement is the reduction in amplitude of an oscillation to make more readable the observation of the measured quantity. This may be accomplished by introducing resistance, friction, filtering, constriction, or other means to attenuate the undesirable effect that is adversely influencing readability. Such an effect is accomplished by electrical filters in roundness measurement, so that the true geometric configuration can be distinguished from the local variations in surface topography. In a hydraulic system, the readability of pressure measurements can be adversely affected by high-frequency pulses generated by pump performance. Here, the simple approach is to constrict the pipe to the pressure gage by a valve closure to the point where stability of the pointer is achieved. Damping in sophisticated strain gage systems is critical in providing the most rapid transient response without overshoot affecting the measured value.

Calibration. The general calibration provisions for a measuring system include:

1. Acceptance calibration of a new system.
2. Periodic calibration of the system in use or when placed in use after storage.
3. Availability of standards traceable to the National Standard for the unit of measure under consideration.

Calibration refers to measurements where the individual values are reported, rather than to measurements indicating only that an instrument is functioning within prescribed limits. It also refers to the disciplines necessary to control measuring systems to assure their functioning within prescribed accuracy objectives.

Normally, a calibration chain or pyramid of echelons is involved in the discipline of metrology control and surveillance. These levels include:

Level 1. The product tolerance or measured quantity.

Level 2. The calibration of the product measuring system.

Level 3. The calibration of the measuring system used to calibrate the product measuring system.

Level 4. Local standards, such as gage blocks or standard cells (volts), used for calibration of *level 3* above.

Level 5. Referencing local standards of *level 4* to the National Standard.

Each of these levels attempts to achieve an accuracy/tolerance ratio that will satisfy requirements of the preceding level. This achievement is, of course, subject to the limitations of the state of the art as well as the cost-accuracy equation previously discussed.

The aim of all calibration activities is ascertaining that a measuring system will function to assure attainment of its accuracy objectives.

Evaluation of Accuracy

Error. Error in measurement is the difference between the indicated value and the true value of a measured quantity. (The true value of a quantity to be measured is seldom known.) Errors are classified as random and systematic. Random errors are accidental in nature. They fluctuate in a way that cannot be predicted from the detailed employment of the measuring system or from knowledge of its functioning. Sources of error (such as hysteresis, ambient influences, or variations in the workpiece) are typical but not completely all-inclusive in the random category. Systematic errors are those not usually detected by repetition of the measurement operations. An error resulting from either faulty calibration of a local standard or a defect in contact configuration of an internal measuring system is typical but not completely inclusive in the systematic class of errors.

It is important to know all sources of error in a measuring system, rather than merely be aware of the details of their classification. The classification and analysis of the causes of errors are helpful in attaining the necessary knowledge of achieved accuracy.

Accuracy. Accuracy is the quality of conformity. Measurement science encompasses two basic approaches to determining conformity to measurement accuracy objectives. These are: (a) an engineering analysis to determine all causes of error, and (b) a statistical evaluation of data after stripping or eliminating the errors revealed by the engineering analysis (a). The latter point is discussed later in this chapter.

The following delineation of the error analysis that should be considered is typical of some disciplines. It is based on *accuracy analysis* of a measured quantity, such as the determination of a pitch diameter of a Class W thread setting plug gage (U.S. Handbook H28).

The basic components of an accuracy evaluation can well be the five elements of a measuring system.

1. Factors affecting the *standard*:
   (a) Traceability.
   (b) Geometric compatibility.
   (c) Coefficient of thermal expansion.
   (d) Calibration interval.
   (e) Stability.
   (f) Elastic properties.
   (g) Position of use—Airy points.*
2. Factors affecting the *workpiece*:
   (a) Geometric truth—hidden geometry.
   (b) Related characteristics, such as surface finish, waviness, scratch depth. The following table lists the National Bureau of Standards practice on related characteristics for internal diameter measurement.

Accuracy objective	10	5	3	2	1
Roundness and uniformity of diameter along axis†	5	3	2	1	0
Waviness†	5	2	1	1	0
Surface finish† (arithmetic average)	2.5	1.2	0.8	0.4	0.2
Average scratch depth† (peak to valley)	12	6	4	2	1
Load	8 oz	3 oz	1.3 oz	0.5 oz	0.17 oz

†Measurements are in microinches.

*See "Measuring the Geometry of Form or Shape," Chapter 11.

    (c) Elastic properties.

    (d) Cleanliness.

    (e) Surface defects.

    (f) Thermal equalization.

    (g) Mass affecting elastic deformation.

    (h) Truth of supporting features.

    (i) Clear definition of characteristic to be measured.

    (j) Adequate *datums* on the workpiece.

3. Factors affecting the *instrument*:

    (a) Adequate amplification for accuracy objective.

    (b) Amplification checked under conditions of use.

    (c) Effects of friction, backlash, hysteresis, or zero drift.

    (d) Electric, optical, or pneumatic input to amplifying system functioning within prescribed limits.

    (e) Contact geometry correct for both workpiece and standard.

    (f) Contact pressure control functioning within prescribed limits.

    (g) Contacts in correct geometrical relationship and inspected for wear or chipping.

    (h) Slides, ways, or moving elements not adversely affected by wear or damage.

    (i) Deformation effects in the instrument when heavy workpieces are measured.

    (j) Auxiliary elements (such as wires, rolls, angles, plates) calibrated and checked for function.

    (k) Magnification of errors by contact geometry.

    (l) Repeatability and readability adequate for accuracy objective.

4. Factors affecting the *person*:

    (a) Training.

    (b) Skill.

    (c) Sense of precision appreciation.

    (d) Complacent or opinionated attitudes towards personal accuracy achievements.

    (e) Open-minded, competent attitudes towards personal accuracy achievements.

    (f) Planning measurements techniques for minimum cost, consistent with precision requirements.

    (g) Appreciation of scope of accuracy evaluation.

    (h) Ability to select high-quality measuring instruments and standards with required geometrical and precision capabilities.

    (i) Sensible appreciation of measurement costs.

5. Factors affecting the *environment*:

    (a) Standard length-measuring temperature is 68°F (20°C); for electrical measurements, it is 73.4°F(23°C).

(b) Temperature equalization between standard, workpiece, and instrument. Deficiency of one degree in equalization could introduce in steel an error of 6.5 millionths inch per inch of length.

(c) Thermal expansion effects due to heat radiation from lights, heating components, sunlight, and people.

(d) Effects of cycles in temperature control.

(e) Impinging drafts of air which may introduce thermal expansion size errors.

(f) Manual handling may introduce thermal expansion errors. Human body temperature is 30°F higher than standard measuring temperature. For a one-inch length of steel, this could cause error up to 0.0002 inch.

(g) Clean surroundings and minimum vibration enhance precision.

(h) Adequate lighting.

(i) Atmospheric refraction effects in optical measuring systems, such as autocollimators.

(j) Thermal gradients, either vertical or lateral, in the measuring area.

The above arrangement and analysis of the five basic metrology elements can be composed into the acronym SWIPE for convenient reference:

S = STANDARD

W = WORKPIECE

I = INSTRUMENT

P = PERSON

E = ENVIRONMENT

In summary, the essential elements of a generalized measuring system are those that assure attainment of required accuracy objectives.

2

STATISTICAL CONCEPTS

IN METROLOGY*†

STATISTICAL CONCEPTS OF
A MEASUREMENT PROCESS

Arithmetic Numbers and Measurement
Numbers

In metrological work, digital numbers are used for different purposes and consequently these numbers have different interpretations. It is therefore important to differentiate the two types of numbers which will be encountered.

*By Harry H. Ku, Statistical Engineering Laboratory, Institute for Basic Standards, National Bureau of Standards.

†A contribution of the National Bureau of Standards, not subject to copyright.

Arithmetic numbers are exact numbers. 3, $\sqrt{2}$, $\frac{1}{3}$, e, or π are all exact numbers by definition, although in expressing some of these numbers in digital form, approximation may have to be used. Thus, π may be written as 3.14 or 3.1416, depending on our judgment of which is the proper one to use from the combined point of view of accuracy and convenience. By the usual rules of rounding, the approximations do not differ from the exact values by more than ± 0.5 units of the last recorded digit. The accuracy of the result can always be extended if necessary.

Measurement numbers, on the other hand, are not approximations to exact numbers, but numbers obtained by operation under approximately the same conditions. For example, three measurements on the diameter of a steel shaft with a micrometer may yield the following results:

No.	Diameter in cm	General notation
1	0.396	x_1
2	0.392	x_2
3	0.401	x_3
Sum	1.189	$\sum\limits_{i=1}^{n} x_i$
Average	0.3963	$\bar{x} = \dfrac{1}{n} \sum\limits_{1}^{n} x_i$
Range	0.009	$R = x_{\max} - x_{\min}$

There is no rounding off here. The last digit in the measured value depends on the instrument used and our ability to read it. If we had used a coarser instrument, we might have obtained 0.4, 0.4, and 0.4; if a finer instrument, we might have been able to record to the fifth digit after the decimal point. In all cases, however, the last digit given certainly does not imply that the measured value differs from the diameter D by less than ± 0.5 unit of the last digit.

Thus we see that measurement numbers differ by their very nature from arithmetic numbers. In fact, the phrase "significant figures" has little meaning in the manipulation of numbers resulting from measurements. Reflection on the simple example above will help to convince one of this fact.

Computation and Reporting of Results. By experience, the metrologist can usually select an instrument to give him results adequate for his needs, as illustrated in the example above. Unfortunately, in the process of computation, both arithmetic numbers and measurement numbers are present, and frequently confusion reigns over the number of digits to be kept in successive arithmetic operations.

No general rule can be given for all types of arithmetic operations. If the instrument is well-chosen, severe rounding would result in loss of information. One suggestion, therefore, is to treat all measurement numbers as exact numbers in the operations and to round off the final result only.

Another recommended procedure is to carry two or three extra figures throughout the computation, and then to round off the final reported value to an appropriate number of digits.

The "appropriate" number of digits to be retained in the final result depends on the "uncertainties" attached to this reported value. The term "uncertainty" will be treated later under "Precision and Accuracy"; our only concern here is the number of digits in the expression for uncertainty.

A recommended rule is that the uncertainty should be stated to no more than two significant figures, and the reported value itself should be stated to the last place affected by the qualification given by the uncertainty statement. An example is:

> "The apparent mass correction for the nominal 10 g weight is +0.0420 mg with an overall uncertainty of ±0.0087 mg using three standard deviations as a limit to the effect of random errors of measurement, the magnitude of systematic errors from known sources being negligible."

The sentence form is preferred since then the burden is on the reporter to specify exactly the meaning of the term uncertainty, and to spell out its components. Abbreviated forms such as $a \pm b$, where a is the reported value and b a measure of uncertainty in some vague sense, should always be avoided.

Properties of Measurement Numbers

The study of the properties of measurement numbers, or the Theory of Errors, formally began with Thomas Simpson more than two hundred years ago, and attained its full development in the hands of Laplace and Gauss. In the next subsections some of the important properties of measurement numbers will be discussed and summarized, thus providing a basis for the statistical treatment and analysis of these numbers in the following major section.

The Limiting Mean. As shown in the micrometer example above, the results of *repeated measurements of a single physical quantity under essentially the same conditions* yield a set of measurement numbers. Each member of this set is an estimate of the quantity being measured, and has equal claims on its value. By convention, the numerical values of these n measurements are denoted by $x_1, x_2, \ldots, x_n$, the arithmetic mean by $\bar{x}$, and the range by R, i.e., the difference between the largest value and the smallest value obtained in the n measurements.

If the results of measurements are to make any sense for the purpose at hand, we must require these numbers, though different, to behave as a group in a certain predictable manner. Experience has shown that this is indeed the case under the conditions stated in italics above. In fact, let us adopt as the postulate of measurement a statement due to N. Ernest Dorsey (reference 2)*

> "The mean of a family of measurements—of a number of measurements for a given quantity carried out by the same apparatus, procedure, and observer—approaches a definite value as the number of measurements is indefinitely increased. Otherwise, they could not properly be called measurements of a given quantity. In the theory of errors, this limiting mean is frequently called the 'true' value, although it bears no necessary relation to the true quaesitum, to the actual value of the quantity that the observer desires to measure. This has often confused the unwary. Let us call it the limiting mean."

Thus, according to this postulate, there exists a limiting mean m to which $\bar{x}$ approaches as the number of measurements increases indefinitely, or, in symbols $\bar{x} \to m$ as $n \to \infty$. Furthermore, if the true value is τ, there is usually a difference between m and τ, or $\Delta = m - \tau$, where Δ is defined as the bias or systematic error of the measurements.

In practice, however, we will run into difficulties. The value of m cannot be obtained since one cannot make an infinite number of measurements. Even for a large number of measurements, the conditions will not remain constant, since changes occur from hour to hour, and from day to day. The value of τ is unknown and usually unknowable, hence also the bias. Nevertheless, this seemingly simple postulate does provide a sound foundation to build on toward a mathematical model, from which estimates can be made and inference drawn, as will be seen later on.

Range, Variance, and Standard Deviation. The range of n measurements, on the other hand, does not enjoy this desirable property of the arithmetic mean. With one more measurement, the range may increase but cannot decrease. Since only the largest and the smallest numbers enter into its calculation, obviously the additional information provided by the measurements in between is lost. It will be desirable to look for another measure of the dispersion (spread, or scattering) of our measurements which will utilize each measurement made with equal weight, and which will approach a definite number as the number of measurements is indefinitely increased.

A number of such measures can be constructed; the most frequently used are the variance and the standard deviation. The choice of the variance as the measure of dispersion is based upon its mathematical convenience and maneuverability. Variance is defined as the value approached by the average of the sum of squares of the deviations of individual measurements from the limiting mean as the number of measurements is indefinitely

*References are listed at the end of this chapter.

increased, or in symbols:

$$\frac{1}{n} \sum (x_i - m)^2 \longrightarrow \sigma^2 = \text{variance, as } n \longrightarrow \infty$$

The positive square root of the variance, σ, is called the standard deviation (of a single measurement); the standard deviation is of the same dimensionality as the limiting mean.

There are other measures of dispersion, such as average deviation and probable error. The relationships between these measures and the standard deviation can be found in reference 1.

Population and the Frequency Curve. We shall call the limiting mean m the location parameter and the standard deviation σ the scale parameter of the population of measurement numbers generated by a particular measurement process. By population is meant the conceptually infinite number of measurements that can be generated. The two numbers m and σ describe this population of measurements to a large extent, and specify it completely in one important special case.

Our model of a measurement process consists then of a defined population of measurement numbers with a limiting mean m and a standard deviation σ. The result of a single measurement X^* can take randomly any of the values belonging to this population. The probability that a particular measurement yields a value of X which is less than or equal to x' is the proportion of the population that is less than or equal to x', in symbols

$$P\{X \leq x'\} = \text{proportion of population less than or equal to } x'$$

Similar statements can be made for the probability that X will be greater than or equal to x'', or for X between x' and x'' as follows: $P\{X \geq x''\}$, or $P\{x' \leq X \leq x''\}$.

For a measurement process that yields numbers on a continuous scale, the distribution of values of X for the population can be represented by a smooth curve, for example, curve C in Fig. 2-1. C is called a frequency curve. The area between C and the abscissa bounded by any two values (x_1 and x_2) is the proportion of the population that takes values between the two values, or the probability that X will assume values between x_1 and x_2. For example, the probability that $X \leq x'$, can be represented by the shaded area to the left of x'; the total area between the frequency curve and the abscissa being one by definition.

Note that the shape of C is not determined by m and σ alone. Any curve C' enclosing an area of unity with the abscissa defines the distribution of a particular population. Two examples, the uniform distribution and

---

*Convention is followed in using the capital X to represent the value that might be produced by employing the measurement process to obtain a measurement (i.e., a random variable), and the lower case x to represent a particular value of X observed.

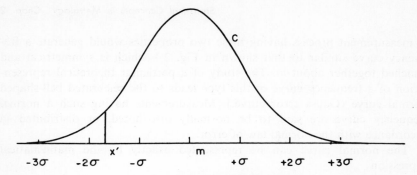

Fig. 2-1. A symmetrical distribution.

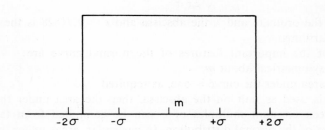

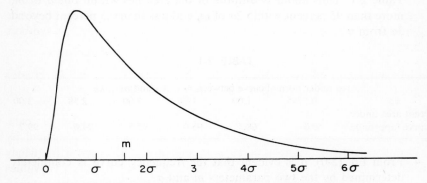

Fig. 2-2. (A) The uniform distribution. (B) The log-normal distribution.

the log-normal distribution are given in Figs. 2-2A and 2-2B. These and other distributions are useful in describing certain populations.

The Normal Distribution. For data generated by a measurement process, the following properties are usually observed:

1. The results spread roughly symmetrically about a central value.
2. Small deviations from this central value are more frequently found than large deviations.

25

A measurement process having these two properties would generate a frequency curve similar to that shown in Fig. 2-1 which is symmetrical and bunched together about *m*. The study of a particular theoretical representation of a frequency curve of this type leads to the celebrated bell-shaped normal curve (Gauss error curve.). Measurements having such a normal frequency curve are said to be normally distributed, or distributed in accordance with the normal law of error.

The normal curve can be represented exactly by the mathematical expression

$$y = \frac{1}{\sqrt{2\pi}\,\sigma}\, e^{-1/2[(x-m)^2/\sigma^2]} \qquad (2\text{-}0)$$

where *y* is the ordinate and *x* the abscissa and $e \doteq 2.71828$ is the base of natural logarithms.

Some of the important features of the normal curve are:

1. It is symmetrical about *m*.
2. The area under the curve is one, as required.
3. If σ is used as unit on the abscissa, then the area under the curve between constant multiples of σ can be computed from tabulated values of the normal distribution. In particular, areas under the curve for some useful intervals between $m - k\sigma$ and $m + k\sigma$ are given in Table 2-1. Thus about two-thirds of the area lies within one σ of *m*, more than 95 percent within 2σ of *m*, and less than 0.3 percent beyond 3σ from *m*.

TABLE 2-1

Area under normal curve between $m - k\sigma$ and $m + k\sigma$						
k:	0.6745	1.00	1.96	2.00	2.58	3.00
Percent area under curve (approx.):	50.0	68.3	95.0	95.5	99.0	99.7

4. From Eq. (2-0), it is evident that the frequency curve is completely determined by the two parameters *m* and σ.

The normal distribution has been studied intensively during the past century. Consequently, if the measurements follow a normal distribution, we can say a great deal about the measurement process. The question remains: How do we know that this is so from the limited number of repeated measurements on hand?

The answer is that we don't! However, in most instances the metrologist may be willing

1. to assume that the measurement process generates numbers that follow a normal distribution approximately, and act as if this were so,
2. to rely on the so-called Central Limit Theorem, one version of which

is the following*: "If a population has a finite variance σ^2 and mean m, then the distribution of the sample mean (of n independent measurements) approaches the normal distribution with variance σ^2/n and mean m as the sample size n increases." This remarkable and powerful theorem is indeed tailored for measurement processes. First, every measurement process must by definition have a finite mean and variance. Second, the sample mean $\bar{x}$ is the quantity of interest which, according to the theorem, will be approximately normally distributed for large sample sizes. Third, the measure of dispersion, i.e., the standard deviation of the sample mean, is reduced by a factor of $1/\sqrt{n}$! This last statement is true in general for all measurement processes in which the measurements are "independent" and for all n. It is therefore not a consequence of the Central Limit Theorem. The theorem guarantees, however, that the distribution of sample means of *independent* measurements will be *approximately* normal with the specified limiting mean and standard deviation $\sigma/\sqrt{n}$ *for large* n.

In fact, for a measurement process with a frequency curve that is symmetrical about the mean, and with small deviations from the mean as compared to the magnitude of the quantity measured, the normal approximation to the distribution of $\bar{x}$ becomes very good even for n as small as 3 or 4. Figure 2-3 shows the uniform and normal distribution having the same mean and standard deviation. The peaked curve is actually two curves, representing the distribution of arithmetic means of four independent measurements from the respective distributions. These curves are indistinguishable to this scale.

A formal definition of the concept of "independence" is out of the scope here. Intuitively, we may say that n normally distributed measurements are independent if these measurements are not correlated or associated in any way. Thus, a sequence of measurements showing a trend or pattern are not independent measurements.

There are many ways by which dependence or correlation creeps into a set of measurement data; several of the common causes are the following:

1. Measurements are correlated through a factor that has not been considered, or has been considered to be of no appreciable effect on the results.
2. A standard correction constant has been used for a factor, e.g., temperature, but the constant may overcorrect or undercorrect for particular samples.
3. Measurements are correlated through time of the day, between days, weeks, or seasons.

*From Chapter 7, *Introduction to the Theory of Statistics*, by A. M. Mood, McGraw-Hill Book Company, New York, 1950.

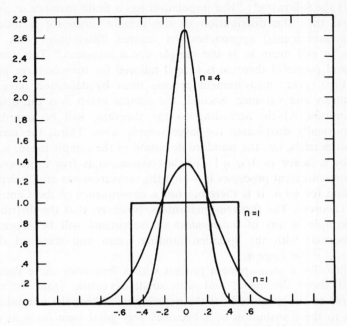

Fig. 2-3. Uniform and normal distribution of individual measurements having the same mean and standard deviation, and the corresponding distribution(s) of arithmetic means of four independent measurements.

4. Measurements are correlated through rejection of valid data, when the rejection is based on the size of the number in relation to others of the group.

The traditional way of plotting the data in the sequence they are taken, or in some rational grouping, is perhaps still the most effective way of detecting trends or correlation.

Estimates of Population Characteristics. In the above section it is shown that the limiting mean m and the variance σ^2 completely specify a measurement process that follows the normal distribution. In practice, m and σ^2 are not known and cannot be computed from a finite number of measurements. This leads to the use of the sample mean $\bar{x}$ as an estimate of the limiting mean m and s^2, the square of the computed standard deviation of the sample, as an estimate of the variance. The standard deviation of the average of n measurements, $\sigma/\sqrt{n}$, is sometimes referred to as the standard error of the mean, and is estimated by $s/\sqrt{n}$.

We note that the making of n independent measurements is equivalent to drawing a sample of size n at random from the population of measurements. Two concepts are of importance here:

1. The measurement process is established and under control, meaning that the limiting mean and the standard deviation do possess definite values which will not change over a reasonable period of time.
2. The measurements are randomly drawn from this population, implying that the values are of equal weights, and there is no prejudice in the method of selection. Suppose out of three measurements the one which is far apart from the other two is rejected, then the result will not be a random sample.

For a random sample we can say that $\bar{x}$ is an unbiased estimate of m, and s^2 is an unbiased estimate of σ^2, i.e., the limiting mean of $\bar{x}$ is equal to m and of s^2 to σ^2, where

$$\bar{x} = \frac{1}{n} \sum_{i=1}^{n} x_i$$

and

$$s^2 = \frac{1}{n-1} \sum_{i=1}^{n} (x_i - \bar{x})^2 = \frac{1}{n-1} \left[\sum x_i^2 - \frac{(\sum x_i)^2}{n} \right]$$

In addition, we define

$$s = \sqrt{s^2} = \text{computed standard deviation}$$

Examples of numerical calculations of $\bar{x}$ and s^2 and s are shown in Tables 2-5 and 2-6.

Interpretation and Computation of Confidence Interval and Limits

By making k sets of n measurements each, we can compute and arrange k, $\bar{x}$'s, and s's in a tabular form as follows:

Set	Sample mean	Sample standard deviation
1	$\bar{x}_1$	s_1
2	$\bar{x}_2$	s_2
.	.	.
.	.	.
.	.	.
j	$\bar{x}_j$	s_j
.	.	.
.	.	.
.	.	.
k	$\bar{x}_k$	s_k

In the array of $\bar{x}$'s, no two will be likely to have exactly the same value. From the Central Limit Theorem it can be deduced that the $\bar{x}$'s will be approximately normally distributed with standard deviation $\sigma/\sqrt{n}$. The frequency curve of $\bar{x}$ will be centered about the limiting mean m and will have the scale factor $\sigma/\sqrt{n}$. In other words, $\bar{x} - m$ will be centered about zero, and the quantity

$$z = \frac{\bar{x} - m}{\sigma/\sqrt{n}}$$

has the properties of a single observation from the "standardized" normal distribution which has a mean of zero and a standard deviation of one.

From tabulated values of the standardized normal distribution it is known that 95 percent of z values will be bounded between -1.96 and $+1.96$. Hence the statement

$$-1.96 < \frac{\bar{x} - m}{\sigma/\sqrt{n}} < +1.96$$

or its equivalent,

$$\bar{x} - 1.96\frac{\sigma}{\sqrt{n}} < m < \bar{x} + 1.96\frac{\sigma}{\sqrt{n}}$$

will be correct 95 percent of the time in the long run. The interval $\bar{x} - 1.96(\sigma/\sqrt{n})$ to $\bar{x} + 1.96(\sigma/\sqrt{n})$ is called a *confidence interval* for m. The probability that the confidence interval will cover the limiting mean, 0.95 in this case, is called the confidence level or confidence coefficient. The values of the end points of a confidence interval are called confidence limits. It is to be borne in mind that $\bar{x}$ will fluctuate from set to set, and the interval calculated for a particular $\bar{x}_j$ may or may not cover m.

In the above discussion we have selected a two-sided interval symmetrical about $\bar{x}$. For such intervals the confidence coefficient is usually denoted by $1 - \alpha$, where $\alpha/2$ is the percent of the area under the frequency curve of z that is cut off from each tail.

In most cases, σ is not known and an estimate of σ is computed from the same set of measurements we use to calculate $\bar{x}$. Nevertheless, let us form a quantity similar to z, which is

$$t = \frac{\bar{x} - m}{s/\sqrt{n}}$$

and if we know the distribution of t, we could make the same type of statement as before. In fact the distribution of t is known for the case of normally distributed measurements.

The distribution of t was obtained mathematically by William S. Gosset under the pen name of "Student," hence the distribution of t is called the Student's distribution. In the expression for t, both $\bar{x}$ and s fluctuate from set to set of measurements. Intuitively we will expect the value of t to be larger than that of z for a statement with the same probability of being correct. This is indeed the case. The values of t are listed in Table 2-2.

TABLE 2-2. A BRIEF TABLE OF VALUES OF t^*

Degrees of freedom ν	Confidence Level: $1 - \alpha$			
	0.500	0.900	0.950	0.990
1	1.000	6.314	12.706	63.657
2	.816	2.920	4.303	9.925
3	.765	2.353	3.182	5.841
4	.741	2.132	2.776	4.604
5	.727	2.015	2.571	4.032
6	.718	1.943	2.447	3.707
7	.711	1.895	2.365	3.499
10	.700	1.812	2.228	3.169
15	.691	1.753	2.131	2.947
20	.687	1.725	2.086	2.845
30	.683	1.697	2.042	2.750
60	.679	1.671	2.000	2.660
∞	.674	1.645	1.960	2.576

*Adapted from *Biometrika Tables for Statisticians*, Vol. I, edited by E. S. Pearson and H. O. Hartley, The University Press, Cambridge, 1958.

To find a value for t, we need to know the "degrees of freedom" (ν) associated with the computed standard deviation s. Since $\bar{x}$ is calculated from the same n numbers and has a fixed value, the nth value of x_i is completely determined by $\bar{x}$ and the other $(n-1)x$ values. Hence the degrees of freedom here are $n-1$.

Having the table for the distribution of t, and using the same reasoning as before, we can make the statement that

$$\bar{x} - t\frac{s}{\sqrt{n}} < m < \bar{x} + t\frac{s}{\sqrt{n}}$$

and our statement will be correct $100(1 - \alpha)$ percent of the time in the long run. The value of t depends on the degrees of freedom ν and the probability level. From the table, we get for a confidence level of 0.95, the following lower and upper confidence limits:

ν	$L_l = \bar{x} - t(s/\sqrt{n})$	$L_u = \bar{x} + t(s/\sqrt{n})$
1	$\bar{x} - 12.706(s/\sqrt{n})$	$\bar{x} + 12.706(s/\sqrt{n})$
2	$\bar{x} - 4.303(s/\sqrt{n})$	$\bar{x} + 4.303(s/\sqrt{n})$
3	$\bar{x} - 3.182(s/\sqrt{n})$	$\bar{x} + 3.182(s/\sqrt{n})$

The value of t for $\nu = \infty$ is 1.96, the same as for the case of known σ. Notice that very little can be said about m with two measurements. However, for n larger than 2, the interval predicted to contain m narrows down steadily, due to both the smaller value of t and the divisor $\sqrt{n}$.

It is probably worthwhile to emphasize again that each particular confidence interval computed as a result of n measurements will either include m or fail to include m. The probability statement refers to the fact that if we make a long series of sets of n measurements, and if we compute a confidence interval for m from each set by the prescribed method, we would expect 95 percent of such intervals to include m.

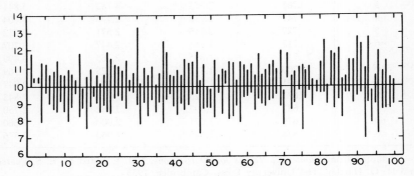

Fig. 2-4. Computed 90% confidence intervals for 100 samples of size 4 drawn at random from a normal population with $m = 10$, $\sigma = 1$.

Figure 2-4 shows the 90 percent confidence intervals ($P = 0.90$) computed from 100 samples of $n = 4$ from a normal population with $m = 10$, and $\sigma = 1$. Three interesting features are to be noted:

1. The number of intervals that include m actually turns out to be 90, the expected number.
2. The surprising variation of the sizes of these intervals.
3. The closeness of the mid-points of these intervals to the line for the mean does not seem to be related to the spread. In samples No. 2 and No. 3, the four values must have been very close together, but both of these intervals failed to include the line for the mean.

From the widths of computed confidence intervals, one may get an intuitive feeling whether the number of measurements n is reasonable and sufficient for the purpose on hand. It is true that, even for small n, the confidence intervals will cover the limiting mean with the specified probability, yet the limits may be so far apart as to be of no practical significance. For detecting a specified magnitude of interest, e.g., the difference between two means, the approximate number of measurements required can be solved by equating the half-width of the confidence interval to this difference and solving for n, using σ when known, or using s by trial and error if σ is not known. Tables of sample sizes required for certain prescribed conditions are given in reference 4.

Precision and Accuracy

Index of Precision. Since σ is a measure of the spread of the frequency curve about the limiting mean, σ may be defined as an index of precision. Thus a measurement process with a standard deviation σ_1 is said to be more precise than another with a standard deviation σ_2 if σ_1 is smaller than σ_2. (In fact, σ is really a measure of imprecision since the imprecision is directly proportional to σ.)

Consider the means of sets of n independent measurements as a new derived measurement process. The standard deviation of the new process is $\sigma/\sqrt{n}$. It is therefore possible to derive from a less precise measurement process a new process which has a standard deviation equal to that of a more precise process. This is accomplished by making more measurements.

Suppose $m_1 = m_2$, but $\sigma_1 = 2\sigma_2$. Then for a derived process to have $\sigma_1' = \sigma_2$, we need

$$\sigma_1' = \frac{\sigma_1}{\sqrt{n}} = \frac{2\sigma_2}{\sqrt{4}}$$

or we need to use the average of four measurements as a single measurement. Thus for a required degree of precision, the number of measurements, n_1 and n_2, needed for measurement processes I and II is proportional to the squares of their respective standard deviations (variances), or in symbols

$$\frac{n_1}{n_2} = \frac{\sigma_1^2}{\sigma_2^2}$$

If σ is not known, and the best estimate we have of σ is a computed standard deviation s based on n measurements, then s could be used as an estimate of the index of precision. The value of s, however, may vary considerably from sample to sample in the case of a small number of measurements as was shown in Fig. 2-4, where the lengths of the intervals are constant multiples of s computed from the samples. The number n or the degrees of freedom ν must be considered along with s in indicating how reliable an estimate s is of σ. In what follows, whenever the terms standard deviation about the limiting mean (σ), or standard error of the mean ($\sigma_{\bar{x}}$), are used, the respective estimates s and $s/\sqrt{n}$ may be substituted, by taking into consideration the above reservation.

In metrology or calibration work, the precision of the reported value is an integral part of the result. In fact, precision is the main criterion by which the quality of the work is judged. Hence, the laboratory reporting the value must be prepared to give evidence of the precision claimed. Obviously an estimate of the standard deviation of the measurement process based only on a small number of measurements cannot be considered as convincing evidence. By the use of the control chart method for standard deviation and by the calibration of one's own standard at frequent intervals, as subsequently described, the laboratory may eventually claim that the standard deviation is in fact known and the measurement process is stable, with readily available evidence to support these claims.

Interpretation of Precision. Since a measurement process generates numbers as the results of repeated measurements of a single physical quantity under essentially the same conditions, the method and procedure in obtaining these numbers must be specified in detail. However, no amount of detail would cover all the contingencies that may arise, or cover all the factors that may affect the results of measurement. Thus a single operator in a single day with a single instrument may generate a process with a precision index measured by σ. Many operators measuring the same quantity over a period of time with a number of instruments will yield a precision index measured by σ'. Logically σ' must be larger than σ, and in practice it is usually considerably larger. Consequently, modifiers of the words "precision" are recommended by ASTM* to qualify in an unambiguous manner what is meant. Examples are "single-operator-machine," "multi-laboratory," "single-operator-day," etc. The same publication warns against the use of the terms "repeatability" and "reproducibility" if the interpretation of these terms is not clear from the context.

The standard deviation σ or the standard error $\sigma/\sqrt{n}$ can be considered as a yardstick with which we can gage the difference between two results obtained as measurements of the same physical quantity. If our interest is to compare the results of one operator against another, the single-operator precision is probably appropriate, and if the two results differ by an amount considered to be large as measured by the standard errors, we may conclude that the evidence is predominantly against the two results being truly equal. In comparing the results of two laboratories, the single-operator precision is obviously an inadequate measure to use, since the precision of each laboratory must include factors such as multi-operator-day-instruments.

Hence the selection of an index of precision depends strongly on the purposes for which the results are to be used or might be used. It is common experience that three measurements made within the hour are closer together than three measurements made on, say, three separate days. However, an index of precision based on the former is generally not a justifiable indicator of the quality of the reported value. For a thorough discussion on the *realistic* evaluation of precision see Section 4 of reference 2.

Accuracy. The term "accuracy" usually denotes in some sense the closeness of the measured values to the true value, taking into consideration

---

*"Use of the Terms Precision and Accuracy as Applied to the Measurement of a Property of a Material," ASTM Designation, E177-61T, 1961.

both precision and bias. Bias, defined as the difference between the limiting mean and the true value, is a constant, and does not behave in the same way as the index of precision, the standard deviation. In many instances, the possible sources of biases are known but their magnitudes and directions are not known. The overall bias is of necessity reported in terms of estimated bounds that reasonably include the combined effect of all the elemental biases. Since there are no accepted ways to estimate bounds for elemental biases, or to combine them, these should be reported and discussed in sufficient detail to enable others to use their own judgment on the matter.

It is recommended that an index of accuracy be expressed as a pair of numbers, one the credible bounds for bias, and the other an index of precision, usually in the form of a multiple of the standard deviation (or estimated standard deviation). The terms "uncertainty" and "limits of error" are sometimes used to express the sum of these two components, and their meanings are ambiguous unless the components are spelled out in detail.

STATISTICAL ANALYSIS
OF MEASUREMENT DATA

In the last section the basic concepts of a measurement process were given in an expository manner. These concepts, necessary to the statistical analysis to be presented in this section, are summarized and reviewed below. By making a measurement we obtain a number intended to express quantitatively a measure of "the property of a thing." Measurement numbers differ from ordinary arithmetic numbers, and the usual "significant figure" treatment is not appropriate. Repeated measurement of a single physical quantity under essentially the same conditions generates a sequence of numbers $x_1, x_2, \ldots, x_n$. A measurement process is established if this conceptually infinite sequence has a limiting mean m and a standard deviation σ.

For many measurement processes encountered in metrology, the sequence of numbers generated follows approximately the normal distribution, specified completely by the two quantities m and σ. Moreover, averages of n independent measurement numbers tend to be normally distributed with the limiting mean m and the standard deviation $\sigma/\sqrt{n}$, regardless of the distribution of the original numbers. Normally distributed measurements are independent if they are not correlated or associated in any way. A sequence of measurements showing a trend or pattern are not independent measurements. Since m and σ are usually not known, these quantities are estimated by calculating $\bar{x}$ and s from n measurements, where

$$\bar{x} = \frac{1}{n} \sum_{1}^{n} x_i$$

and

$$s = \sqrt{\frac{1}{n-1} \sum_{1}^{n} (x_i - \bar{x})^2} = \sqrt{\frac{1}{n-1} \left[\sum_{1}^{n} x_i^2 - \frac{(\sum x_i)^2}{n} \right]}$$

The distribution of the quantity $t = (\bar{x} - m)/(s/\sqrt{n})$ (for x normally distributed) is known. From the tabulated values of t (see Table 2-2), confidence intervals can be constructed to bracket m for a given confidence coefficient $1 - \alpha$ (probability of being correct in the long run).

The confidence limits are the end points of confidence intervals defined by

$$L_l = \bar{x} - t \frac{s}{\sqrt{n}}$$

$$L_u = \bar{x} + t \frac{s}{\sqrt{n}}$$

where the value of t is determined by two parameters, namely, the degrees of freedom v associated with s and the confidence coefficient $1 - \alpha$.

The width of a confidence interval gives an intuitive measure of the uncertainty of the evidence given by the data. Too wide an interval may merely indicate that more measurements need to be made for the objective desired.

Algebra for the Manipulation of Limiting Means and Variances

Basic Formulas. A number of basic formulas are extremely useful in dealing with a quantity which is a combination of other measured quantities.

1. Let m_x and m_y be the respective limiting means of two measured quantities X and Y, and a, b be constants, then

$$\left. \begin{aligned} m_{x+y} &= m_x + m_y \\ m_{x-y} &= m_x - m_y \\ m_{ax+by} &= am_x + bm_y \end{aligned} \right\} \quad (2\text{-}1)$$

2. If, in addition, X and Y are independent, then it is also true that

$$m_{xy} = m_x m_y \tag{2-2}$$

For paired values of X and Y, we can form the quantity Z, with

$$Z = (X - m_x)(Y - m_y) \tag{2-3}$$

Then by formula (2-2) for independent variables,

$$\begin{aligned} m_z &= m_{(x-m_x)} m_{(y-m_y)} \\ &= (m_x - m_x)(m_y - m_y) = 0 \end{aligned}$$

Thus $m_z = 0$ when X and Y are independent.

3. The limiting mean of Z in (2-3) is defined as the covariance of X and Y and is usually denoted by cov (X, Y), or σ_{xy}. The covariance, similar to the variance, is estimated by

$$s_{xy} = \frac{1}{n-1} \sum (x_i - \bar{x})(y_i - \bar{y}) \qquad (2\text{-}4)$$

Thus if X and Y are correlated in such a way that paired values are likely to be both higher or lower than their respective means, then s_{xy} tends to be positive. If a high x value is likely to be paired with a low y value, and vice versa, then s_{xy} tends to be negative. If X and Y are not correlated, s_{xy} tends to zero (for large n).

4. The correlation coefficient ρ is defined as:

$$\rho = \frac{\sigma_{xy}}{\sigma_x \sigma_y} \qquad (2\text{-}5)$$

and is estimated by

$$r = \frac{s_{xy}}{s_x s_y} = \frac{\sum (x_i - \bar{x})(y_i - \bar{y})}{\sqrt{\sum (x_i - \bar{x})^2 \sum (y_i - \bar{y})^2}} \qquad (2\text{-}6)$$

Both ρ and r lie between -1 and $+1$.

5. Let σ_x^2 and σ_y^2 be the respective variances of X and Y, and σ_{xy} the covariance of X and Y, then

$$\sigma_{x+y}^2 = \sigma_x^2 + \sigma_y^2 + 2\sigma_{xy}$$
$$\sigma_{x-y}^2 = \sigma_x^2 + \sigma_y^2 - 2\sigma_{xy} \qquad (2\text{-}7)$$

If X and Y are independent, $\sigma_{xy} = 0$, then

$$\sigma_{x+y}^2 = \sigma_x^2 + \sigma_y^2 = \sigma_{x-y}^2 \qquad (2\text{-}8) .$$

Since the variance of a constant is zero, we have

$$\sigma_{ax+b}^2 = a^2 \sigma_x^2$$
$$\sigma_{ax+by}^2 = a^2 \sigma_x^2 + b^2 \sigma_y^2 + 2ab\sigma_{xy} \qquad (2\text{-}9)$$

In particular, if X and Y are independent and normally distributed, then $aX + bY$ is normally distributed with limiting mean $am_x + bm_y$ and variance $a^2 \sigma_x^2 + b^2 \sigma_y^2$.

For measurement situations in general, metrologists usually strive to get measurements that are independent, or can be assumed to be independent. The case when two quantities are dependent because both are functions of other measured quantities will be treated under propagation of error formulas (see Eq. 2-13).

6. Standard errors of the sample mean and the weighted means (of independent measurements) are special cases of the above. Since $\bar{x} = (1/n) \sum x_i$ and the x_i's are independent with variance σ_x^2, it follows, by (2-9), that

$$\sigma_{\bar{x}}^2 = \left(\frac{1}{n}\right)^2 \sigma_{x_1}^2 + \left(\frac{1}{n}\right)^2 \sigma_{x_2}^2 + \cdots \left(\frac{1}{n}\right)^2 \sigma_{x_n}^2 = \frac{\sigma_x^2}{n} \qquad (2\text{-}10)$$

as previously stated.

If $\bar{x}_1$ is an average of k values, and $\bar{x}_2$ is an average of n values, then for the over-all average, $\bar{\bar{x}}$, it is logical to compute

$$\bar{\bar{x}} = \frac{x_1 + \cdots + x_k + x_{k+1} + \cdots + x_{k+n}}{k + n}$$

and $\sigma_{\bar{\bar{x}}}^2 = \sigma_x^2/(k + n)$. However, this is equivalent to a weighted mean of $\bar{x}_1$ and $\bar{x}_2$, where the weights are proportional to the number of measurements in each average, i.e.,

$$w_1 = k, \qquad w_2 = n$$

and

$$\bar{\bar{x}} = \left(\frac{w_1}{w_1 + w_2}\right)\bar{x}_1 + \left(\frac{w_2}{w_1 + w_2}\right)\bar{x}_2$$

$$= \frac{k}{n + k}\,\bar{x}_1 + \frac{n}{n + k}\,\bar{x}_2$$

Since

$$\frac{\sigma_{\bar{x}_1}^2}{\sigma_{\bar{x}_2}^2} = \frac{\sigma^2/k}{\sigma^2/n} = \frac{n}{k} = \frac{w_2}{w_1}$$

the weighting factors w_1 and w_2 are therefore also inversely proportional to the respective variances of the averages. This principle can be extended to more than two variables in the following manner.

Let $\bar{x}_1, \bar{x}_2, \ldots, \bar{x}_k$ be a set of averages estimating the same quantity. The over-all average may be computed to be

$$\bar{\bar{x}} = \frac{1}{w_1 + w_2 + \cdots + w_k}(w_1\bar{x}_1 + w_2\bar{x}_2 + \cdots + w_k\bar{x}_k)$$

where

$$w_1 = \frac{1}{\sigma_{\bar{x}_1}^2}, \qquad w_2 = \frac{1}{\sigma_{\bar{x}_2}^2}, \qquad \ldots, \qquad w_k = \frac{1}{\sigma_{\bar{x}_k}^2}$$

The variance of $\bar{\bar{x}}$ is, by (2-9),

$$\sigma_{\bar{\bar{x}}}^2 = \frac{1}{w_1 + w_2 + \cdots + w_k} \qquad (2\text{-}11)$$

In practice, the estimated variances $s_{\bar{x}}^2$ will have to be used in the above formulas, and consequently the equations hold only as approximations.

Propagation of error formulas. The results of a measurement process can usually be expressed by a number of averages $\bar{x}, \bar{y}, \ldots$, and the standard errors of these averages $s_{\bar{x}} = s_x/\sqrt{n}$, $s_{\bar{y}} = s_y/\sqrt{k}$, etc. These results, however, may not be of direct interest; the quantity of interest is in the functional relationship $m_w = f(m_x, m_y)$. It is desired to estimate m_w by $\bar{w} = f(\bar{x}, \bar{y})$ and to compute $s_{\bar{w}}$ as an estimate of $\sigma_{\bar{w}}$.

If the errors of measurements of these quantities are small in comparison with the values measured, the propagation of error formulas usually work surprisingly well. The $\sigma_{\bar{w}}^2$, $\sigma_{\bar{x}}^2$, and $\sigma_{\bar{y}}^2$ that are used in the following formulas will often be replaced in practice by the computed values $s_{\bar{w}}^2$, $s_{\bar{x}}^2$, and $s_{\bar{y}}^2$.

The general formula for $\sigma_{\bar{w}}^2$ is given by

$$\sigma_{\bar{w}}^2 \doteq \left[\frac{\partial f}{\partial x}\right]^2 \sigma_{\bar{x}}^2 + \left[\frac{\partial f}{\partial y}\right]^2 \sigma_{\bar{y}}^2 + 2\left[\frac{\partial f}{\partial x}\right]\left[\frac{\partial f}{\partial y}\right]\rho_{\bar{x}\bar{y}}\sigma_{\bar{x}}\sigma_{\bar{y}} \qquad (2\text{-}12)$$

where the partial derivatives in square brackets are to be evaluated at the averages of x and y. If X and Y are independent, $\rho = 0$ and therefore the last term equals zero. If X and Y are measured in pairs, $s_{\bar{x}\bar{y}}$ (Eq. 2-6) can be used as an estimate of $\rho_{\bar{x}\bar{y}}\sigma_{\bar{x}}\sigma_{\bar{y}}$.

If W is functionally related to U and V by

$$m_w = f(m_u, m_v)$$

TABLE 2-3. PROPAGATION OF ERROR FORMULAS FOR SOME SIMPLE FUNCTIONS

(*X* and *Y* are assumed to be independent.)

Function form	Approximate formula for $s_{\bar{w}}^2$
$m_w = Am_x + Bm_y$	$A^2 s_{\bar{x}}^2 + B^2 s_{\bar{y}}^2$ (exact)
$m_w = \dfrac{m_x}{m_y}$	$\left(\dfrac{\bar{x}}{\bar{y}}\right)^2\left(\dfrac{s_{\bar{x}}^2}{\bar{x}^2} + \dfrac{s_{\bar{y}}^2}{\bar{y}^2}\right)$
$m_w = \dfrac{1}{m_y}$	$\dfrac{s_{\bar{y}}^2}{\bar{y}^4}$
$m_w = \dfrac{m_x}{m_x + m_y}$	$\left(\dfrac{\bar{w}}{\bar{x}}\right)^4(\bar{y}^2 s_{\bar{x}}^2 + \bar{x}^2 s_{\bar{y}}^2)$
$m_w = \dfrac{m_x}{1 + m_x}$	$\dfrac{s_{\bar{x}}^2}{(1 + \bar{x})^4}$
*$m_w = m_x m_y$	$(\bar{x}\bar{y})^2\left(\dfrac{s_{\bar{x}}^2}{\bar{x}^2} + \dfrac{s_{\bar{y}}^2}{\bar{y}^2}\right)$
*$m_w = m_x^2$	$4\bar{x}^2 s_{\bar{x}}^2$
$m_w = \sqrt{m_x}$	$\dfrac{1}{4}\dfrac{s_{\bar{x}}^2}{\bar{x}}$
*$m_w = \ln m_x$	$\dfrac{s_{\bar{x}}^2}{\bar{x}^2}$
*$m_w = km_x^a m_y^b$	$\bar{w}^2\left(a^2\dfrac{s_{\bar{x}}^2}{\bar{x}^2} + b^2\dfrac{s_{\bar{y}}^2}{\bar{y}^2}\right)$
*$m_w = e^{m_x}$	$e^{2\bar{x}} s_{\bar{x}}^2$
$W = 100\dfrac{s_x}{\bar{x}}$ (=coefficient of variation)	$\dfrac{\bar{w}^2}{2(n-1)}$ (not directly derived from the formulas)†

*Distribution of $\bar{w}$ is highly skewed and normal approximation could be seriously in error for small n.

†See, for example, *Statistical Theory with Engineering Applications*, by A. Hald, John Wiley & Sons, Inc., New York, 1952, p. 301.

and both U and V are functionally related to X and Y by

$$m_u = g(m_x, m_y)$$
$$m_v = h(m_x, m_y)$$

then U and V are functionally related. We will need the covariance $\sigma_{\bar{u}\bar{v}} = \rho_{\bar{u}\bar{v}}\sigma_{\bar{u}}\sigma_{\bar{v}}$ to calculate $\sigma_{\bar{w}}^2$. The covariance $\sigma_{\bar{u}\bar{v}}$ is given approximately by

$$\sigma_{\bar{u}\bar{v}} \doteq \left[\frac{\partial g}{\partial x} \cdot \frac{\partial h}{\partial x}\right]\sigma_{\bar{x}}^2 + \left[\frac{\partial g}{\partial y} \cdot \frac{\partial h}{\partial y}\right]\sigma_{\bar{y}}^2$$
$$+ \left\{\left[\frac{\partial g}{\partial x} \cdot \frac{\partial h}{\partial y}\right] + \left[\frac{\partial g}{\partial y} \cdot \frac{\partial h}{\partial x}\right]\right\}\rho_{\bar{x}\bar{y}}\sigma_{\bar{x}}\sigma_{\bar{y}}$$

$$(2\text{-}13)$$

The square brackets mean, as before, that the partial derivatives are to be evaluated at $\bar{x}$ and $\bar{y}$. If X and Y are independent, the last term again vanishes.

These formulas can be extended to three or more variables if necessary. For convenience, a few special formulas for commonly encountered functions are listed in Table 2-3 with X, Y assumed to be independent. These may be derived from the above formulas as exercises.

In these formulas, if

(a) the partial derivatives when evaluated at the averages are small, and

(b) σ_x, σ_y are small compared to $\bar{x}$, $\bar{y}$,

then the approximations are good and $\bar{w}$ tends to be distributed normally (the ones marked by asterisks are highly skewed and normal approximation could be seriously in error for small n).

Pooling Estimates of Variances. The problem often arises that there are several estimates of a common variance σ^2 which we wish to combine into a single estimate. For example, a gage block may be compared with the master block n_1 times, resulting in an estimate of the variance s_1^2. Another gage block compared with the master block n_2 times, giving rise to s_2^2, etc. As long as the nominal thicknesses of these blocks are within a certain range, the precision of calibration can be expected to remain the same. To get a better evaluation of the precision of the calibration process, we would wish to combine these estimates. The rule is to combine the computed variances weighted by their respective degrees of freedom, or

$$s_p^2 = \frac{\nu_1 s_1^2 + \nu_2 s_2^2 + \cdots + \nu_k s_k^2}{\nu_1 + \nu_2 + \cdots + \nu_k} \tag{2-14}$$

The pooled estimate of the standard deviation, of course, is $\sqrt{s_p^2} = s_p$. In the example, $\nu_1 = n_1 - 1$, $\nu_2 = n_2 - 1, \ldots,$ $\nu_k = n_k - 1$, thus the expression reduces to

$$s_p^2 = \frac{(n_1 - 1)s_1^2 + (n_2 - 1)s_2^2 + \cdots + (n_k - 1)s_k^2}{n_1 + n_2 + \cdots + n_k - k} \tag{2-15}$$

The degrees of freedom for the pooled estimate is the sum of the degrees of freedom of individual estimates, or $v_1 + v_2 + \cdots v_k = n_1 + n_2 + \cdots + n_k - k$. With the increased number of degrees of freedom, s_p is a more dependable estimate of σ than an individual s. Eventually, we may consider the value of s_p to be equal to that of σ and claim that we know the precision of the measuring process.

For the special case where k sets of duplicate measurements are available, the above formula reduces to:

$$s_p^2 = \frac{1}{2k} \sum_1^k d_i^2 \qquad (2\text{-}16)$$

where d_i = difference of duplicate readings. The pooled standard deviation s_p has k degrees of freedom.

For sets of normally distributed measurements where the number of measurements in each set is small, say less than ten, an estimate of the standard deviation can be obtained by multiplying the range of these measurements by a constant. Table 2-4 lists these constants corresponding to the number n of measurements in the set. For large n, considerable information is lost and this procedure is not recommended.

TABLE 2-4. ESTIMATE OF σ FROM THE RANGE*

n	*Multiplying factor*
2	0.886
3	0.591
4	0.486
5	0.430
6	0.395
7	0.370
8	0.351
9	0.337
10	0.325

*Adapted from *Biometrika Tables for Statisticians*, Vol. I, edited by E. S. Pearson and H. O. Hartley, The University Press, Cambridge, 1958.

If there are k sets of n measurements each, the average range $\bar{R}$ can be computed. The standard deviation can be estimated by multiplying the average range by the factor for n.

Component of Variance Between Groups. In pooling estimates of variances from a number of subgroups, we have increased confidence in the value of the estimate obtained. Let us call this estimate the within-group standard deviation, σ_w. The within-group standard deviation σ_w is a proper measure of dispersions of values within the same group, but not necessarily the proper one for dispersions of values belonging to different groups.

If in making calibrations there is a difference between groups, say from day to day, or from set to set, then the limiting means of the groups are not equal. These limiting means may be thought of as individual measurements; thus, it could be assumed that the average of these limiting means will approach a limit which can be called the limiting mean for all the groups. In estimating σ_w^2, the differences of individuals from the respective group means are used. Obviously σ_w does not include the differences between groups. Let us use σ_b^2 to denote the variance corresponding to the differences between groups, i.e., the measure of dispersion of the limiting means of the respective groups about the limiting mean for all groups.

Thus for each individual measurement x, the variance of x has two components, and

$$\sigma^2 = \sigma_b^2 + \sigma_w^2$$

For the group mean $\bar{x}$ with n measurements in the group,

$$\sigma_{\bar{x}}^2 = \sigma_b^2 + \frac{\sigma_w^2}{n}$$

If k groups of n measurements are available giving averages $\bar{x}_1, \bar{x}_2, \ldots, \bar{x}_k$, then an estimate of $\sigma_{\bar{x}}^2$ is

$$s_{\bar{x}}^2 = \frac{1}{k-1} \sum_{i=1}^{k} (\bar{x}_1 - \bar{\bar{x}})^2$$

with $k - 1$ degrees of freedom, where $\bar{\bar{x}}$ is the average of all nk measurements.

The resolution of the total variance into components attributable to identifiable causes or factors and the estimation of such components of variances are topics treated under analysis of variance and experimental design. For selected treatments and examples see references 5, 6, and 8.

Comparison of Means and Variances

Comparison of means is perhaps one of the most frequently used techniques in metrology. The mean obtained from one measurement process may be compared with a standard value; two series of measurements on the same quantity may be compared; or sets of measurements on more than two quantities may be compared to determine homogeneity of the group of means.

It is to be borne in mind in all of the comparisons discussed below, that we are interested in comparing the limiting means. The sample means and the computed standard errors are used to calculate confidence limits on the difference between two means. The "t" statistic derived from normal distribution theory is used in this procedure since we are assuming either the measurement process is normal, or the sample averages are approximately normally distributed.

Comparison of a Mean with a Standard Value. In calibration of weights at the National Bureau of Standards, the weights to be calibrated are intercompared with sets of standard weights having "accepted" corrections. Accepted corrections are based on years of experience and considered to be exact to the accuracy required. For instance, the accepted correction for the NB'10 gram weight is −0.4040 mg.

The NB'10 is treated as an unknown and calibrated with each set of weights tested using an intercomparison scheme based on a 100-gm standard weight. Hence the observed correction for NB'10 can be computed for each particular calibration. Table 2-5 lists eleven observed corrections of NB'10 during May 1963.

TABLE 2-5. COMPUTATION OF CONFIDENCE LIMITS FOR
OBSERVED CORRECTIONS, NB'10 gm*

Date	i	X_i Observed Corrections to standard 10 gm wt in mg
5–1–63	1	−0.4008
5–1–63	2	−0.4053
5–1–63	3	−0.4022
5–2–63	4	−0.4075
5–2–63	5	−0.3994
5–3–63	6	−0.3986
5–6–63	7	−0.4015
5–6–63	8	−0.3992
5–6–63	9	−0.3973
5–7–63	10	−0.4071
5–7–63	11	−0.4012

$$\sum x_i = -4.4201 \qquad \sum x_i^2 = 1.77623417$$

$$\bar{x} = -0.40183 \text{ mg} \qquad \frac{(\sum x_i)^2}{n} = 1.77611673$$

$$\text{difference} = 0.00011744$$

$$s^2 = \frac{1}{n-1}(0.00011744) = 0.000011744$$

$s = 0.00343 =$ computed standard deviation of an observed correction about the mean.

$\dfrac{s}{\sqrt{n}} = 0.00103 =$ computed standard deviation of the mean of eleven corrections.

$\qquad\qquad = $ computed standard error of the mean.

For a two-sided 95 percent confidence interval for the mean of the above sample of size 11, $\alpha/2 = 0.025$, $v = 10$, and the corresponding value of t is equal to 2.228 in the table of t distribution. Therefore,

$$L_l = \bar{x} - t\frac{s}{\sqrt{n}} = -0.40183 - 2.228 \times 0.00103 = -0.40412$$

and

$$L_u = \bar{x} + t\frac{s}{\sqrt{n}} = -0.40183 + 2.228 \times 0.00103 = -0.39954$$

*Data supplied by Robert Raybold, Metrology Division, National Bureau of Standards.

Calculated 95 percent confidence limits from the eleven observed corrections are -0.4041 and -0.3995. These values include the accepted value of -0.4040, and we conclude that the observed corrections agree with the accepted value.

What if the computed confidence limits for the observed correction do not cover the accepted value? Three explanations may be suggested:

1. The accepted value is correct. However, in choosing $\alpha = 0.05$, we know that 5 percent of the time in the long run we will make an error in our statement. By chance alone, it is possible that this particular set of limits would not cover the accepted value.

2. The average of the observed corrections does not agree with the accepted value because of certain systematic error, temporary or seasonal, particular to one or several members of this set of data for which no adjustment has been made.

3. The accepted value is incorrect, e.g., the mass of the standard has changed.

In our example, we would be extremely reluctant to agree to the third explanation since we have much more confidence in the accepted value than the value based only on eleven calibrations. We are warned that something may have gone wrong, but not unduly alarmed since such an event will happen purely by chance about once every twenty times.

The control chart for mean with known value, to be discussed in a following section, would be the proper tool to use to monitor the constancy of the correction of the standard mass.

Comparison Among Two or More Means. The difference between two quantities X and Y to be measured is the quantity

$$m_{x-y} = m_x - m_y$$

and is estimated by $\bar{x} - \bar{y}$, where $\bar{x}$ and $\bar{y}$ are averages of a number of measurements of X and Y respectively.

Suppose we are interested in knowing whether the difference m_{x-y} could be zero. This problem can be solved by a technique previously introduced, i.e., the confidence limits can be computed for m_{x-y}, and if the upper and lower limits include zero, we could conclude that m_{x-y} may take the value zero; otherwise, we conclude that the evidence is against $m_{x-y} = 0$.

Let us assume that measurements of X and Y are independent with known variances σ_x^2 and σ_y^2 respectively.

By Eq. (2.10)

$$\sigma_{\bar{x}}^2 = \frac{\sigma_x^2}{n} \text{ for } \bar{x} \text{ of } n \text{ measurements}$$

$$\sigma_{\bar{y}}^2 = \frac{\sigma_y^2}{k} \text{ for } \bar{y} \text{ of } k \text{ measurements}$$

then by (2.8),

$$\sigma_{\bar{x}-\bar{y}}^2 = \frac{\sigma_x^2}{n} + \frac{\sigma_y^2}{k}$$

Therefore, the quantity

$$z = \frac{(\bar{x} - \bar{y}) - 0}{\sqrt{\dfrac{\sigma_x^2}{n} + \dfrac{\sigma_y^2}{k}}} \tag{2-17}$$

is approximately normally distributed with mean zero and a standard deviation of one under the assumption $m_{x-y} = 0$.

If σ_x and σ_y are not known, but the two can be assumed to be approximately equal, e.g., $\bar{x}$ and $\bar{y}$ are measured by the same process, then s_x^2 and s_y^2 can be pooled by Eq. (2-15), or

$$s_p^2 = \frac{(n-1)s_x^2 + (k-1)s_y^2}{n+k-2}$$

This pooled computed variance estimates

$$\sigma^2 = \sigma_x^2 = \sigma_y^2$$

so that

$$\sigma_{\bar{x}-\bar{y}}^2 = \frac{\sigma_x^2}{n} + \frac{\sigma_y^2}{k} = \frac{n+k}{nk}\sigma^2$$

Thus, the quantity

$$t = \frac{(\bar{x} - \bar{y}) - 0}{\sqrt{\dfrac{n+k}{nk}}\, s_p} \tag{2-18}$$

is distributed as Student's "t", and a confidence interval can be set about m_{x-y} with $\nu = n + k - 2$ and $p = 1 - \alpha$. If this interval does not include zero, we may conclude that the evidence is strongly against the hypothesis $m_x = m_y$.

As an example, we continue with the calibration of weights with NB'10 gm. For 11 subsequent observed corrections during September and October, the confidence interval (computed in the same manner as in the preceding example) has been found to be

$$L_l = -0.40782$$
$$L_u = -0.40126$$

Also,

$$\bar{Y} = -0.40454 \quad \text{and} \quad \frac{s}{\sqrt{k}} = 0.00147$$

It is desired to compare the means of observed corrections for the two sets of data. Here

$$n = k = 11$$
$$\bar{x} = -0.40183, \qquad \bar{y} = -0.40454$$
$$s_x^2 = 0.000011669, \qquad s_y^2 = 0.000023813$$

$$s_p^2 = \tfrac{1}{2}(0.000035482) = 0.000017741$$

$$\frac{n+k}{nk} = \frac{11+11}{121} = \frac{2}{11}$$

$$\sqrt{\frac{n+k}{nk}}\,s_p = \sqrt{\frac{2}{11} \times 0.000017741} = 0.00180$$

For $\alpha/2 = 0.025$, $1 - \alpha = 0.95$, and $\nu = 20$, $t = 2.086$. Therefore,

$$L_u = (\bar{x} - \bar{y}) + t\sqrt{\frac{n+k}{nk}}\,s_p = 0.00271 + 2.086 \times 0.00180$$

$$= 0.00646$$

$$L_l = (\bar{x} - \bar{y}) - t\sqrt{\frac{n+k}{nk}}\,s_p = -0.00104$$

Since $L_l < 0 < L_u$ shows that the confidence interval includes zero, we conclude that there is no evidence against the hypothesis that the two observed average corrections are the same, or $m_x = m_y$. Note, however, that we would reach a conclusion of no difference wherever the magnitude of $\bar{x} - \bar{y}$ (0.00271 mg) is less than the half-width of the confidence interval (2.086 $\times$ 0.00180 = 0.00375 mg) calculated for the particular case. When the true difference m_{x-y} is large, the above situation is not likely to happen; but when the true difference is small, say about 0.003 mg, then it is highly probable that a conclusion of no difference will still be reached. If a detection of difference of this magnitude is of interest, more measurements will be needed.

The following additional topics are treated in reference 4.
1. Sample sizes required under certain specified conditions—Tables A-8 and A-9.
2. σ_x^2 cannot be assumed to be equal to σ_y^2—Section 3-3.1.2.
3. Comparison of several means by Studentized range—Sections 3-4 and 15-4.

Comparison of variances or ranges. As we have seen, the precision of a measurement process can be expressed in terms of the computed standard deviation, the variance, or the range. To compare the precision of two processes a and b, any of the three measures can be used, depending on the preference and convenience of the user.

Let s_a^2 be the estimate of σ_a^2 with ν_a degrees of freedom, and s_b^2 be the estimate of σ_b^2 with ν_b degrees of freedom. The ratio $F = s_a^2/s_b^2$ has a distribution depending on ν_a and ν_b. Tables of upper percentage points of F are given in most statistical textbooks, e.g., reference 4, Table A-5 and Section 4-2.

In the comparison of means, we were interested in finding out if the absolute difference between m_a and m_b could reasonably be zero; similarly, here we may be interested in whether $\sigma_a^2 = \sigma_b^2$, or $\sigma_a^2/\sigma_b^2 = 1$. In practice, however, we are usually concerned with whether the imprecision of one process exceeds that of another process. We could, therefore, compute the ratio of s_a^2 to s_b^2, and the question arises: If in fact $\sigma_a^2 = \sigma_b^2$, what is the probability of getting a value of the ratio as large as the one observed? For each pair of values of ν_a and ν_b, the tables list the values of F which are exceeded with probability α, the upper percentage point of the distribution of F. If the computed value of F exceeds this tabulated value of $F_{\alpha', \nu_a, \nu_b}$, then we conclude that the evidence is against the hypothesis $\sigma_a^2 = \sigma_b^2$; if it is less, we conclude that σ_a^2 could be equal to σ_b^2.

For example, we could compute the ratio of s_y^2 to s_x^2 in the preceding two examples.

Here the degrees of freedom $\nu_y = \nu_x = 10$, the tabulated value of F which is exceeded 5 percent of the time for these degrees of freedom is 2.98, and

$$\frac{s_y^2}{s_x^2} = \frac{0.000023813}{0.000011669} = 2.041$$

Since 2.04 is less than 2.98, we conclude that there is no reason to believe that the precision of the calibration process in September and October is poorer than that of May.

For small degrees of freedom, the critical value of F is rather large, e.g., for $\nu_a = \nu_b = 3$, and $\alpha' = 0.05$, the value of F is 9.28. It follows that a small difference between σ_a^2 and σ_b^2 is not likely to be detected with a small number of measurements from each process. The table below gives the approximate number of measurements required to have a four-out-of-five chance of detecting whether σ_a is the indicated multiple of σ_b (while maintaining at 0.05 the probability of incorrectly concluding that $\sigma_a > \sigma_b$, when in fact $\sigma_a = \sigma_b$).

Multiple	No. of measurements
1.5	39
2.0	15
2.5	9
3.0	7
3.5	6
4.0	5

Table A-11 in reference 4 gives the critical values of the ratios of ranges, and Tables A-20 and A-21 give confidence limits on the standard deviation of the process based on computed standard deviation.

Control Charts Technique for
Maintaining Stability and Precision

A laboratory which performs routine measurement or calibration operations yields, as its daily product, numbers—averages, standard deviations, and ranges. The control chart techniques therefore could be applied to these numbers as products of a manufacturing process to furnish graphical evidence on whether the measurement process is in statistical control or out of statistical control. If it is out of control, these charts usually also indicate where and when the trouble occurred.

Control Chart for Averages. The basic concept of a control chart is in accord with what has been discussed thus far. A measurement process with limiting mean m and standard deviation σ is assumed. The sequence of numbers produced is divided into "rational" subgroups, e.g., by day, by a set of calibrations, etc. The averages of these subgroups are computed. These averages will have a mean m and a standard deviation $\sigma/\sqrt{n}$ where n is the number of measurements within each subgroup. These averages are approximately normally distributed.

In the construction of the control chart for averages, m is plotted as the center line, $m + k(\sigma/\sqrt{n})$ and $m - k(\sigma/\sqrt{n})$ are plotted as control limits, and the averages are plotted in an orderly sequence. If k is taken to be 3, we know that the chance of a plotted point falling outside of the limits, if the process is in control, is very small. Therefore, if a plotted point falls outside these limits, a warning is sounded and investigative action to locate the "assignable" cause that produced the departure, or corrective measures, are called for.

The above reasoning would be applicable to actual cases only if we have chosen the proper standard deviation σ. If the standard deviation is estimated by pooling the estimates computed from each subgroup and denoted by σ_w (within group), obviously differences, if any, between group averages have not been taken into consideration. Where there are between-group differences the variance of the individual $\bar{x}$ is not σ_w^2/n, but, as we have seen before, $\sigma_b^2 + (\sigma_w^2/n)$, where σ_b^2 represents the variance due to differences between groups. If σ_b^2 is of any consequence as compared to σ_w^2, many of the $\bar{x}$ values would exceed the limits constructed by using σ_w alone.

Two alternatives are open to us: (1) remove the cause of the between-group variation; or, (2) if such variation is a proper component of error, take it into account as has been previously discussed.

As an illustration of the use of a control chart on averages, we use again the NB'10 gram data. One hundred observed corrections for NB'10 are plotted in Fig. 2-5, including the two sets of data given under comparison of means (points 18 through 28, and points 60 through 71). A three-sigma limit of 8.6 μg was used based on the "accepted" value of standard deviation.

We note that all the averages are within the control limits, excepting numbers 36, 47, 63, 85, and 87. Five in a hundred falling outside of the three-sigma limits is more than predicted by the theory. No particular reasons, however, could be found for these departures.

Since the accepted value of the standard deviation was obtained by pooling a large number of computed standard deviations for within-sets of

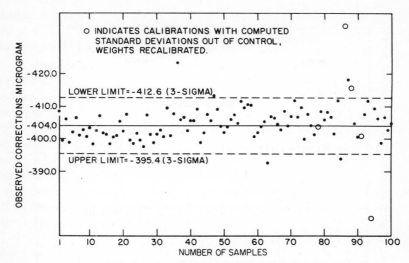

Fig. 2-5. Control chart on $\bar{x}$ for NB'10 gram.

calibrations, the graph indicates that a "between-set" component may be present. A slight shift upwards is also noted between the first 30 points and the remainder.

Control Chart for Standard Deviations. The computed standard deviation, as previously stated, is a measure of imprecision. For a set of calibrations, however, the number of measurements is usually small, and consequently also the degrees of freedom. These computed standard deviations with few degrees of freedom can vary considerably by chance alone, even though the precision of the process remains unchanged. The control chart on the computed standard deviations (or ranges) is therefore an indispensable tool.

The distribution of s depends on the degrees of freedom associated with it, and is not symmetrical about m_s. The frequency curve of s is limited on the left side by zero, and has a long "tail" to the right. The limits, therefore, are not symmetrical about m_s. Furthermore, if the standard deviation of the process is known to be σ, m_s is not equal to σ, but is equal to $c_2\sigma$, where c_2 is a constant associated with the degrees of freedom in s.

The constants necessary for the construction of three-sigma control limits for averages, computed standard deviations, and ranges, are given in most textbooks on quality control. Section 18-3 of reference 4 gives such a table. A more comprehensive treatment on control charts is given in ASTM "Manual on Quality Control of Materials," Special Technical Publication 15-C.

Unfortunately, the notation employed in quality control work differs

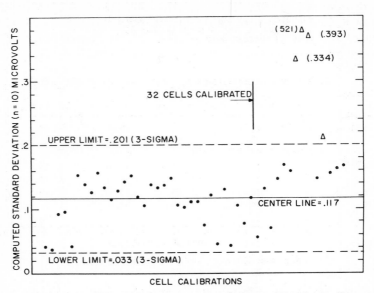

Fig. 2-6. Control chart on s for the calibration of standard cells.

in some respect from what is now standard in statistics, and correction factors have to be applied to some of these constants when the computed standard deviation is calculated by the definition given in this chapter. These corrections are explained in the footnote under the table.

As an example of the use of control charts on the precision of a calibration process, we will use data from NBS calibration of standard cells.* Standard cells in groups of four or six are usually compared with an NBS standard cell on ten separate days. A typical data sheet for a group of six cells, after all the necessary corrections, appears in Table 2-6. The standard deviation of a comparison is calculated from the ten comparisons for each cell and the standard deviation for the average value of the ten comparisons is listed in the line marked SDA. These values were plotted as points 6 through 11 in Fig. 2-6.

Let us assume that the precision of the calibration process remains the same. We can therefore pool the standard deviations computed for each cell (with nine degrees of freedom) over a number of cells and take this value as the current value of the standard deviation of a comparison, σ. The corresponding current value of standard deviation of the average of ten comparisons will be denoted by $\sigma' = \sigma/\sqrt{10}$. The control chart will be made on $s' = s/\sqrt{10}$.

*Illustrative data supplied by Miss Catherine Law, Electricity Division, National Bureau of Standards.

For example, the SDA's for 32 cells calibrated between June 29 and August 8, 1962, are plotted as the first 32 points in Fig. 2-6. The pooled standard deviation of the average is 0.114 with 288 degrees of freedom. The between-group component is assumed to be negligible.

TABLE 2-6. CALIBRATION DATA FOR SIX STANDARD CELLS

Day	Corrected Emf's and standard deviations, Microvolts					
1	27.10	24.30	31.30	33.30	32.30	23.20
2	25.96	24.06	31.06	34.16	33.26	23.76
3	26.02	24.22	31.92	33.82	33.22	24.02
4	26.26	24.96	31.26	33.96	33.26	24.16
5	27.23	25.23	31.53	34.73	33.33	24.43
6	25.90	24.40	31.80	33.90	32.90	24.10
7	26.79	24.99	32.19	34.39	33.39	24.39
8	26.18	24.98	32.18	35.08	33.98	24.38
9	26.17	25.07	31.97	34.27	33.07	23.97
10	26.16	25.16	31.96	34.06	32.96	24.16
R	1.331	1.169	1.127	1.777	1.677	1.233
AVG	26.378	24.738	31.718	34.168	33.168	24.058
SD	0.482	0.439	0.402	0.495	0.425	0.366
SDA	0.153	0.139	0.127	0.157	0.134	0.116

Position	Emf, volts	Position	Emf, volts
1	1.0182264	4	1.0182342
2	1.0182247	5	1.0182332
3	1.0182317	6	1.0182240

Since $n = 10$, we find our constants for three-sigma control limits on s' in Section 18-3 of reference 4 and apply the corrections as follows:

$$\text{Center line} = \sqrt{\frac{n}{n-1}}\ c_2\sigma' = 1.111 \times 0.9227 \times 0.114 = 0.117$$

$$\text{Lower limit} = \sqrt{\frac{n}{n-1}}\ B_1\sigma' = 1.111 \times 0.262 \times 0.114 = 0.033$$

$$\text{Upper limit} = \sqrt{\frac{n}{n-1}}\ B_2\sigma' = 1.111 \times 1.584 \times 0.114 = 0.201$$

The control chart (Fig. 2-6) was constructed using these values of center line and control limits computed from the 32 calibrations. The standard deviations of the averages of subsequent calibrations are then plotted.

Three points in Fig. 2-6 far exceed the upper control limit. All three cells, which were from the same source, showed drifts during the period of calibration. A fourth point barely exceeded the limit. It is to be noted that the data here were selected to include these three points for purposes of illustration only, and do not represent the normal sequence of calibrations.

The main function of the chart is to justify the precision statement on the report of calibration, which is based on a value of σ estimated with

perhaps thousands of degrees of freedom and which is shown to be in control.
The report of calibration for these cells ($\sigma = 0.117 \doteq 0.12$) could read:

> "Each value is the mean of ten observations made between ____
> and ____. Based on a standard deviation of 0.12 microvolts for the
> means, these values are correct to 0.36 microvolts relative to the
> volt as maintained by the national reference group."

Linear Relationship and Fitting of Constants by Least Squares

In using the arithmetic mean of n measurements as an estimate of the
limiting mean, we have, knowingly or unknowingly, fitted a constant to
the data by the method of least squares, i.e., we have selected a value $\hat{m}$
for m such that

$$\sum_{1}^{n} (y_i - \hat{m})^2 = \sum_{1}^{n} d_i^2$$

is a minimum. The solution is $\hat{m} = \bar{y}$. The deviations $d_i = y_i - \hat{m} = y_i - \bar{y}$
are called residuals.

Here we can express our measurements in the form of a mathematical
model

$$Y = m + \epsilon \tag{2-19}$$

where Y stands for the observed values, m the limiting mean (a constant),
and ϵ the random error (normal) of measurement with a limiting mean zero
and a standard deviation σ. By (2-1) and (2-9), it follows that

$$m_y = m + m_\epsilon = m$$

and

$$\sigma_y^2 = \sigma^2$$

The method of least squares requires us to use that estimator $\hat{m}$ for m such
that the sum of squares of the residuals is a minimum (among all possible
estimators). As a corollary, the method also states that the sum of squares
of residuals divided by the number of measurements n less the number of
estimated constants p will give us an estimate of σ^2, i.e.,

$$s^2 = \frac{\sum (y_i - \hat{m})^2}{n - p} = \frac{\sum (y_i - \bar{y})^2}{n - 1} \tag{2-20}$$

It is seen that the above agrees with our definition of s^2.

Suppose Y, the quantity measured, exhibits a linear functional relationship with a variable which can be controlled accurately; then a model can
be written as

$$Y = a + bX + \epsilon \tag{2-21}$$

where, as before, Y is the quantity measured, a (the intercept) and b (the slope) are two constants to be estimated, and ϵ the random error with limiting mean zero and variance σ^2. We set X at x_i, and observe y_i. For example, y_i might be the change in length of a gage block steel observed for n equally spaced temperatures x_i within a certain range. The quantity of interest is the coefficient of thermal expansion b.

For any estimates of a and b, say $\hat{a}$ and $\hat{b}$, we can compute a value $\hat{y}_i$ for each x_i, or

$$\hat{y}_i = \hat{a} + \hat{b}x_i$$

If we require the sum of squares of the residuals

$$\sum_{i=1}^{n} (y_i - \hat{y}_i)^2$$

to be a minimum, then it can be shown that

$$\hat{b} = \frac{\sum_{i=1}^{n} (x_i - \bar{x})(y_i - \bar{y})}{\sum_{i=1}^{n} (x_i - \bar{x})^2} \tag{2-22}$$

and

$$\hat{a} = \bar{y} - \hat{b}\bar{x} \tag{2-23}$$

The variance of Y can be estimated by

$$s^2 = \frac{\sum (y_i - \hat{y}_i)^2}{n - 2} \tag{2-24}$$

with $n - 2$ degrees of freedom since two constants have been estimated from the data.

The standard errors of $\hat{b}$ and $\hat{a}$ are respectively estimated by $s_{\hat{b}}$ and $s_{\hat{a}}$, where

$$s_{\hat{b}}^2 = \frac{s^2}{\sum (x_i - \bar{x})^2} \tag{2-25}$$

$$s_{\hat{a}}^2 = s^2 \left[\frac{1}{n} + \frac{\bar{x}^2}{\sum (x_i - \bar{x})^2} \right] \tag{2-26}$$

With these estimates and the degrees of freedom associated with s^2, confidence limits can be computed for $\hat{a}$ and $\hat{b}$ for the confidence coefficient selected if we assume that errors are normally distributed.

Thus, the lower and upper limits of a and b, respectively, are:

$$\hat{a} - ts_{\hat{a}}, \qquad \hat{a} + ts_{\hat{a}}$$
$$\hat{b} - ts_{\hat{b}}, \qquad \hat{b} + ts_{\hat{b}}$$

for the value of t corresponding to the degree of freedom and the selected confidence coefficient.

The following problems relating to a linear relationship between two variables are treated in reference 4, Section 5-4.

1. Confidence intervals for a point on the fitted line.
2. Confidence band for the line as a whole.
3. Confidence interval for a single predicted value of Y for a given X.

Polynomial and multivariate relationships are treated in Chapter 6 of the same reference.

REFERENCES

The following references are recommended for topics introduced in the first section of this chapter:

1. Wilson, Jr., E. B., *An Introduction to Scientific Research*, McGraw-Hill Book Company, New York, 1952, Chapters 7, 8, and 9.

2. Eisenhart, Churchill, "Realistic Evaluation of the Precision and Accuracy of Instrument Calibration System," *Journal of Research of the National Bureau of Standards*, Vol. 67C, No. 2, 1963.

3. Youden, W. J., *Experimentation and Measurement*, National Science Teacher Association Vista of Science Series No. 2, Scholastic Book Series, New York.

In addition to the three general references given above, the following are selected with special emphasis on their ease of understanding and applicability in the measurement science:

Statistical Methods

4. Natrella, M. G., *Experimental Statistics*, NBS Handbook 91, U.S. Government Printing Office, Washington, D.C., 1963.

5. Youden, W. J., *Statistical Methods for Chemists*, John Wiley & Sons, Inc., New York, 1951.

6. Davies, O. L., *Statistical Method in Research and Production* (3rd ed.), Hafner Publishing Co., Inc., New York, 1957.

Textbooks

7. Dixon, W. J. and F. J. Massey, *Introduction to Statistical Analysis* (2nd ed.), McGraw-Hill Book Company, New York, 1957.

8. Brownlee, K. A., *Statistical Theory and Methodology in Science and Engineering*, John Wiley & Sons, Inc., New York, 1960.

9. Areley, N. and K. R. Buch, *Introduction to the Theory of Probability and Statistics*, John Wiley & Sons, Inc., New York, 1950.

3

GENERAL PRINCIPLES OF

MEASUREMENT

The topics of "Linear Measurements" and "Physical Measurements" are treated in this chapter. The linear data deal with datum deformation, stress and strain, size and geometrical shape, and contours. (See also Chapter 11, "Geometric Considerations in Linear Measurements.")

Because of the extreme breadth of physical measurements, only mechanical measurements are discussed system-wise. For detailed data on all physical measurements, reference should be made to the bibliography at the end of the chapter.

LINEAR MEASUREMENTS*

Basically, linear measurement is conducted for the determination of spatial relationship between points by the assignment of numbers of units

*By Theodore R. Young, Chief, Length Section, Metrology Division, Institute for Basic Standards, National Bureau of Standards.

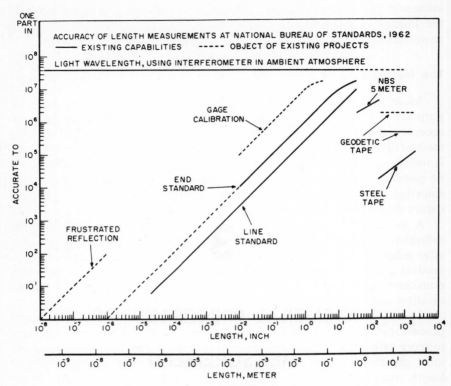

Fig. 3-1. Accuracy of linear length measurement at the National Bureau of Standards. Uncertainty limiting the accuracy is represented at the three sigma level.

indicating length. Length is the minimum or "straight-line" geometrical distance between points. The unit is proportionately related to the standard of length, the meter. The meter is exactly 1,650,763.73 vacuum wavelengths of light resulting from the unperturbed atomic energy level transition $2p_{10} - 5d_5$ of the isotope of krypton having atomic weight 86.[1]† Specifications, defining a source of such wavelengths, make possible a standard of length limited to an uncertainty estimated to be 1 part in 10^8.[1] The state of the art of transferring from this standard to the calibration of material standards such as gage blocks, length scales and tapes is shown in Fig. 3-1.[2]

Length characteristics of material embodiments are defined by lines, edges, and surfaces, identities that are called datums, and these datums are coupled together by matter reactive to factors such as heat, dilational and shearing stresses, and electromagnetic radiation. These factors and their

†Superior numbers indicate specific references at the end of this section.

influences upon length measurement are limited by specifying the setup of the linear measurement. The setup of a measurement defines material, environment, procedure, and techniques involved in the measurement.

The Importance of Setup and Datum Definition

As in all measurement, linear measurement is performed to serve a purpose. It is the purpose that determines the significant datum and the accuracy required and thus indicates the method of measurement. The method of measurement is a specification of setup and datum to be employed. It includes a definition of the equipment to be employed, the operations to be performed, the sequence of those operations, the condition of the surrounding environment, and the definition of all factors known to influence datum deformation and the accuracy of measurement at the level required.

A measurement process is then employed in an attempt to realize the definitions forming the method of measurement. The data from this process, after reduction, is the end product of the linear measurement. Does the end product achieve the accuracy required and is it of a form that can be communicated intelligently to other related efforts? Reference 3 provides an excellent review of this subject.

To answer these questions, it is necessary to scrutinize the measurement process, the method of measurement, and the purpose of the measurement in more detail. The length measurement is a direct product of the measurement process. Immediately the question arises: How characteristic of the length measurement process is the length measurement? An answer is provided by making successive measurements. If the precision of these measurements proves unfavorable in relation to the accuracy required, refinement is necessary. The nature of this refinement is implied by the usual meaning of precision, that is, the degree of mutual agreement of measurements of a *single quantity* by a process *under specific conditions*. If the precision is unsatisfactory, the measured specimen must be more stable and/or the conditions of the process must be more specific. Need for better setup and datum definition is indicated.

With refinements applied sufficient to the need, the end product of the measurement is a value that approaches the limiting mean, a value that would be obtained if the measurement process were applied to the same test specimen an infinite number of times. A value of precision is also obtained as an end product. This is an estimate of the possible magnitude of the dissimilarity between the value and the limiting mean. The precision is often stated in terms of the magnitude of the probable error or the magnitude of the standard error of the measurement process. Both the value of the measurement and the value of the precision are related to the measurement process, and have no significance unless the measurement process is recorded. This is usually accomplished by defining the setup and the datum, including the specification of all factors known to influence accuracy and precision of the measurement.

Occasionally the concepts defining a method of measurement are so detailed and so generally followed in a standard practice that there is little uncertainty as to the specifications of the measurement process. In such cases, a complete description of the measurement process is unnecessary. However, it is important to recognize the fact that no particular measurement process exactly follows the conceptual method of measurement.

These exceptions to the concept of the method of measurement may be purposely introduced to expedite the measurement, but they should be considered suitable only if they satisfy certain conditions. First, the exceptions should be noted and detailed, and be presented as part of the end product of the measurement process. Second, a method generally accepted as being reliable should exist whereby the measured value obtained in the modified measurement process can be reduced to the value likely to be achieved by adhering to concepts of the method of measurement. Third, the magnitude of the uncertainties introduced by this reduction, when added to the uncertainties of the measurement process, should not abrogate the measurement effort in regard to its being suitable to the purpose.

Other exceptions of the measurement process to the concepts of the method of measurement are not purposely introduced. They are subtle, recurring differences of the measurement process from that which is truly representative of the method of measurement. The accumulation of error due to such differences is often called systematic error. Because of the recurring nature of such differences, an estimate of this type of error cannot be achieved by reference to the precision of the measurement process. Precision indicates the degree of similarity of the measured value to the limiting mean value of the process; it does not measure the similarity of the process to the conceptual method of measurement. How is an estimate of this similarity achieved?

It has been stated previously that the purpose for which measurement is made dictates the accuracy required, and this requirement in turn indicates the method of measurement to be employed. Since accuracy may be defined as the degree of the measured value's agreement with the true value, and since the true value is incapable of identification, how can accuracy be estimated and why are certain methods of measurement associated with certain accuracies? The solution is obtained by introducing a pragmatic concept of true value. This "true" value might be defined as the limiting mean of a series of measured values, each value being a limiting mean obtained from an independent measurement process. Independent processes would employ different laboratories, observers, equipment, etc.; the same test sample would be measured by each process. The measurement processes are similar in that each one is a nominal representation of the method of measurement. The probability of the "true" value being between the extreme values of a series of independent measurement processes may be determined by a method indicated by Youden.[4] The probability of the "true" value falling between the extreme values of a series of n independent measurement processes is expressed, in percent, as

$$\frac{2^{n-1} - 1}{2^{n-1}} \times 100$$

It is evident that the probability is dependent upon the number of measurement processes composing the series and not upon the extreme limits of values obtained from the series. The accuracy of the method of measurement is estimated by the magnitude of dispersion of the extreme values of the series of measurement processes; the "true" value is between these extreme limits. Thus a "true" value is associated with a method of measurement whose reputation for accuracy is established by the agreement of results of measurement processes, each of which attempts to duplicate the method.

The foregoing indicates a method of comparing a particular measurement process with the conceptual method of measurement. The measurement process may be related to other independent measurement processes that attempt to duplicate the method of measurement. This relation can be achieved by an audit survey utilizing a group of independent measurement processes in measuring the same test specimens, and evaluating the results with respect to the reputed accuracy of the method.

In summary, the purpose to be served by linear measurement usually defines the accuracy required. A method of measurement is chosen that is reputed to be capable of providing this accuracy. This method is a concept. Its reputation for accuracy is founded on man's knowledge of physical laws, the consistency of results obtained in application of this concept, and the agreement of such results with those derived by following other concepts of similar merit. The concept provides guidance as to the setup and datum to be used; it defines equipment, procedures, and conditions of the surrounding environment.

The actual length measurement is a product of a measurement *process*, not of the method of measurement. The setup and datum employed in the measurement process are, in general, different from those conceptually defined in the method of measurement. The consistency of the setup employed and the datum used is indicated by the precision achieved. This consistency is considered satisfactory only when the precision is favorable in respect to the accuracy required. Finally, the degree to which the setup and datum employed in the process agree with the concepts indicated by the method is tested practically by comparing the results obtained in the process with those of other processes designed to follow the same method

of measurement. Such tests, called measurement audits, are usually conducted periodically and involve the measurement of a representative group
of specimens by several independent measurement processes.

Datum Deformation, Stress and Strain

It is the intent of this section to define deformation, review some simple
engineering concepts and terminology useful in describing and predicting
deformation and show, by example, some of the deformation conditions
encountered in the field of linear metrology. The scope of this section does
not cover all the cases of deformation likely to be encountered by the
metrologist; the intent is to create an awareness that deformation does
generally exist and that it must be considered in the measurement method
or process. Some important but specialized cases, such as the deformation
between a radius probe and surface, will be considered in other chapters.
It is assumed that the material under consideration is homogeneous and
isotropic throughout in regard to elastic properties, and that deformations
are limited to small values such that squared and higher-order terms are
negligible.

When the distance between any two incremental elements of a material
changes from that of its unperturbed state, the material is considered to be
deformed.

Types of Deformations. Deformations are classified into two types,
dilational deformations and shear deformations. Dilational deformations
are the type causing a change of density of the material. Therefore, if the
material is finite in extent, a change of size occurs. A shear deformation
causes no change of density, but creates a change of shape.

The size and shape of a material in the unperturbed state results from
an equilibrium of internal forces within the material. Application of other
external or internal forces creates an inequilibrium of forces across imaginary surfaces within the material. Deformations occur of magnitudes sufficient to provide a new equilibrium of forces within the material. A different
size and/or shape results. Such an applied force expressed in terms of force
per unit area of the surface involved is termed a stress.

Types of Stresses. Corresponding to the two types of deformation there
are two types of stress, dilational stresses producing a change of density
and size of the material, and shear stresses producing a change in shape
of the material. An arbitrary force acting on a surface has two components,
one normal to the surface and one parallel to the surface. The former
produces dilational stress; the latter creates shearing stress.

For convenience, dilational stresses are divided into two subcategories
in accord with two general kinds of situation encountered. If the normal

force per unit area is constant over all the surface area enclosing a volume, the dilational stress is called a compressional stress. Such situations are encountered when a body is subjected to a hydrostatic pressure of a surrounding fluid, or to a change of temperature. On the other hand, if the dilational stress acts only upon surfaces whose normals are parallel, the stress is called a tensile stress. A rectangular parallelopiped held in the jaws of a C-clamp would be subject to a tensile stress.

The deformations a body experiences under stress are conventionally described by dimensionless quantities called *strains*. A body under dilational stress experiences a change of density. The ratio of this change in density to the density is termed a dilational strain. Thus a finite body under compressive stress experiences a change of volume. The ratio of this change of volume to the total volume is termed a volume strain. Similarly, the normal distance between parallel surfaces of a body changes under tensile stress. The ratio of this change to the normal distance between the surfaces is called a *linear strain*. On the other hand, forces acting as a couple parallel to these surfaces produce a shearing stress. The resulting deformation is one that displaces one surface with respect to the other in a direction perpendicular to the surface normals. This displacement in ratio to the distance between the surfaces is a *shearing strain*.

The concepts of stress and strain are used in the evaluation of the deformation of elastic material. A material is considered to be elastic for a range of stress if it deforms according to Hooke's Law; that is, the material deforms such that a constant ratio of stress to strain exists over the range of stress applied. For higher stresses, exceeding the elastic limit of the material, the linear relationship between stress and strain breaks down and finally exceeds the yield point, the strain becomes time dependent, and the material becomes plastic in character.

In general the needs of metrology dictate that stresses in the measurement setup be limited to values less than the elastic limit. As stress has dimensions of force per unit area, setups including small contact area must be particularly suspect.

Elastic materials, stressed at values less than the material's elastic limit, obey Hooke's Law, i.e., the ratio of stress to strain remains constant. The constant is called an elastic modulus of the material, and values of such moduli for different materials may be found in engineering handbooks. As strain is a dimensionless quantity, the modulus, in general, has the same dimensions as stress, i.e., force per unit area.

As a matter of convenience, different types of moduli are given, appropriate for use with the different types of stress. A body of finite extent, under compressional stress, will experience volume strain. The ratio of compressional stress to volume strain is called the bulk modulus or the modulus of volume elasticity. Similarly, a body under tensile stress will experience a linear strain. The ratio of this type of stress to strain is known as Young's Modulus. A body under shearing stress will experience a shearing strain. The ratio is given by the shear modulus.

On other quantity pertaining to the elastic characteristics of material is commonly found in the handbooks. A body under tensile stress will experience linear strain in the direction of the applied stress. In addition to this longitudinal strain, the body will also experience a lateral linear strain, generally of opposite sense. The ratio of the lateral strain to the longitudinal strain is called Poisson's ratio.

Relationships exist between the three moduli and Poisson's ratio. Knowing the magnitude of any two of the quantities, the other two may be calculated. The relating equations are

$$E = 3k(1 - 2\sigma) = 2G(1 + \sigma)$$

where E = Young's modulus
$\quad k$ = bulk modulus
$\quad G$ = shear modulus
$\quad \sigma$ = Poisson's ratio

From these equations, it may be determined that

$$E = \frac{9kG}{G + 3k}$$

and as E, G, and k are positive, $-1 < \sigma < \frac{1}{2}$. For most engineering materials σ has a magnitude between 0.2 and 0.4.

To review the foregoing and to illustrate the utility of these relations to metrology problems, some examples are considered.

Example 1: The length of a horizontal, continuously supported 10-in. brass bar, having a uniform cross-sectional area of 0.04 square inch, is compared with a steel gage block standard having cross-sectional area of 1.0 square inch. The comparison is performed on a measuring machine equipped with flat anvil and spindle and adjusted to operate at a measuring force of 2.5 lb. What correction is to be applied to the measured length of the brass bar to compensate the difference in applied stress?

(a) Type of stress: tensile.

    1. For brass bar: stress $= \dfrac{\text{force}}{\text{area}} = \dfrac{2.5}{0.04} = 62.5$ psi

    2. For steel gage: stress $= \dfrac{2.5}{1.0} = 2.5$ psi

(b) Applicable modulus: Young's modulus (from the handbook).
    1. For brass bar: $E = 13 \times 10^6$ psi
    2. For steel gage: $E = 30 \times 10^6$ psi
(c) Type of strain: longitudinal linear strain

1. For brass bar: strain $= \dfrac{\text{stress}}{\text{modulus}} = \dfrac{62.5}{13 \times 10^6}$

$\qquad\qquad\qquad\qquad\qquad\quad = 4.8 \times 10^{-6}$ in./in.

2. For steel gage: strain $= \dfrac{2.5}{30 \times 10^6} = 0.08 \times 10^{-6}$ in./in.

(d) Difference in strain $= 4.7 \ \mu$in./in.

(e) Correction to 10-in. brass bar $= +47 \ \mu$in.

Example 2: A continuously supported brass bar of uniform cross-sectional area A is oriented with its length axis in the horizontal. In this orientation, its length is 20 in. What is the change of length of this bar when oriented with length axis in the vertical? Note that the force on an incremental cross section of the bar will equal the weight of material above the cross section.

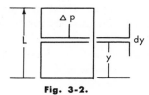

Fig. 3-2.

(a) The axial force on cross-sectional wafer dy (Fig. 3-2) is equal to the partial volume of the bar above the wafer multiplied by the density of brass, ρ.

$$\Delta P = \rho A (L - y)$$

(b) The tensile stress on the wafer, ΔS, is equal to the axial load divided by the area of the wafer

$$S = \rho \frac{A(L - y)}{A} = \rho (L - y)$$

(c) Under the load the wafer will deform an amount, dl.

(d) As linear strain is the change of length per unit length, the strain, $\Delta \Sigma$, experienced by the wafer is

$$\Delta \Sigma = \frac{dl}{dy}$$

(e) As Young's modulus E is the ratio of tensile stress to linear strain, the strain experienced by the wafer is

$$\Delta \Sigma = \frac{dl}{dy} = \frac{\rho (L - y)}{E}$$

(f) The total deformation l experienced by the bar is the sum of the deformations experienced by the wafers

$$l = \int dl = \int_0^L (L - y)\, dy$$

$$l = \frac{\rho}{E} \cdot \frac{L^2}{2}$$

(g) Values for brass, from the handbook, are

$$\rho = 0.314 \text{ lb/in.}^3$$

$$E = 13 \times 10^6 \text{ psi}$$

(h) For a 20-in. bar,

$$l = \frac{0.314 \times 400}{2 \times 13 \times 10^6} = 4.8 \ \mu\text{in.}$$

Example 3: The length of a brass, rectangular parallelopiped is measured in air at atmospheric pressure of 15 psi. What change of length will occur if the bar is measured in vacuum? Assume the bar to have a nominal length of 20 in.

(a) Type of stress: compressive stress = 15 psi

(b) Applicable modulus: bulk modulus, k.

$$k = \frac{E}{3(1 - 2\sigma)}$$

(c) Type of strain: volume strain, $\Delta V / V$.

$$\text{strain} = \frac{\text{stress}}{\text{modulus}}$$

$$\frac{\Delta V}{V} = \frac{15}{k} = \frac{3 \times 15(1 - 2\sigma)}{E}$$

(d) If the dimensions of the bar are x, y, z and the deformations are $\Delta x, \Delta y,$ and Δz,

$$V = xyz$$

$$\Delta V = (x + \Delta x)(y + \Delta y)(z + \Delta z) - xyz$$

Neglecting squared and higher orders of deformation,

$$\frac{\Delta V}{V} = \frac{\Delta x}{x} + \frac{\Delta y}{y} + \frac{\Delta z}{z}$$

Thus, a volume strain is represented by three linear strains. As the material is homogeneous,

$$\frac{\Delta x}{x} = \frac{\Delta y}{y} = \frac{\Delta z}{z} = \frac{\Delta l}{l}$$

(e) Thus,

$$\frac{\Delta V}{V} = \frac{3\Delta l}{l} = \frac{3 \times 15 \, (1 - 2\sigma)}{E}$$

$$\Delta l = \frac{15l\,(1 - 2\sigma)}{E}$$

(f) For brass,

$$E = 13 \times 10^6 \text{ lbs/in.}^2$$

$$\sigma = 0.25$$

(g) Therefore,

$$\Delta l = \frac{15 \times 20\,(1 - 0.5)}{13 \times 10^6} = 11.5\ \mu\text{in.}$$

The simple examples above are selected to indicate the use of stress-strain relationships in the field of metrology. Many more complex problems are encountered in precise measurement work, but these are beyond the scope of this chapter.

Reference is made to two stress-strain analyses of particular use in the field of linear metrology. An excellent analysis of equations describing the bending of bars of uniform cross section, when supported at two positions symmetrical to center, is provided by F. H. Rolt.[5] Another excellent work pertains to the bending of optical flats of circular cross section.[6]

Size and Geometrical Shape

In the preceding section, it was shown that the strain experienced by a bar in a measuring machine is dependent upon the bar's cross-sectional area. In the second example, the strain generated by the bar's weight would be of different magnitude if the bar varied in cross-sectional area. In the references cited—those by Rolt and Emerson—shearing strains are shown to be dependent upon size and shape. In general, stresses generated in the measurement setup will depend upon the test specimen's size and shape. Resulting strains in the specimen and in the measuring equipment will influence the measurement.

Size and shape of the test specimen also has an important influence upon the rate at which it will react to temperature variation. Most laboratories equipped to perform precise measurements are environmentally controlled. Temperature cycling of the ambient air is a characteristic of such control. Test specimens, similar in material and surface finish but differing in mass because of shape, will react at different rates to such cycling. Thus the effective temperature of the specimens will, in general, be different.

What general measurement principles are indicated from these considerations? In essence, all linear measurements are comparisons, usually of an unknown against a standard. When the unknown and the standard are nominally alike in size, shape, surface finish, and material, the effects mentioned are identical and the potential for accuracy of the comparison is the greatest. When they are unlike, sources of error, such as those indicated, perturb the measurement process. Conscientious work can minimize the resultant error but can never reduce it to zero.

The vast array of measurement problems faced by the laboratory metrologist precludes the possibility that his standards will always duplicate his test specimens. In practice he must endeavor to compensate for these errors by calculations, by technique, and by additional measurement. When shape differs to such extent that the mass of the standard becomes significantly different from that of the test specimen, he might support the measurement specimens independently of the measuring equipment and thus avoid errors generated by strain in the equipment. To correct for differences in strain within the standard and the test specimen, he might calculate the magnitude of correction from stress-strain equations. This is feasible when simple shapes are involved. Finally, he may find it necessary to measure strain, such as by appropriate positioning of strain gages on the measurement specimens. Temperature effects resulting from difference in shape are sometimes reduced by placing the standard and the unknown in thermal contact, either directly or by means of a soak plate.

This section has considered macroscopic shape effects. Obviously, microscopic shape of the datum is always of importance in precise linear measurement. Gage blocks with flat parallel measuring surfaces can be calibrated and used with less uncertainty. They not only wring more reliably but the measurement point on the datum surface requires less critical definition. Many experienced metrologists believe that gage block quality is defined more by flatness and parallelism of measuring surfaces than by adherence of length to nominal value. Errors of the latter type can be nullified by calibration, whereas departures from flatness and parallelism set limits on the accuracy to which calibration can be made.

Irregular Plane Areas

Materials of regular shape such as cylinders, rectangular parallelopipeds, spheres, helicoids, and involutes comprise much of the work load of metrology laboratories. Occasionally, the characteristics of irregular shapes or a combination of shapes must be defined. Description of such characteristics is sometimes attempted by specification of area, i.e., the specification of the area of a surface as projected into a common plane. For instance, it might be required to determine a cross-sectional area of an abrasive grit. The magnified profile of this grift might be obtained on the screen of a contour projector or in the field of a microscope. Knowing the magnification of the optical system, the area of the grit can be determined, if the area of the magnified profile is measured. The latter is sometimes accomplished by superimposing the profile on a grid of squares of known area placed in the image plane of the optical system. Counting the number of whole squares and summing the estimate of fractional squares bounded by the periphery of the profile provides the area of the profile.

Another procedure for area determination employs an instrument known as a polar planimeter. Basically, the periphery of the area to be measured is traced with the stylus of the instrument. A wheel attached to the stylus arm, with axis parallel to the arm, records the movement of the arm in a direction normal to the arm's length. The area traced is then calculated from the equation

$$A = \pi dln$$

where A = area
d = diameter of the wheel
l = length of the stylus arm
n = number of turns of the wheel

A vernier scale on the wheel allows n to be determined to 0.001 turn. From the equation above, it can be seen that errors in the scale and errors in defining d and l cause error in determining the area. Therefore it is the usual practice to calibrate by using the planimeter to measure known areas of regular shape. Normally a series of measurements is made, using different ranges of the scale and tracing both in clockwise and counterclockwise directions. Beckwith and Buck[7] show that this is not sufficient. One error source, not indicated by the equation above, derives from non-parallelism of the wheel axis to the length axis of the stylus arm. In such cases, the wheel does not record the proper movement. Its measurement includes an unwanted component of movement parallel to the arm's axis. The magnitude of the resulting error in the area measurement depends upon the shape that is traced. To detect this source of error, calibrations should be made using standard areas of different shapes. If a compensating planimeter is employed, this error can be detected by the difference in the measured values obtained from a given trace.

Contours

With simple shapes such as parallelopipeds, cylinders, and spheres, the problems of measurement are relatively more simple than problems of measurement of contours such as threads and gears. Instead of facing the formidable task of precisely defining the complete dimensional form of a particular thread or gear, the metrologist measures particular dimensional characteristics. For such measurements to be meaningful, the characteristics chosen must be significant relative to the function of the part. Recognized significant characteristics usually form the basis of standardized measurement practice. Details of such methods for threads and gears are given in Chapters

14 and 15. In this section we will discuss some of the more general measurement concepts that apply.

Pitch diameter of a thread is usually determined by the two-wire or three-wire method. The measurement is obtained between flat anvils of a measuring machine adjusted to operate at a standard measuring force. The nature of the measurement is, as usual, a comparison between a standard and the unknown, the dimensional difference being indicated by the difference in reading of the micrometer head. If the standard and unknown were alike in form and material, and if "best size" wires were used, the difference in micrometer reading would indicate the difference in pitch diameter. However, thread gages sufficiently accurate for reference use are not generally available. Gage blocks and cylinders provide more accurate reference standards, but because they differ in form from the unknown, the metrologist is faced with added complexity.

For instance, in the British system the standard is a cylinder of known diameter. This cylinder, sandwiched between the thread wires, is positioned between and references the anvils. The cylinder is replaced with the screw plug; the wires are positioned between the crests. The difference in micrometer reading is added algebraically to the known diameter of the cylinder. The resultant value added to the calculated thread wire contribution provides a value of the pitch diameter of the thread. What are the systematic errors?

Looking at the process more critically, one observes that the contact conditions for the unknown are not the same as for the standard. When using the standard, the thread wires are compressed between a cylindrical surface and a flat surface. For the unknown, the thread wires are compressed between the flanks of the thread and the flat surfaces of the anvils. Different contact areas are involved, different stress is exerted, and different strain results. The difference in strain is such that a small correction must be added to the measured pitch diameter. The magnitude of the positive correction is dependent upon the diameter, pitch and angle of the thread, and upon the measuring force applied. For a screw of $\frac{1}{4}$-in. diameter, the magnitude can be as large as a few tenths of a mil. Of course, if the materials of the standard and the unknown differ in elastic constants, the magnitude of the correction can be even larger.

Another error that results from this process is the obliquity or "rake" error. When the standard cylinder-thread wire combination is aligned between the anvils of the measuring machine, the thread wires are nominally aligned perpendicular to the axis of the cylinder. Small variations from this condition have negligible effect. However, when the cylinder is replaced with the screw plug, the thread wires position themselves between the crests, and in so doing, assume the direction of the lead angle of the thread. The result is that they ride up the flanks of the thread, producing a measurement too large. The magnitude of the negative correction required is also dependent upon the diameter, the pitch, and the thread angle of the screw.

In the United States practice of measurement, gage blocks (no thread wires) are used for referencing the anvils. The gage block reference is then replaced with the screw plug-thread wire combination. The difference in micrometer reading is added algebraically to the known gage block length. A calculated thread-wire contribution is subtracted from the resultant value to obtain the magnitude of the pitch diameter of the thread. As in the British system, stresses prevail for the unknown, different from those for the standard. The thread wires, as in the British system, also follow the direction of the lead angle of the thread. Normally, no corrections are made for either of these effects. Why?

In the British system, a positive deformation correction is applied to compensate for the difference in deformation resulting from comparing the screw plug with a standard cylinder. This positive deformation correction tends to equal the negative obliquity correction. Thus the algebraic sum of both is usually small compared to accuracies generally achieved in pitch diameter measurement.

The remaining discrepancy between the two systems results from the fact that the British system employs a cylinder-thread wire combination as a standard, whereas the United States system employs gage blocks, without thread wires, as a standard. This discrepancy is limited to small values because of the system used in the United States to calibrate thread wires. In this system, thread wires are calibrated between a flat anvil and a cylindrical anvil with standard measuring forces. The resulting thread-wire diameter values, uncorrected for deformation, are used for the calculation of thread-wire contribution to the pitch diameter measurement. Thus, while thread-wire diameter calibrations will be of different magnitude in the two systems, the differences tend to compensate for the differences in pitch diameter measurement methods.

The balancing of systematic errors of methods described above should not be assumed to occur in all contour measurement. Various elements of systematic error in thread measurement were described in an attempt to show that they must first be identified and their characteristics determined. It is then sometimes possible to devise measurement methods that tend to nullify their effect.

PHYSICAL MEASUREMENTS*

The basic symbols and concepts that may be used in various combinations to provide the units of all physical measurements consist of five independently defined quantities. These basic concepts are:

*By W. Richard Struwin, Senior Specialist, Scientific Facilities, General Motors Institute.

1. Displacement.
2. Mass.
3. Time interval.
4. Relative temperature.
5. Electric current.

In order to define any possible measurement that might be required, the units of that measurement must be expressed in terms of various combinations of these units. In turn, these primary units, which cannot be defined in terms of still simpler concepts, must rely upon physical properties or mechanical concepts for their absolute meaning and standardizations. It is important to ascertain that the basic units used in an exact scientific equation balance the same as the numerical quantities involved. If they do not balance, an error exists. Empirical equations usually do not have their units obviously balanced, but serve useful purposes in engineering plans and estimates.

Of the five basic concepts listed above, all except electric current are established and defined in Chapter 4, "Standards of Measurement."

In the measurement of electrical quantities, the standards by which they are evaluated derive from *absolute* measurements, from which the magnitudes of the electrical units can be expressed in terms of the basic mechanical units.

Measurement Systems

Generally, a given measurement system is based upon the fewest fundamental units which can be so combined mathematically as to express all the physical concepts needed in the particular scientific and/or engineering problem, in the terms of fundamental and derived dimensions.

There are many measurement systems, some in little current use, and some restricted to special areas of science. Of the classic branches of engineering, mechanics requires three fundamental units: length l, mass m, and time t; thermodynamics requires these three units plus temperature θ; electromagnetism requires these four units plus electric current I.

For the mechanical measurement systems, with length l and time t as a basis, instead of mass m, the third unit can be force f, power P, energy E, pressure p, torque T, momentum M, or others.

Units for the three most common mechanical measurement systems are shown in Table 3-1.

TABLE 3-1. MECHANICAL MEASUREMENTS

	British Gravitational or FPS system	Metric (small) CGS system	Metric (large) MKS system
	I. Fundamental Measurements		
1. Basic units.			
a. Length (l)	ft	cm	m
b. Mass (m)	slug	g	kg
c. Time (t)	sec	sec	sec
d. Temperature (θ)	Rankine	Kelvin	
	Fahrenheit	Celsius (centigrade)	
e. Electric current (I)			ampere
2. Standards.	Primary	Secondary	
a. Length	Standard meter	Kr^{86} orange line; also Hg^{198} 1,650,763.73 λ = 1 meter	
b. Mass	Standard kg	(Originally 1000 cubic cm of water, but this was not precise)	
c. Time	sec	$\dfrac{1}{86,400}$ of a mean solar day	
d. Temperature	Thermodynamic absolute zero and triple point of water.	Melting and boiling point of water (old standard)	
e. Current	ampere	Magnetic forces between current-carrying conductors	
3. Multiples of units.			
a. Smaller.			
Mil, inch			
atto 10^{-18}, femto 10^{-15}, pico 10^{-12}, nano 10^{-9}, micro 10^{-6}, milli 10^{-3}, centi 10^{-2}, deci 10^{-1}			
b. Larger.			
yard, rod, mile			

TABLE 3-1. MECHANICAL MEASUREMENTS (cont.)

British Gravitational or FPS system	Metric (small) CGS system	Metric (large) MKS system

tera 10^{12}, giga 10^9, mega 10^6, kilo 10^3, hecto 10^2, deka 10^1,

c. Conversions.
    39.37 in. = 1 m
    2.54 cm = 1 in.
d. Special units.
    circular mil = area of 0.001-in. diam circle = 0.7854 sq mil
    rod = 16.5 ft
    acre = 160 sq rods
    barn (unit of nucleus cross section) = 10^{-24} sq cm
    light year (in a vacuum) = 5,878 × 10^9 miles
    Angstrom = 10^{-10} m

II. Linear Quantities

1. Velocity: length/time, provided linear or particle velocity u = constant, otherwise $v = ds/dt$ or $v = s/t$.

a. Basic units	ft/sec	cm/sec	m/sec
b. Other units	miles/hour		

c. Velocity is a *vector* quantity and therefore requires special mathematics for addition of combination

2. Acceleration: velocity/time or length/time², provided linear acceleration a = constant, otherwise $a = dv/dt = d^2s/dt^2$.

a. Basic units	ft/sec²	cm/sec²	m/sec²
b. Other units	miles/hr/sec		
c. Acceleration is a *vector* quantity	32 ft/sec²	980 cm/sec²	9.8 m/sec²

d. Acceleration due to gravitational field of earth = 978.0495 cm sec⁻²

3. Force: mass × acceleration is the basic equation, provided velocities involved are less than 10 percent of the velocity of light.

a. Basic units	$\dfrac{\text{slug ft}}{\text{sec}^2}$ = lb	$\dfrac{\text{g cm}}{\text{sec}^2}$ = dyne	$\dfrac{\text{kg m}}{\text{sec}^2}$ = newton

b. Force is a *vector* quantity
c. Weight is *force* acting on a *mass* due to the acceleration of earth's gravitational field.

TABLE 3-1. MECHANICAL MEASUREMENTS (cont.)

	British Gravitational or FPS system	Metric (small) CGS system	Metric (large) MKS system
d. Newton's First Law:	A body at rest remains at rest, and a body in motion continues to move at constant speed along a straight line, unless the body is acted upon, in either case by an unbalanced force.		
e. Newton's Second Law:	An unbalanced force acting on a body causes the body to accelerate in the direction of the force. The acceleration is directly proportional to the unbalanced force and inversely proportional to the mass of the body.		
f. Newton's Third Law:	For every action, there is an equal and opposite reaction, and the two are along the same straight line.		
4. Momentum: mass $\times$ velocity.			
a. Basic units	slug ft/sec	g cm/sec	kg m/sec
b. Momentum is a *vector* quantity			
c. Momentum is conserved in each direction (this is of utmost importance)			
d. Calculations show transfer of velocities when *any* bodies collide			
5. Impulse: force $\times$ time.			
a. Basic units	lb sec	dyne sec	newton sec
b. Change of momentum = impulse			
c. Impulse is a *vector* quantity			
6. Work: force $\times$ displacement (must be in same direction).			
a. Basic units	ft lb	dyne cm = erg	newton m = joule
b. Work is a scalar quantity			
7. Power: work/time.			
a. Basic units	ft lb/sec	erg/sec	joule/sec
b. Other units	$\dfrac{550 \text{ ft lb}}{\text{sec}} = 1$ horsepower		watt
8. Potential energy: stored up work.			
a. Gravitational potential energy mgh	$\dfrac{\text{slug ft}^2}{\text{sec}^2} = \text{ft lb}$	$\dfrac{\text{g cm}^2}{\text{sec}^2} = \text{erg}$	$\dfrac{\text{kgm}^2}{\text{sec}^2} = \text{joule}$

TABLE 3-1. MECHANICAL MEASUREMENTS (cont.)

	British Gravitational or FPS system	Metric (small) CGS system	Metric (large) MKS system
b. Mechanical potential energy of springs, $E = \frac{1}{2} KX^2$ of compressed gas, $E =$ Btu/lb			
c. Electrical. of charged capacitor, $W = \frac{1}{2} CV^2$ of magnetic field, Emf $= W/Q$ (joules/coulombs)			
d. Atomic and nuclear (considered later)			
9. Kinetic energy: due to mass in motion.			
a. Macroscopic mass at velocity less than 10 percent that of light.		$KE = 1/2\,mv^2$	
b. Atomic particles with velocity greater than 10 percent that of light.		$KE = m_0 c^2 \left[\left(1 - \dfrac{v^2}{c^2}\right)^{-1/2} - 1 \right]$	

III. Rotational Units

	British Gravitational or FPS system	Metric (small) CGS system	Metric (large) MKS system
1. Angular displacement.	θ		
a. Units	deg	rev	radians (2π radians $= 1$ rev) 1 radian $= 57.3°$
b. Conversion to linear (tangental) units.		length $= R\theta$, where $R =$ radius and θ is in radians.	
2. Angular velocity:	$\omega = \theta/$time		
a. Units	deg/sec	rev/sec or radians/sec rev/min	
b. Conversion to linear (tangental) units:		$v_t = R\omega$	
3. Angular acceleration:	α		
a. Units	deg/sec^2	rev/sec^2	radians/sec^2
b. Conversion:		$a = R\alpha$	

TABLE 3-1. MECHANICAL MEASUREMENTS (cont.)

4. Radial acceleration.
   a. Changes *direction* of velocity vector (not magnitude).
   b. Results in *centripetal force* $F = mv^2/R = mR\omega^2$
5. Torque:
   a. Units $t = I\alpha$
   b. Conversion: lb ft   dyne cm   newton m
   c. Moment of force.   Same as torque = force × perpendicular distance to center. $t = $ force × radius
   d. Couple.   Two equal and opposite forces at equal, but opposite, distances from center.
6. Moment of inertia.   Equivalent of mass in linear equations.
   a. Units.   Mass × distance squared from axis of rotation for each particle making up body.
   b. For common rigid bodies:

Small mass on end of long cord	mr^2
Slender rod, axis through center	$\frac{1}{12}\,mL^2$
Slender rod, axis through one end	$\frac{1}{3}\,mL^2$
Annular cylinder	$\frac{1}{2}\,m(R_1^2 + R_2^2)$
Solid cylinder	$\frac{1}{2}\,mR^2$
Thin-walled hollow cylinder	mR^2
Solid sphere	$\frac{2}{5}\,mR^2$

       Add the moment of inertia through the center of gravity to the mass of the body times the square of the distance from the center of

   c. Parallel axis theorem.   gravity to the axis of rotation. $I = I_G + ML^2$
7. Angular momentum: $I\omega$
       Angular momentum of a body about an axis is the algebraic sum of the angular momentum of its particles.
8. Kinetic energy of rotation.
   a. $\frac{1}{2}\,I\omega^2(\frac{1}{2}$ moment of inertia × angular velocity squared)
   b. Used in flywheels, stabilizers, etc.
   c. Rate of change of rotational kinetic energy is power.

TABLE 3-1. MECHANICAL MEASUREMENTS (cont.)

IV. Other Mechanical Units

1. Friction.
   a. Force of friction = constant depending on materials involved × force holding surfaces in contact.
   b. Force of friction does *not* depend on area of contact.
   c. Coefficient of friction is greater when surfaces are at rest than when moving.
2. Center of gravity.
   a. The centroid of the forces of gravitation acting upon all of a body's particles.
   b. For rotational motion, the center of percussion is the distance from the axis of suspension to the center of percussion, $L = I/ml$ where L is distance from axis to center of percussion, I is moment of inertia, m is mass of body, l is distance from axis to center of gravity.
3. Equilibrium.
   a. For a body to be at rest or in constant velocity motion in a straight line:
      (1) The sum of all forces acting on body must be zero (vector addition).
      (2) The sum of all moments (torques) about *any* point must be zero.
   b. If unbalanced forces exist, the body has linear acceleration.
      If unbalanced torques exist, the body has angular acceleration.
   c. Falling bodies.
      Constant acceleration in vertical direction.
   d. Projectiles.
      Constant velocity in horizontal direction
      Constant acceleration in vertical direction.
      Combination gives a parabola.
4. Surface tension = force/length
   a. Work is required to create surface tension, hence to make mist of liquid.
   b. Capillary actions depend upon surface tension.
5. Viscosity: $\dfrac{\text{dyne sec}}{\text{cm}^2}$ = poise
   a. Not to be confused with density.
   b. Equation: $\eta = \dfrac{F/A}{v/h}$, where F/A = force applied to test faces, v = velocity, h = distance between test faces

TABLE 3-1. MECHANICAL MEASUREMENTS (cont.)

c. Using a precision capillary tube: $Q = \dfrac{\pi P r^4}{8\eta l}$

d. Reynold's number for liquid in large tube: $N_R = \dfrac{\rho v D}{\eta}$, where v = average velocity.

e. Stoke's Law for velocity of body falling in medium: $v = \dfrac{2dgr^2}{9\eta}$ where r = radius of spherical body.

6. Fluid flow.

a. Bernoulli equation $Q = A\sqrt{\dfrac{2gh}{(A^2/B^2) - 1}}$ for Venturi meter

b. Velocity of flow may be determined using Pitot tube: $v = \sqrt{\dfrac{2\Delta p}{\rho}}$

V. Derived Mechanical Units.

1. Elasticity:

a. Hooke's Law: *Stress* (distortion) is directly proportional to *strain* (force per unit area).

b. Elastic constant: Young's modulus = ratio of stress to strain.

c. Applies for less than elastic limit, that is, position of permanent deformation or breakage.

d. May involve tension, compression, torsion, shear, volume or bulk.
   Liquids and gases have only bulk modulus.

e. Energy stored by elastic media: $E = \frac{1}{2} K X^2$

f. Coefficient of restitution.

2. Density: mass/volume

a. Specific gravity is ratio of density of substance to the density of water.

b. A solid will displace an amount of liquid equal to its volume, and hence will have buoyancy equal to the mass of the displaced liquid.

3. Pressure: force/area   lb/in²   dynes/cm²   kg/m²

a. Pressure due to head of liquid: $p = mgh$

b. Absolute pressure refers to a perfect vacuum as base, and is used in most calculations.

c. Gauge pressure uses atmospheric pressure (14.7 lb/in.²) as zero. This must be changed to absolute for most calculations.

TABLE 3-1. MECHANICAL MEASUREMENTS (cont.)

d. Atmospheric pressure expressed in inches on a mercury barometer, or millibars (1000 millibars = atmospheric pressure.)

e. Curve banking
   provides equilibrium since resultant of gravitational and centripetal forces is perpendicular to road bed.

4. Machines:
   a. Used to change direction or mode of application of forces or torques.
   b. Used to change force and velocity.
   c. Never increase energy, but have internal losses giving efficiency less than 1.
   d. Theoretical mechanical advantage based on velocity ratios.
   e. Actual mechanical advantage based on forces or torques.

REFERENCES

1. *Onzième Conférence Général des Poids et Mesures*, Gauthier-Villars, Paris, 1960, p. 85.

2. *Proceedings of 1962 Standard Laboratory Conference*, NBS Miscellaneous Publication 248, U.S. Government Printing Office, Washington, D.C., p. 9–13.

3. Eisenhart, Churchill, "Realistic Evaluation of the Precision and Accuracy of Instrument Calibration Systems," *Journal of Research of the National Bureau of Standards*, Vol. 67c, No. 2, 1963, p. 161.

4. Youden, W. J., "Systematic Errors in Physical Constants," *Physics Today*, Vol. 14, p. 32–42, 1961.

5. Rolt, F. H., *Gauges and Fine Measurement*, Vol. 11, The Macmillan Company, New York, 1929, p. 340.

6. Emerson, W. B., *Determination of Planeness and Bending of Optical Flats*, NBS Handbook 77, Vol. 111, U.S. Government Printing Office, Washington, D.C.

7. Beckwith, T. G. and N. Lewis Buck, *Mechanical Measurements*, Addison-Wesley Publishing Co., Inc., Reading, Mass., 1961, p. 114–117.

BIBLIOGRAPHY

General Texts and Reference Books

Blackwood, Oswald H., William C. Kelly and Raymond M. Bell, *General Physics*, John Wiley & Sons, Inc., New York, 1963.

Condon, E. U., *Handbook of Physics*, McGraw-Hill Book Company, New York, 1958.

Eshbach, O. W., *Handbook of Engineering Fundamentals* (2nd ed.), John Wiley & Sons, Inc., New York, 1952.

Goble, Alfred T. and David K. Baker, *Elements of Modern Physics*, The Ronald Press Co., New York, 1962.

Gray, D. E. (editor), *American Institute of Physics Handbook*, McGraw-Hill Book Company, New York, 1963.

Lewin, G. F., *Physics for Engineers*, Butterworth, Inc., Washington, D.C., 1963.

Marks, L. S. and T. Baumeister (editors), *Mechanical Engineers Handbook*, McGraw-Hill Book Company, New York, 1958.

Sears, Frances W. and Mark W. Zemansky, *University Physics* (3rd ed.), Addison-Wesley Publishing Co., Inc., Reading, Mass., 1964.

Shortley, George and Dudley Williams, *Elements of Physics* (3rd ed.), Prentice-Hall, Inc., Englewood Cliffs, N. J., 1961.

Weber, Robert L., Marsh W. White, and Kenneth V. Manning, *College Physics* (3rd. ed.), McGraw-Hill Book Company, New York, 1959.

Mechanical Engineering

Beckwith, Thomas G. and N. Lewis Buck, *Mechanical Measurements*, Addison-Wesley Publishing Co., Inc., Reading, Mass., 1961.

Daugherty, R. L. and A. C. Ingersoll, *Fluid Mechanics* (5th ed.), McGraw-Hill Book Company, New York, 1954.

Faires, V. M., *Kinematics*, McGraw-Hill Book Company, New York, 1959.

Rothbart, H. A. (editor), *Mechanical Design and Systems Handbook*, McGraw-Hill Book Company, New York, 1964.

Timoshenko, Stephen P. and D. H. Young, *Engineering Mechanics* (4th ed.), McGraw-Hill Book Company, New York, 1956.

Thermodynamics

Eckert, E. R. G. and Robert M. Drake, Jr., *Heat and Mass Transfer* (2nd ed.), McGraw-Hill Book Company, New York, 1959.

Hall, Newman A. and Warren E. Ibele, *Engineering Thermodynamics*, Prentice-Hall, Inc., Englewood Cliffs, N. J., 1960.

Kenyon, Richard A. and Hilbert Schenck, Jr., *Fundamentals of Thermodynamics*, The Ronald Press Company, New York, 1962.

Lee, John F. and Francis W. Sears, *Thermodynamics: An Introductory Text for Engineering Students* (2nd ed.), Addison-Wesley Publishing Co., Inc., Reading, Mass., 1963.

Obert, Edward F. and Richard A. Gaggiolo, *Thermodynamics* (2nd ed.), McGraw-Hill Book Company, New York, 1963.

Rossini, F. D., *Chemical Thermodynamics*, John Wiley & Sons, Inc., New York, 1950.

Acoustics

Berancek, L. L., *Acoustics*, McGraw-Hill Book Company, New York, 1954.

Blitz, J., *Elements of Acoustics*, Butterworth, Inc., Washington, D.C., 1964.

Kinsler, Lawrence E. and Austin R. Frey, *Fundamentals of Acoustics* (2nd ed.), John Wiley & Sons, Inc., New York, 1962.

Morse, P. M., *Vibration and Sound* (2nd ed.), McGraw-Hill Book Company, New York, 1948.

Electricity

Angus, R. B., Jr., *Electrical Engineering Fundamentals*, Addison-Wesley Publishing Co., Inc., Reading, Mass., 1961.

Cockrell, W. D. (editor), *Industrial Electronics Handbook*, McGraw-Hill Book Company, New York, 1958.

Cook, Arthur L. and Clifford C. Carr, *Elements of Electrical Engineering* (6th ed.), John Wiley & Sons, Inc., New York, 1954.

Fitzgerald, A. E. and David E. Higginbotham, *Basic Electrical Engineering* (2nd ed.), McGraw-Hill Book Company, New York, 1957.

Gray, Alexander and G. A. Wallace, *Principles and Practice of Electrical Engineering* (8th ed.), McGraw-Hill Book Company, New York, 1962.

Knowlton, A. E. (editor), *Standard Handbook for Electrical Engineers* (9th ed.), McGraw-Hill Book Company, New York, 1957.

Lewis, Walter W. and Clarence F. Goodheart, *Basic Electrical Circuit Theory*, The Ronald Press Company, New York, 1958.

Stout, M. B., *Basic Electrical Measurements* (2nd ed.), Prentice-Hall, Inc., Englewood Cliffs, N. J., 1960.

Optics

Jenkins, Francis A. and Harvey E. White, *Fundamentals of Optics* (3rd ed.), McGraw-Hill Book Company, New York, 1957.

Longhurst, R. S., *Geometrical and Physical Optics*, John Wiley & Sons, Inc., New York, 1957.

Rossi, B., *Optics*, Addison-Wesley Publishing Co., Inc., Reading, Mass., 1957.

Sears, F. W., *Optics* (3rd ed.) (Principles of Physics III), Addison-Wesley Publishing Co., Inc., Reading, Mass., 1949.

Atomic and Nuclear Physics

Bonilla, C. F., *Nuclear Engineering*, McGraw-Hill Book Company, New York, 1957.

DeBeneditti, Sergio, *Nuclear Interactions*, John Wiley & Sons, Inc., New York, 1964.

Eisberg, R. M., *Fundamentals of Modern Physics*, John Wiley & Sons, Inc., New York, 1961.

Etherington, H., *Nuclear Engineering Handbook*, McGraw-Hill Book Company, New York, 1958.

Kittel, C., *Introduction to Solid State Physics* (2nd ed.), John Wiley & Sons, Inc., New York, 1956.

4

STANDARDS OF MEASUREMENT*

THE ROLE OF STANDARDS

A standard is defined in *Webster's Third New International Dictionary* as "something that is set up and established by authority as a rule for the measure of quantity, weight, extent, value, or quality." For example, the meter is the standard established by an international organization for the measure of extent. Industry, commerce, international trade, and, in fact, modern civilization itself would be impossible without a good system of standards. The complex technological structure of contemporary civilization requires uniform, consistent, and repeatable measurements in all units of physics. In the broadest scope, the role of standards is to support the systems which make such measurements possible throughout the world.

Man has always converted the natural resources of this planet into devices and products to meet his needs and desires, and he has always been concerned

*By Julian C. Moody, Length and Mass Standards Section, and Maurice K. Laufer, Environmental Standards Section, Sandia Corporation.

with the shape, size, proportions, and performances of the devices he has produced. Prehistoric man made spears for his hunting. His primary concern was that the length and weight of his spears be compatible with his strength and stature. These were his design criteria. As his experience with the spear grew, he observed that certain changes would produce better performance (a more efficient weapon) and he modified his spears accordingly. He used as a standard a simple and convenient yardstick—parts of his body such as the length of his arm or the span of his hand. Even in a simple culture where progress was probably measured in tens of centuries, standards, as crude as they were, played a part in man's achievement.

Today, progress is measured perhaps in terms of months, and the features and configurations of many devices are controlled to extremely close limits. Tolerances of millionths of an inch are required in areas where physical phenomena have shown that the efficient performance of a part or a device depends on a close approach to perfection. Some fuel injection parts used in high-speed aircraft, for example, are made to tolerances of 5 μin. Some accelerometer pistons and cylinders have a tolerance envelope of 20 μin.

Today, our entire industrial economy is based on the interchangeability-of-parts method of manufacture. To make this duplicate-parts system work efficiently and to achieve complete interchangeability of parts, a measuring system adequate to define features to the accuracy required and standards of sufficient accuracy to support the measuring system are necessary. Because of the strict requirements imposed by the duplicate-parts system and the tight tolerances on many components imposed by performance, many standards laboratories have been established in industrial plants and industrial complexes in the past decade. The purpose of these laboratories is to assure that products are being fabricated according to standards based on the national physical standards maintained by the National Bureau of Standards. In many industries, components and subassemblies are made in different, sometimes geographically remote, plants and assembled at some central location. For such a system to work, all dimensions which affect the important characteristics such as size, shape, volume, and mass must be directly related to the same master standards.

Figure 4-1 shows how the characteristics and features of a product in a large industrial complex are related to national standards. The system standards laboratory maintains standards that are primary to the entire system and supports two or more plant standards laboratories. The system standards are calibrated periodically by the National Bureau of Standards, the frequency of calibration depending on the stability and wear resistance of the standard. Master wires, for example, should be calibrated annually, while the primary mass standards of the system would normally need calibration by the National Bureau of Standards only every five years. In the calibration of gage blocks, it is more efficient for the system standards laboratory to calibrate the master

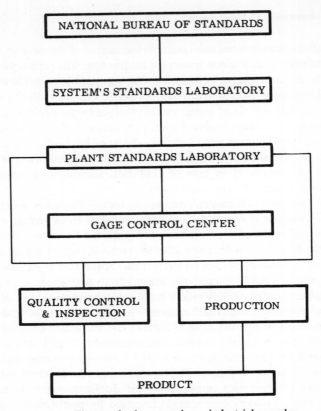

Fig. 4-1. The standards system in an industrial complex.

gage blocks of the plant standards laboratories by interferometry. To provide a high confidence level for the values supplied by the interferometric work of the system standards laboratory, an annual cross test of a small number of gage blocks, say 12, is made with the National Bureau of Standards. The use of interferometry is a step toward the goal of basing all primary standards on physical constants. The achievement of this goal would make primary standards directly available to every technological laboratory.

The system standards laboratory periodically compares the plant standards to the system standards, the frequency of calibration depending on the usage and stability of the standards. Each plant standards laboratory supports a gage-control center, inspection groups, and production facilities by periodically comparing the various standards which these groups use as references for their measurements to the plant standards. In companies which have only one manufacturing plant, the functions of the system standards laboratory and the plant standards laboratory are combined. The gage-control center, using references calibrated by the plant standards laboratory, calibrates all special-design gages used by the production and inspection groups to check the product.

With such a calibration and standards system, all references used to check or set instruments, gages, and testers for measuring the characteristics and features of the product are directly traceable to national standards through the several echelons that make up the system.

LEGAL BASES FOR STANDARDS

The authority to establish and control national standards is vested in the Congress of the United States. Article I, Section 8, Paragraph E of the Constitution reads, in part, "The Congress shall have Power to fix the Standards of Weights and Measures." Although Congress has this power, it has left the establishment of measurement standards, for the most part, up to science and industry. It has neither passed mandatory legislation of standards nor taken unnecessary action to approve the English system of standards, which has been the common measuring system of most American industry and commerce. In the Act of July 28, 1866, however, Congress gave official recognition to the metric system by approving the weights and measures of the metric system as lawful measures for "any contract or dealing or pleading in court" throughout the United States. This act also established the relations of the meter and gram to the inch and pound:

1 meter = 39.37 inches (exactly)

1 avoirdupois pound = 453.592 427 7 grams

In an order dated April 5, 1893, Superintendent Mendenhall of the Coast and Geodetic Survey (CGS) declared the international prototype meter and kilogram to be fundamental standards and the yard and the pound to be derived from them in accordance with the relationships established by the Act of 1866. This famous order in effect recognized the metric units as standard and the English units as derivatives.

In 1901, Congress authorized the establishment of the National Bureau of Standards. This authorization included the transfer of the standards program in the CGS to the Bureau. The NBS was charged with the responsibility of providing basic measuring services to commerce, to governmental and military agencies, and to industry. Its two major assigned functions are: (1) to develop and maintain the national standards, and (2) to carry on a broad program of research in the measurement of physical quantities. It should be pointed out that Congress gave no regulatory authority to the National Bureau of Standards; rather it required that the NBS maintain standards and calibration services which industry and others can use at their option. The Bureau calibrates master measurement standards for government, industry, and others for nominal fees at the accuracy levels needed, insofar as those levels are obtainable. It has always been the practice of the NBS to encourage industrial laboratories to calibrate their own working standards.

From a small beginning, the Bureau has grown into a dynamic scientific institution guarding our standards and assuring our country the highest order in measurement capability and continued leadership in metrology.

SYSTEMS OF MEASUREMENT

The Metric System

The metric system, completed in 1799 after ten years of work by a group of French scientists, is one of the two important systems of weights and measures used throughout the world today. It is the official system for almost all but the English-speaking countries, and even in the English-speaking world it is used extensively in scientific work. Most industries in the English-speaking countries, however, use the other important system of weights and measures, the Anglo-Saxon system.

The metric system is a decimal system of weights and measures based on the meter and the kilogram. Its basic units are the meter, the are (unit of surface measure, equal to 100 square meters), the liter, and the gram, the meter being the fundamental unit to which all others are related. Multiples and submultiples of these units are denoted by universally accepted prefixes:

Multiples and submultiples	Prefixes	Symbols	Pronunciations
10^{12}	tera	T	tĕr′ à
10^{9}	giga	G	jĭ′gà
10^{6}	mega	M	mĕg′ à
10^{3}	kilo	k	kĭl′ ō
10^{2}	hecto	h	hĕk′ tō
10	deka	da	dĕk′ à
10^{-1}	deci	d	dĕs′ ĭ
10^{-2}	centi	c	sĕn′ tĭ
10^{-3}	milli	m	mĭl′ ĭ
10^{-6}	micro	μ	mĭ′ krō
10^{-9}	nano	n	năn′ ō
10^{-12}	pico	p	pē′ cō
10^{-15}	femto	f	fĕm′ tō
10^{-18}	atto	a	ăt′ tō

Thus, a millimeter is 0.001 m, a milligram is 0.001 gm, a kilometer is 1000 m, and a kilogram is 1000 gm.

The meter was defined by the French scientists as 1/10,000,000 part of the meridian quadrant that passes through Paris. The first physical embodiment of this magnitude was an end standard; later it became line a standard. The kilogram was originally defined as being equal to the mass of one cubic decimeter of distilled water at its maximum density, which occurs at 4°C. The material form of this standard was a platinum cylinder the diameter of which was equal to its height. These were the first material prototype standards of the metric system and were called the Metre and Kilogramme des Archives.

It is interesting to note that both of these standards deviated slightly from their definitions. The meter bar was about 0.2 mm shorter than the 1/10,000,000 part of the meridian quadrant because of a slight error in the original survey measurement of the quadrant. But this error was of no significance because the meter is the base for the entire system; the space between the parallel faces on the meter bar could have been any reasonable distance. Later studies in volume found, however, that the volume of a kilogram of water at standard conditions was equal to 1.000028 cu dm. Unlike the difference between the meter and its original definition, this error of 28 millionths did have significance. It introduced an inconsistency in an otherwise coherent measuring system. For many years the liter, the unit of capacity, was defined as being equal to the volume occupied by a kilogram of water at standard conditions. The liter was therefore equal to 1.000028 cu dm and differed from 1 cu dm by 28 millionths. Because of this discrepancy, the units of cubical volume and units of capacity were not equal. To correct this discrepancy, the Twelfth General Conference of Weights and Measures abrogated the old definition in October, 1964 and made the liter a special name for the cubic decimeter. The word liter should not be used in volume measurement of high precision because of the possible confusion with the old definition. It is better to use the term cubic decimeter.

In the middle of the nineteenth century the need for world-wide unification of measures became increasingly manifest to European scientific academies and societies. At the request of these institutions, the French government, in 1870, called a conference composed of representatives from 24 countries to establish an international bureau of weights and measures. At the Convention du Mètre, May 20, 1875, 28 countries, including the United States, agreed to set up and maintain at commom expense an International Bureau of Weights and Measures at Sèvres, a suburb of Paris. The original mission of this new international bureau was to construct and maintain an international prototype meter and kilogram, to furnish to the various countries copies of these standards after comparing them to the international standards, and to advance measuring capability in all fields of metrology. The Bureau's scope has now been extended to include standards for geodetic work, thermometry, acceleration due to gravity, volume of water, wavelengths of light, electric, and photometric units. Today, 35 countries belong to the Convention du Mètre and send delegates to the General Conference of Weights and

Measures, which meets periodically. The General Conference controls the organization of the Bureau and is responsible for its effective operations.

In the 1870's, after a search for more stable and convenient standards, the International Bureau of Weights and Measures constructed a new meter bar and a new kilogram. The Bureau made these new standards equal to the values of the Mètre and Kilogramme des Archives, or as close to those values as possible at the time. In September, 1889, the First General Conference of Weights and Measures approved the new standards, calling them the International Prototype Meter and the International Prototype Kilogram. The Conference also redefined the meter and the kilogram in terms of these physical standards. Strict adherence to the original definitions would have led to new values each time the quadrant was remeasured and each time the mass of a cubic decimeter of water was redetermined. Thus, the new definition gave to length and mass standards a permanence that depended only on the stability of the platinum-iridium prototypes.

The International Prototype Kilogram is a platinum-iridium cylinder the diameter of which is equal to its height (39 mm). This prototype still remains the world's standard of mass. The International Prototype Meter, which is no longer used as an international standard, was a platinum-iridium bar with an X-shaped cross section. On the neutral plane near either end were three engraved parallel lines perpendicular to the longitudinal axis of the bar. The meter was defined as the distance between the axes of the two median lines when the temperature of the bar was 0°C. Because the length of a body changes as its temperature rises or falls, the scientists had to associate temperature with length to determine when the distance between the lines was exactly one meter. They selected zero degree Celsius because, as the temperature of melting ice, it was the easiest temperature to reproduce at that time. This meter bar remained the world's standard of length until it was replaced by the wavelength of light in 1960.

It has been said in jest that although the French gave the world the meter, it took an American to tell them how long it was. In 1892–93, the American scientist A. A. Michelson, using an interferometer that he had developed and with the aid of M. Benoit, the Director of the International Bureau, determined the length of the meter in terms of the wavelength of light. His light source was a high-temperature, two-ring-electrode cadmium lamp. For his measuring references, he used several etalons—interferometers consisting of two parallel plates of glass separated by a short distance, and with the adjacent surfaces partially silvered, varying in length from 0.390 to 100 mm, and an auxiliary meter line standard. He computed the number of wavelengths of the several lines of cadmium (when reduced to conditions of 15°C and 760 mm Hg) in the meter. The final mean figure in this famous test by Michelson and Benoit indicated that in one meter there were 1,553,163.5 wavelengths of the red line of cadmium.

By demonstrating that the meter could be expressed in terms of light-waves, Michelson had found a practical method of accurately relating any linear dimension to the meter or any other standard of length. By using the principles of interferometry, he laid the ground work for a future standard that could be reproduced any time and anywhere.

In 1906, three French scientists, Messrs. Benoit, Fabry, and Perot, again determined the distance between the two median parallel lines on the International Prototype Meter in terms of the red line of cadmium. Averaging the results of four observations and correcting these results to standard conditions (760 mm Hg, 15°C, dry air), they found that the meter was equal to 1,553,164.13 wavelengths of cadmium red. This figure differed by only four parts in 10^8 from Michelson's figure. This value at standard conditions and dry air with a carbon dioxide content of 0.03 percent became the generally accepted reference for measurements of the wavelengths of light. All measurements in spectroscopy and interferometry are based on it. In 1927, the Seventh General Conference on Weights and Measures officially adopted this relationship between the meter and the red line of cadmium.

The English System

The English system of weights and measures is based on two fundamental units, the yard and the pound, and is the common system of the English-speaking countries. Originated by the British around the twelfth century and frequently changed with different periods, it developed into a rather cumbersome and ambiguous system. For example, to obtain multiples and submultiples of the yard, one has to use such unrelated numbers as 3, 36, and 1760 to obtain feet, inches, and a mile. The word *pound* is used for a unit of mass, a unit of weight, or a unit of force.

The yard was originally defined by Henry I of England around 1120 A.D. as the distance from the tip of his nose to the end of his thumb when his arm was extended. A later monarch established the physical embodiment of this definition by creating an end standard made of iron, the Iron Ulna. The distance between the parallel end faces was one yard. This standard was replaced several times during subsequent periods. Finally, in the early nineteenth century British scientists created a line standard from a bronze alloy bar. By an act of Parliament in 1855, this line standard became the Imperial Standard Yard, the legal standard of length of the British Commonwealth. The yard was defined as the distance between the two scribed lines of the Imperial Yard when its temperature was 62°F. This remained the legal standard of length in Britain until 1963. To establish a relationship between the yard and the meter for scientific and trade purposes, intercomparisons between the Imperial Yard and the British copy of the International Prototype Meter were made at intervals of ten years. Because of length changes in the Imperial Yard in the meter, this relationship did not remain constant. A different relationship resulted from each intercomparison. For example, in 1898 one yard was equal to 0.914,399,2 m; in 1947, one yard equalled 0.914,397,5 m; and in 1959, just before the establishment of the International Yard, the National Physical Laboratory considered a yard as equal to 0.914,398,4 m.

The development of the English pound was very similar to that of the yard. The first mass standard of the English system was the Saxon pound. A weight having similar mass later became the Tower pound. In the fourteenth century, a weight which replaced the Tower pound became the avoirdupois pound. This has remained the British standard of mass, although its representations have varied with different periods. The Imperial Standard Pound was defined as the mass of a cylinder of pure platinum, 1.15 in. in diameter and 1.35 in. in length, which was equal to 7000 grains.

Like the Imperial Yard, the Imperial Pound was related to the kilogram by intercomparison with the British copy of the International Prototype Kilogram. And, like the relationship of the yard and the meter, this relationship has changed with each intercomparison. Prior to the International Pound, one pound was equal to 0.453, 592, 338 kg.

It is interesting to note the differences between the legal foundation of the British and the American fundamental units of weights and measures. The British pound and yard are established by Parliament. The American units are established by the executive branch of the government and have always been fixed by edict as certain fractions of the International Meter and Kilogram. For many decades the British pound and yard were unique and independent standards. But in 1963, to be consistent with the rest of the English-speaking world, an act of Parliament related these two units to international standards.

For decades, scientists throughout the world recognized the merits of the metric system and wished to see it universally adopted. But, they also realized that the English-speaking world was unlikely to change from the English system of measure. The following relationships were in use in English-speaking countries before the adoption of the International units:

1 in. (United States)	=	24.400,0508 mm
1 in. (Britain)	=	25.399,956 mm
1 in. (Canada)	=	25.4 (exactly) mm
1 lb (United States)	=	0.453,592,4277 kg
1 lb (Britain)	=	0.453,592,388 kg
1 lb (Canada)	=	0.453,592,37 kg

For many years, national standardizing laboratories in the English-speaking world tried unsuccessfully to obtain from the governing bodies of their respective countries legislative action that would legalize a uniform conversion from the metric system to the English. But in the late 1950's, the need for a uniform English Yard and Pound was becoming more intense. Representatives of the national standardizing laboratories of Canada, New Zealand, the United States of America, the United Kingdom, South Africa, and Australia met in a conference in London and agreed to adopt the uniform yard and a new pound for industrial and scientific use. They called these units the International Yard and the International Pound. The International Yard is equal to 0.9144 m, and the International Inch, derived from the International Yard, is equal to 25.4 mm exactly (0.9144/36 = 0.0254 m = 25.4 mm). The International Pound is equal to 0.453,592,37 kg. Since the value is exactly divisible by 7, it gives an exact value for the grain, the one unit common to the three important systems of mass in the English system—the avoirdupois, the troy, and the apothecarian. On July 1, 1959, industry throughout the English-speaking world started using this new inch and pound, and an important milestone in world standardization was reached. The National Bureau of Standards officially recognized these units on this date and has since used them in calibration services to American industry. Official recognition of these units in Britain did not come until Parliament redefined the British pound and yard to conform to international units in 1963.

The present practice throughout the English-speaking world of deriving the basic English units from the metric standards gives the English system a uniformity which was previously lacking. Since the English standards are now the same standards used in the metric system except for fixed numerical ratios, they are, and will remain, in step with the standards that are used by the rest of the world.

MASTER STANDARDS

The fundamental basis of all standardization in measurement is not in the physical world, but is in psychology. It is agreement among men that is important. But to be useful, accurate, and efficient, standards and measuring systems must meet certain qualifications and requirements. The chief requirements of any measuring system is that it be simple, logical, and coherent. The metric system meets these qualifying conditions quite well, and this is why this system is used by scientists and most industrial nations. Since the English system does not meet these requirements very well, it has many critics.

The three main characteristics which physical standards must have are stability, reproducibility, and transferability. Mass, length, time, and temperature (aside from electrical and illumination standards) are the four standards basic to various measuring systems. All other physical quantities can be expressed in terms of these fundamentals. Until recent years, the physical representations of these standards have had the required characteristics to a degree sufficient for science and industry. Temperature was based on a physical constant, but the other three basic standards were man-made standards. But because of science and technology, man-made standards are no longer adequate. Scientists, therefore, are gradually replacing man-made standards with standards expressed in terms of immutable physical constants. At present three of these standards, length, time, and temperature, are based on physical constants. Mass, a man-made constant, will probably remain so for some time to come.

Mass

Mass may be defined as the quantity of matter in a body. So long as no matter is added to or taken from the body, its mass remains constant. Mass is a measure of the inertia of a body, i.e., it is a measure of the resistance of the body to any alteration in its state of motion.

The weight of a body is defined as the net natural force that the body experiences. For instance, the natural forces acting on a body at the surface of the earth are the gravitational attraction of the earth, the buoyancy of the atmosphere, and the centrifugal force due to the rotation of the earth. The usual weight of a body is a resultant of these forces. The values of acceleration due to gravity usually include the value of the centrifugal force. Thus the weight of a body equals its mass times the acceleration due to gravity and is written $f = ma$. (Note that this equation ignores the effect of air buoyancy.) Since acceleration varies from about 978 cm per sec² at the equator to about 983 cm per sec² at the poles and varies with different elevations from sea level, the weight of a body is not constant, but depends upon the location of the body on the earth.

The amount of matter in the International Prototype Kilogram has been arbitrarily defined as one kilogram of mass. All national prototype kilograms which are furnished to national standardizing laboratories are periodically intercompared with the working standards of the International Bureau of Weights and Measures. To prevent damage and to reduce the risk of any minute change of mass, the International Prototype Kilogram itself has been intercompared with other prototypes only once, in 1946, since its construction and acceptance in 1889.

Using the national prototypes as the mass references, the national standardizing laboratories throughout the world determine the mass of their working standards, which are in multiples and submultiples of a kilogram. Other units of mass, such as the ounce and the pound, can be readily related to the kilogram by use of the defined ratio of their masses to the mass of the kilogram. Master standards for industry are compared periodically to these working standards to an accuracy of one part per million in the case of one-piece weights and three parts per millions in the case of two-piece weights. Thus the mass standards used by industry throughout the world are directly related to one standard of mass, the International Prototype Kilogram.

Length

On October 14, 1960, the wavelength of krypton 86 became the new international standard of length. The Eleventh General Conference on Weights and Measures, which met in Paris, redefined the meter as being equal to 1,650,763.73 wavelengths in a vacuum of the orange-red radiation corresponding to the transition between certain energy levels of the krypton 86 atom. This 0.6058 μ line was chosen over other spectral lines because its wavelength was the most uniform known at that time. This new relationship of the 0.6058 μ line and the meter is based on the ratio of the cadmium red line to the meter which was officially accepted by the General Conference in 1927 and used by science as the secondary definition of the meter since that time. The new definition varies from the old secondary definition only by the insignificant uncertainties associated with the relationship of these lines to each other. Since these uncertainties are of the order of three parts in 10^8, the difference between the secondary definition in terms of cadmium red and the new definition in terms of the orange-red lines of krypton may be about 1 μin.

With the more accurate line standard measuring devices of the 1950's, science estimated that the distance between the engraved lines on the International Prototype Meter was about 8 μin. longer than the value derived by M. Benoit *et al.* in their 1906 work, which has been the basis of all spectroscopic relationships since 1927. If the new definition of the meter in terms of the wavelength of krypton had been based on this more recent determination of the physical length of the meter, all the wavelength tables used in spectroscopy and metrology would have had to be revised. By defining the length of the meter in terms of the existing ratio of cadmium red, the General Conference officially recognized a value for the meter that had been used in spectroscopy and metrology for decades. The adoption of the International Meter caused no significant change of any kind, but the world now has an indestructible standard of length that can be reproduced anywhere and any time to an accuracy of one part in 10^8.

Time

Man's first awareness of time involved the daily succession of sunrise, sun at zenith, sunset, and night. This interval, corresponding to the 360° rotation of the earth about its axis, was for a long time the basis for the scientific unit of time, the second, which was defined as 1/86,400 part of a mean solar day.

Our earth, however, is not a perfect timepiece. Tidal friction produces a heating of the oceans. The source of this energy is stored in the motions of the sun, earth, and moon. Part of this energy drain comes from the earth's rate of rotation. The result is that the duration of the mean solar day is slowly increasing, and any expansion or contraction of the radius of the earth affects the rate of rotation. Other earth phenomena, such as wobbling of the poles, major earthquakes which tend to displace the poles, and changes in the extent of the tides (depending on whether the sun aids or hinders the effect of the moon) contribute to small eccentricities in the rate of rotation of the earth about its north-south pole axis.

A more constant, though not ideal, astronomical time reference is the apparent rotation of the sun about the earth with respect to so-called fixed stars. The *sidereal year* is the duration of time extending from the instant the sun has a certain position relative to a fixed-star background as observed from the earth until the sun again attains the same relative position. But since the earth bulges at the equator and its axis of rotation is not perpendicular to its elliptic plane of motion about the sun, gravitational attraction of the sun and planets attempts to bring the plane of the bulge into coincidence with the elliptic plane. The spinning earth reacts to this tilting force like a gyroscope. The result is that the angle between the spin axis and the tilting force remains constant, but the spin or polar axis precesses with a period of 26,000 years. This precession causes the seasons to progressively get out of phase with the sidereal year by the same relative amount (about 20 minutes per year). The year which keeps the seasons constant is known as the *calendar or tropical year*. It extends from the time when the sun is in the direction of the vernal (spring) equinox until it attains the same direction again.

The present standard ephemeris second is defined as 1/31, 556, 925. 9747 of the tropical year for 1900 beginning January 0 (day), 12 (hours). This definition was adopted as the fundamental invariable unit of time by the International Committee of Weights and Measures in 1957. It replaced the 1/86,400 part of the mean solar day. The ephemeris second has an uncertainty of a few parts in 10^9. Today, standards based on atomic frequencies are stable to a few parts in 10^{12}, and there are indications that a stability to a few parts in 10^{14} may be possible. In terms of frequency, the reciprocal of time, the Twelfth General Conference of Weights and Measures officially adopted temporarily in October, 1964, a new standard of time based on the value of 9,162,631,770 oscillations per second for the cesium 133 atomic clock. This action increases the accuracy of time measurement two hundred times greater than that referred to astronomical observations. The permanent adoption of "atomic time" awaits further evaluation of other atomic clocks as well as cesium 133.

Temperature

Most material properties, such as length, electrical resistance, spectral emissivity, pressure, volume, and viscosity, vary as the material becomes hotter or colder. Several of the thermometric properties of specific materials are employed in thermometers, for example, the volume expansion of mercury in the common mercury-in-glass thermometer, the electromotive force generated by a thermocouple, and the electrical resistance of a platinum resistance thermometer.

If a linear variation of the thermometric property P between a cold fixed point c and a hot fixed point h exists, then

$$\frac{P_h - P_c}{t_h - t_c} = \frac{P_t - P_c}{t - t_c} \tag{1}$$

where P_h, P_c, and P_t are the respective magnitudes of the thermometric property at the arbitrarily fixed temperature values t_h and t_c and for any non-fixed point temperature t. For t, intermediate to t_h and t_c, one has an interpolated value for the temperature as determined by P_t.

The resulting temperature scale depends on the assigned values of t_h and t_c. For the four common temperature scales, the assigned values are given in Table 4-1 for the fixed points, where h and c are the steam and ice points of water at standard pressure (14.696 pounds per square inch) respectively.

TABLE 4-1. FIXED-POINT TEMPERATURES FOR FOUR COMMON TEMPERATURE SCALES

Temperature scale	Steam fixed point	Ice fixed point
Celsius (centigrade), C	100°	0°
Kelvin, K	373.15°	273.15°
Fahrenheit, F	212°	32°
Rankine, R	671.67°	491.67°

The Kelvin and Rankine temperature scales are based on absolute zero temperature, $-273.15°C$ and $-459.67°F$, respectively. An understanding of absolute zero temperature may be gained by a consideration of gas thermometers. The average pressure coefficient of most common gases per degree C is $(P_{100} - P_0) / (100° - 0°) /P_0$ and has an experimental value very close to 0.00366. Extrapolation to temperatures below 0°C indicates that the pressure of the gas reduces to zero in the neighborhood of $-273°C$. The kinetic theory of gases assumes that pressure is the result of the impingement and rebound of the gas molecules on the interior confining walls of the container. Reducing the pressure to zero requires that molecular activities be reduced to zero. Further reduction of temperature is thus void of meaning. Today, theory and measurement have been refined to include the minimizing of all atomic, molecular, and intermolecular energy at the absolute zero temperature of $-273.15°C$ or $0°K$.

Few, if any, materials have a strictly linear variation of any of their thermometric properties with temperature. Consequently, linearly interpolated and extrapolated values, as determined by the thermometric properties of various materials, will not generally agree. Thermodynamics, however, provides a temperature scale which is independent of the material, or working substance. The provision is based on the Carnot cycle of the reversible thermodynamic engine. The work output per cycle is proportional to the area bounded by the two isothermals and the two adiabatics comprising the cycle and is independent of the working substance. If a major cycle consists of (1) any two fixed adiabatics, (2) an isothermal representing a hot reservoir at the temperature of the steam point, and (3) an isothermal representing a cold reservoir at the temperature of the ice point, it is possible to add 99 isothermals, so that the 100 subareas and the work output per cycle of the reversible engine operating between the two fixed adiabatics and any pair of adjacent isothermals are the same. These unique 99 isothermals plus the isothermals at the steam and ice point temperatures define the thermodynamic centesimal temperature scale. A thermodynamic temperature scale was first considered by William Thompson (later to become Lord Kelvin) in 1848. He proposed the thermodynamic centesimal scale in 1854, and the scale was accepted in international scientific circles soon afterward. Extrapolation above the steam point and below the ice point temperatures is obvious. It may be shown that at $-273.15°C$ the reversible thermodynamic engine has no heat to give up to the cold reservoir during the compression portion of the Carnot cycle. For this to be true, the working substance of the engine—and hence, all substances or materials—at this temperature must have no heat or thermal energy which can be released to a cold reservoir.

Only one temperature other than absolute zero needs to be assigned an arbitrary value so that the magnitude of one degree of temperature change can be defined. The triple point of water (that temperature at which, for an otherwise isolated system, ice, liquid water, and water vapor all exist simultaneously) is a more precisely reproducible temperature than those of the ice and steam points at standard pressure. In 1954 the temperature of the triple point of water was accepted internationally as being $273.16°K$. Today the triple point of water is the basis for the interval of one degree Kelvin, viz., $1/273.16$ part of the temperature interval between absolute zero and the triple point of water. The Celsius (centigrade) one-degree interval is the same, and the one-degree Rankine and Fahrenheit interval is $5/9$ as much.

The Kelvin thermodynamic temperature scale is theoretical. It may be

TABLE 4-2. THE INTERNATIONAL PRACTICAL TEMPERATURE SCALE

Fixed point	Temperature, Celsius (degrees centigrade)
Boiling point of oxygen	-182.970
Triple point of water	0.01
Boiling point of water	100.
Boiling point of sulfur*	444.600
Freezing point of silver	960.8
Freezing point of gold	1063.0

*The freezing point of zinc ($419.505°C$) is more reproducible and is preferred to the sulfur point.

closely approximated by gas thermometers, but the gas thermometer is unwieldy and must be used by personnel with specialized training if accurate temperature measurements are to be obtained. Consequently, in 1927 the International Bureau of Weights and Measures adopted a practical temperature scale. The 1960 revision of this scale is known as the International Practical Temperature Scale. It uses the fixed points listed in Table 4-2.

Interpolation from $-182.970°C$ to $0.01°C$ is made by a standard platinum resistance thermometer using the Callendar-Van Dusen quartic formula:

$$R_t = R_0 [1 + C_1 t + C_2 t^2 + C_3(t - 100)t^3] \tag{2}$$

From $0.01°C$ to $630.5°C$ the same standard platinum resistance thermometer is employed for the interpolation, but one uses the Callender quadratic formula:

$$R_t = R_0(1 + C_1 t + C_2 t^2) \tag{3}$$

From 630.5 to $1063.0°C$ a standard platinum and platinum-rhodium thermocouple is used for interpolation based on a quadratic formula relating thermoelectromotive force to temperature when one thermocouple junction is at the measured temperature and the other is at $0°C$. For extrapolation above $1063.0°C$ a narrow-wavelength, band-pass optical pyrometer and the Planck radiation formula are used.

BIBLIOGRAPHY

The American Ephemeris and Nautical Almanac for the Year 1965, U. S. Government Printing Office, Washington, D.C. 1963.

Astin, Allen V., *The Basic Standards for Physical Measurement*, Annual Engineering Conference paper, American Society of Tool and Manufacturing Engineers, Detroit, Michigan, 1960.

Herzfeld, C. (editor), *Temperature, Its Measurement and Control in Science and Industry*, Vols. I–III, Reinhold Publishing Corp., New York, 1941–1962.

Hudson, George E., "Of Time and the Atom," *Physics Today*, Vol. 18, No. 8, 1965, p. 34.

McNish, A. G., "Fundamentals of Measurement," *Electro-Technology*, Science and Engineering Series, No. 53, 1963.

Mozeau, H., "The Genesis of the Metric System and the Work of the International Bureau of Weights and Measures," *Journal of Chemical Education*, January, 1953.

National Bureau of Standards, Technical News Bulletin, Vol. 48, December, 1964.

5

DIRECT MEASURING TOOLS

AND INSTRUMENTS*

Measuring tools and instruments can be divided into direct and indirect or comparative measuring groups. Direct measuring tools are applied directly to the workpiece, as in the case of a micrometer or a caliper. Indirect measuring tools, on the other hand, use optical, electronic, and pneumatic methods to arrive at the final dimensions of a piece.

The direct measuring instruments are either of the graduated manual or non-graduated manual types. The word "manual" implies that both consist of hand-operated instruments. The graduated types have either linear or angular graduations incorporated into the measuring system of the tool. The non-graduated types consist of fixed gages or adjustable tools which compare measurements.

*By Cortland A. Bassett, General Sales Manager, The L.S. Starrett Co., and Hugh G. Collins, Divisional Sales Engineer, Webber Gage Div. of The L.S. Starrett Co.

GRADUATED MANUAL MEASURING TOOLS

Rules

The basic graduated measuring instrument is the rule. It is a graduated length of steel, used for approximately determining linear dimensions. Rules are made with various dimensions, graduations, and accuracies. Lengths vary from 1 in. to 14 ft for steel rules, but flexible steel measuring tapes are manufactured as long as 100 ft, or more. Rule graduations are standardized throughout the United States. Various graduations are provided, of which the finest normally obtainable is 1/100th of an inch (0.01 in.). Rules have from one to four sets of graduations on the two edges and two sides. Figure 5-1* shows the most common of these, in which the four edges are graduated in increments of $\frac{1}{8}$, $\frac{1}{16}$, $\frac{1}{32}$, and $\frac{1}{64}$ in. respectively. Rules graduated on one side in eighths and on the other in tenths or multiples thereof, are also popular.

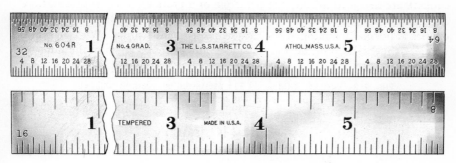

Fig. 5-1. The most widely used rule graduation.

Rules are manufactured of carbon steel or stainless steel and many are chrome plated with enameled graduations.

Shrink rules are commonly employed in the pattern-making trade, where the casting of metals is involved. These rules automatically take into consideration the shrink allowances of the materials being cast. The most common allowances are $\frac{1}{4}$ in. and $\frac{3}{16}$ in. per foot.

Hook rules are frequently used to assure the user that the end of the workpiece is flush with the end of the rule.

Tapered rules find many applications in measuring inside of small holes, narrow slots, and grooves.

Rules are still the most generally used measuring instrument in the industrial metrology field today. Precision-graduated rules are much more accurate

*Unless otherwise indicated, all illustrations through Fig. 5-32 are by courtesy of the authors' company.

than their smallest division, and are limited only by the keenness of the eye
of the individual user.

Effects of normal temperature variations are insignificant in the degree
of accuracy attained in reading a rule.

Calipers

Slide calipers consist of a stationary jaw integral with a graduated beam,
on which the movable jaw slides, with a reference point for inside and outside
reading. Some are made of tool steel; others are of stainless steel. They offer
a means of making direct measurements, both inside and outside, in accuracies as close as $\frac{1}{64}$ in.

One modification of slide calipers gives both the circumference and
diameter of a round workpiece. Its range is usually $3\frac{1}{2}$ in. in diameter. This
tool is accurate to $\frac{1}{32}$ in.

Vernier calipers, one type of which is shown in Fig. 5-2, give 0.001-in.
accuracy throughout the range of 6 to 72 in. Similarly to slide calipers, vernier
calipers are designed around the principle of a graduated bar with a stationary jaw. To the movable jaw, however, a vernier scale has been added. The
caliper is normally equipped with a fine-adjustment feature. With standard
vernier calipers, both inside and outside readings are taken from the same set

Fig. 5-2. Vernier caliper: (A) thousandths reading caliper;
(B) close-up view of the vernier head.

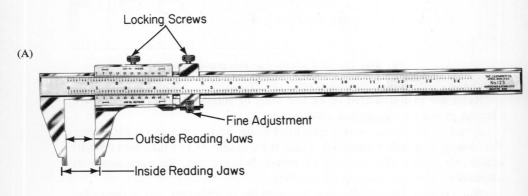

(A)

Locking Screws

Fine Adjustment

Outside Reading Jaws

Inside Reading Jaws

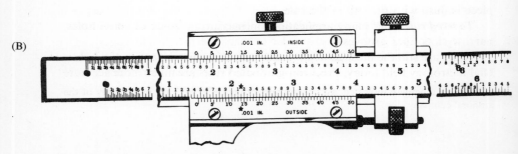

(B)

of jaws. They are available with both English and metric readings. Vernier calipers are available with either a 25- or 50-division vernier plate. Following is a description of how to read a 50-division vernier. The 25-graduation plate is read similarly.

As seen in Fig. 5-2B the bar of the tool is graduated in twentieths of an inch (0.050 in.). Every second division represents a tenth of an inch and is numbered. The vernier plate is divided into fifty parts and numbered 0, 5, 10, . . .45, 50. The fifty divisions on the vernier occupy the same space as forty-nine divisions on the bar.

The difference between the width of one of the fifty spaces on the vernier and one of the forty-nine spaces on the bar is therefore $\frac{1}{50}$ of $\frac{1}{20}$ in. which equals 1/1000 of an inch (0.001 in). If the tool is set so that the 0 line on the vernier coincides with the 0 line on the bar, the line to the right of the 0 on the vernier will differ from the line to the right of the 0 on the bar by 1/1000; the second line by 2/1000 and so on. The difference will continue to increase by 1/1000 of an inch for each division until the line 50 on the vernier coincides with the line 49 on the bar.

To read the tool, note how many inches, tenths (or 0.100 in.) and twentieths (or 0.050 in.) the 0 mark on the vernier is from the 0 mark on the bar. Then note the number of divisions on the vernier from 0 to a line which exactly coincides with a line on the bar. By following this procedure, from Fig. 5-2B we obtain 1.465 in. and 1.765 in. readings for outside or inside dimensions, respectively.

The maximum accuracy obtainable with vernier calipers is one thousandth of an inch. Because of their precision, verniers should be handled with extreme care. They should be periodically checked for accuracy, and adjusted for wear.

Dial calipers, in which the thousandths-of-an-inch readings are taken directly from a dial indicator incorporated into the tool are also available. These calipers do not have a vernier plate.

Vernier Height Gages

The *vernier height gage* illustrated in Fig. 5-3A, is an offspring of vernier calipers and therefore very closely related to them. Here, the graduated bar is held in a vertical position by a finely ground and lapped base. Both the height gage and the workpiece are used in conjunction with a precision-ground surface such as a surface plate, or the work table of a machine tool. They are provided with either a 25- or a 50-division adjustable vernier plate, and they are read similarly to vernier calipers. Vernier height gages can be provided in sizes from 6 to 72 in. All current models have fine-adjustment provision and a scriber attachment which makes it possible to scribe a workpiece with the tool itself, to 0.001 in. accuracy. Some models have a quick-

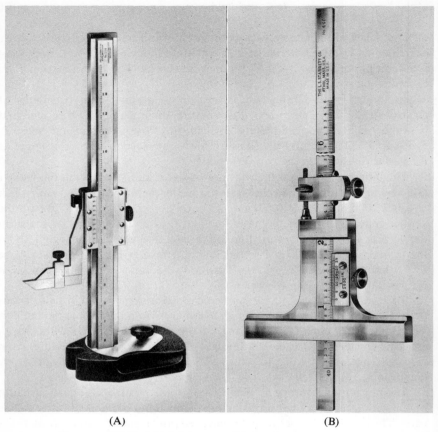

Fig. 5-3. (A) Vernier height gage. (B) Vernier depth gage.

adjusting screw release on the movable jaw which makes it possible to move directly to any point within the range which will approximate the desired reading, and then to zero in by a fine-adjustment mechanism. Vernier height gages are designed for use in toolrooms, inspection departments, or wherever layout and jig and fixture work necessitate accurately measuring or marking off vertical distances and locating center distances, in thousandths of an inch. Checking for accuracy on these gages can be done in many ways. Perhaps the simplest method and the one most widely used is to check by the use of stacks of gage blocks from an accurate surface plate. Modifications, such as optical and electronic height gages, are now available which give accuracies to 0.0001 in. These are discussed in other parts of this book.

The vernier depth gage (Fig. 5-3B) provides a long-range (up to 12 in.) thousands-of-an-inch accuracy tool for determining the depths of holes, slots, and recesses as well as measuring from a plane surface to toolmaker's buttons in locating center distances. It consists of a sliding head and a graduated blade which is perpendicular to the head. This blade may be set at any point with the fine adjustment mechanism, locked, and read from the vernier on the head.

Micrometer Calipers

This group of calipers is one of the most useful close-tolerance measuring devices available. The outside micrometer in particular is one of the few mechanical instruments that can be used to measure to 0.0001-in. accuracy.

Outside Micrometers. These instruments, a standard type of which is shown in Fig. 5-4A, basically consist of a C-shaped frame with an anvil and

Fig. 5-4. Outside micrometer: (A) cutaway view; (B) measuring with a 0.001-in. reading micrometer; (C) measuring with a 0.001-in. reading micrometer.

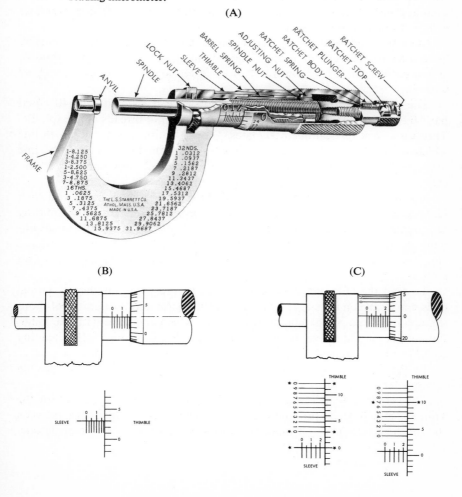

a threaded spindle. The thread is precision ground, to assure uniform movement of the spindle toward or away from the anvil. The spindle moves as it is rotated in the stationary spindle nut. A graduated stationary sleeve and a graduated rotating thimble are the bases for determining the measurement. The measuring surfaces of the anvil and spindle are lapped parallel. When the anvil and spindle are brought together, the tool is set at zero. The movement of the screw conforms with the sets of graduations. A locking mechanism can be provided for holding an established reading. A friction thimble or ratchet stop is also available to establish a uniform "feel" among individual users. The range on micrometer spindles is normally $\frac{1}{2}$ in. or 1 in. Outside micrometers range from $\frac{1}{2}$ in. to 14 ft, and accuracy is either 0.001 in. or 0.0001 in. Micrometers above 12 in. are seldom available with accuracy closer than 0.001 in. Micrometers are normally considered to be able to be read accurately within half a graduation, plus or minus. This means that 0.001-in. accuracy micrometers are read to $\pm$ 0.0005 in. and 0.0001-in. accuracy micrometers, are read to $\pm$ 0.00005 in. Following are examples of how to read a micrometer.

Since the pitch of the screw thread on the spindle is $\frac{1}{40}$ in. in micrometers graduated to measure in inches, one complete revolution of the thimble advances the spindle face toward or away from the anvil face precisely $\frac{1}{40}$ or 0.025 in.

The inch long longitudinal line of the sleeve is divided into 40 equal parts by vertical lines that correspond to the number of threads on the spindle. Therefore, each vertical line designates $\frac{1}{40}$ or 0.025 in., and every fourth line which is longer than the others designates 0.100 in. For example, the line marked "1" represents 0.100 in., the line marked "2" represents 0.200 in., etc.

The beveled edge of the thimble is divided into 25 equal parts with each line representing 0.001 in. and every line numbered consecutively. Rotating the thimble from one of these lines to the next moves the spindle longitudinally $\frac{1}{25}$ of 0.025 in. or 0.001 in.; rotating two divisions represents 0.002 in., etc. Twenty-five divisions indicate a complete revolution, 0.025 or $\frac{1}{40}$ of an inch.

To read the micrometer in thousandths, multiply the number of vertical divisions visible on the sleeve by 0.025 in., and to this add the number of thousandths indicated by the line on the thimble which coincides with the longitudinal line on the sleeve. By following these rules, from Fig. 5-4B a reading of 0.178 in. is obtained.

By the addition of a vernier scale (see Fig. 5-4C), the 0.0001-in. reading micrometer is obtained.

The vernier scale consists of ten divisions on the sleeve, which occupy the same space as nine divisions on the thimble. Therefore, the difference between the width of one space on the vernier and one space on the thimble is one-tenth of a division on the thimble, which corresponds to 0.0001-in. movement of the spindle. To read a 0.0001-in. micrometer, first obtain the thousandths reading, then see which of the lines on the vernier coincides with a line on the thimble. If it is line marked "1", add 0.0001 in.; if it is line marked "2", add 0.0002 in. Accordingly, the left and right parts of Fig. 5-4C show readings of 0.2500 in. and 0.2507 in. respectively. Temperature created by the hand alone will effect a 0.0001-in. reading, even in a small micrometer. The cumulative effect of temperature in larger micrometers and workpieces should definitely be taken into consideration when very accurate measurements are being made. The accuracy of outside micrometers may most easily be checked by the use of gage blocks or end-measuring rods. There are many varieties of special micrometers for different applications. Some of these are described briefly in the next few paragraphs.

Interchangeable anvil micrometers can be provided in intermittent ranges covering from 0 in. to 14 ft. Their advantage lies in applications where only occasional use of a micrometer in various ranges is necessary, and the accuracy needed falls in the 0.001-in. category. Since one interchangeable-anvil set of micrometers covers a multiple range, a fewer number of micrometers are needed to cover a given range. One disadvantage of these tools is that each one inch change in range necessitates a time-consuming change and setting of anvils.

A special adaptation of interchangeable anvil micrometers is the *multiple anvil micrometer* which consists of a vise-jaw frame that holds varying anvils. This micrometer can be used in many ways with its flat, round, and V-shaped anvils. Its accuracy is one-thousandth of an inch.

A high-precision micrometer which assures each operator of applying exactly the same feel, is shown in Fig. 5-5. This micrometer has two thimbles which work interdependently. The inner thimble carries the thousandths graduations. The other spring-loaded thimble, however, contains four consecutive sets of tenths-of-thousandths graduations around the complete

Fig. 5-5. High-precision micrometer.

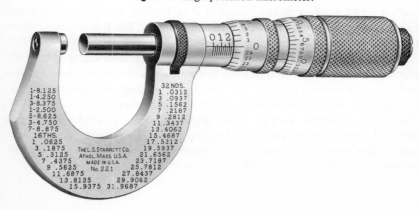

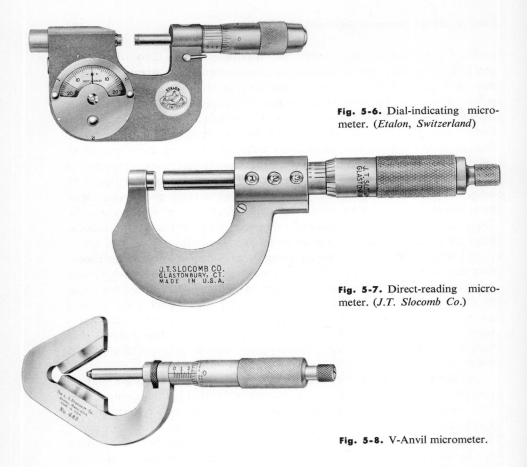

Fig. 5-6. Dial-indicating micrometer. (*Etalon, Switzerland*)

Fig. 5-7. Direct-reading micrometer. (*J.T. Slocomb Co.*)

Fig. 5-8. V-Anvil micrometer.

circumference of the thimble, and all read similarly. These graduations are sufficiently precise for the micrometer to be read in 0.00005-in. accuracy throughout the range.

The dial-indicating micrometer shown in Fig. 5-6 is similar to a standard micrometer except that the tenth-of-thousandths reading is read directly through a small window in the frame. It is of similar accuracy to the high-precision micrometer and can be read slightly faster, but it is a more expensive tool.

Direct reading micrometers such as shown in Fig. 5-7, are read directly in thousandths from figures appearing in small windows on the barrel of the micrometer, "Tenths" (of thousandths) direct reading micrometers, however, employ a vernier for establishing the "tenths" figures.

V-anvil micrometers, as their name implies, have a tapered spindle and a V-shaped carbide-tipped anvil (see Fig. 5-8). They are designed for measuring odd-fluted taps, milling cutters, and reamers, as well as checking out-of-roundness to tenths-of-thousandths accuracy.

Disc-type micrometers are designed with two parallel, $\frac{1}{2}$-in. diameter, thin discs attached to anvil and spindle. The discs fit into narrow slots or grooves. Some applications are ribs, lands, keys, fins, cutting edges on forming tools, and chordal thickness of gear teeth, which can be checked to thousandth accuracy. Because of the large diameter of anvil and spindle, it may also be used to measure soft materials such as rubber.

Blade-type micrometers are an adaptation of standard micrometers in which the anvil and spindle ends are thinned to a blade shape. This thousandths micrometer is used for checking the root diameter of circular form tools as well as the diameter and depth of narrow slots, key-ways, recesses, etc.

Quick-adjusting micrometers allow the spindle to be slid quickly to any point within their range. This feature makes it a particularly efficient thousandths-reading micrometer for checking work where a variety of dimensions are involved.

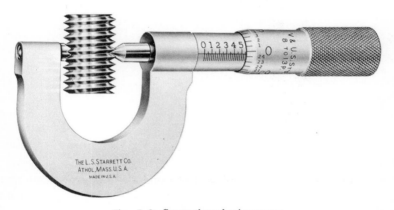

Fig. 5-9. Screw thread micrometer.

Screw thread micrometers such as shown in Fig. 5-9, are designed to measure the pitch diameter of screw threads to thousandths accuracy by the use of a pointed spindle and double-V anvil. These are available for varying diameters of work and each size normally covers a range of threads-per-inch.

Inside Micrometers. These instruments, illustrated in Fig. 5-10, consist of a $\frac{1}{2}$-in. or 1-in. micrometer head with one permanent contact. The other contact consists of accurate rods in various increments which are seated snugly in the opposite end of the head against a shoulder and locked securely. Inside micrometers are available with solid or tubular rods. The range of solid rods normally goes as high as 32 in., whereas the tubular style with their larger diameter can be furnished up to 30 or 40 ft.

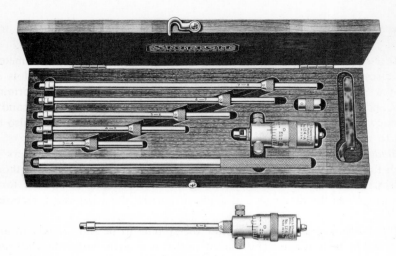

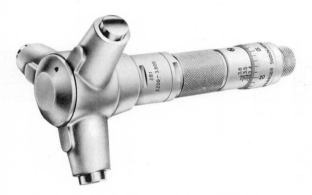

Fig. 5-10. Inside micrometer set.

Fig. 5-11. Micrometer hole gage. (*Brown & Sharpe Mfg. Co.*)

This tool is used for taking inside measurements on any workpiece. Measuring in a comparatively deep hole can often be aided by a handle, temporarily attached to the center of the micrometer head.

Because of the interchangeable rods, accuracies to tenths of thousandths cannot be guaranteed with this tool. Inside micrometers may be checked for accuracy with outside micrometers or end-measuring machines.

Micrometer hole gages graduated in tenths of thousandths, are available in ranges from 0.188 to 8 in. As seen in Fig. 5-11, these consist of a specially designed micrometer head with a three-point contact at the extreme end. This tool makes it possible to measure an exact hole diameter in depths up to 15 in., an operation impossible with gages of fixed dimensions.

Micrometer Depth Gages. These instruments consist of a 1-in. range micrometer head with bases varying from 2 to 6 in. long, centered vertically to the axis of the micrometer head. These heads are so designed that by remov-

Fig. 5-12. Micrometer depth gage.

ing a knurled nut at the end of the head (see Fig. 5-12), rods in 1-in. steps may be interchanged, thus providing total depth ranges up to 9 in. Round rods are available for standard applications, and flat rods are normally used for taking depth measurements in slots and recesses. These tools are accurate to a thousandth of an inch.

In the simple *rule depth gage*, a 6-in. rule is set perpendicularly to the base of the head. The rule can be moved up and down to determine approximate depths of holes.

Protractors

Figure 5-13 shows a *simple protractor*. This consists of a rectangular head graduated in degrees along a semicircle, with a blade pivoted on the center pin. By rotating the blade on the center pin, any angle from 0 to 180° can be set.

Fig. 5-13. Simple protractor.

Combination protractor and depth gages combine a movable graduated blade (depth gage) with a graduated protractor head.

The *universal bevel protractor* shown in Fig. 5-14A consists of a round body with a fixed blade, on which a graduated turret rotates. The turret is slotted to accommodate a 7 or 12-in. non-graduated blade. Through a locking mechanism any desired angle and the blade length can be set. This tool has a vernier reading to 5 minutes ($\frac{1}{12}^{\circ} = 5'$) and can be furnished with or without a fine adjustment feature. Any angle up to 360° can be laid out accurately. The dial of the protractor is graduated around a complete circle from 0° to 90°, 90° to 0°, 0° to 90°, 90° to 0°. As seen in Fig. 5-14B, the vernier scale is

Fig. 5-14. Universal bevel protractor: (A) protractor assembly; (B) enlarged view of the circular vernier plate and surrounding area.

(A)

(B)

also graduated to the right and left of zero up to 60 minutes (60'), each of the 12 vernier graduations representing 5 minutes. Since both the protractor dial and vernier scale have graduations in both directions from zero, any angle can be measured, but it should be remembered that the vernier must be read in the same direction from zero as the protractor, either left or right.

Since 12 graduations on the vernier scale occupy the same space as 23 graduations on the protractor dial, each vernier graduation is $\frac{1}{12}°$ or 5' shorter than two graduations on the protractor dial. Therefore, if the zero graduation on the vernier scale coincides with a graduation on the protractor dial, the reading is in exact degrees, but if some other graduation on the vernier scale coincides with a protractor graduation, the number of vernier graduations multiplied by 5' must be added to the number of degrees read between the zeros on the protractor dial and vernier scale. By using this method, from Fig. 5-14B a reading of 50°20' is obtained.

Since length measurement is not involved, temperature change does not affect the accuracy of this tool. Its accuracy can conveniently be checked with angle gage blocks. Because of the mating parts, with substantial areas rotating or sliding against each other, this tool must be kept clean, and handled carefully.

Combination squares and sets are refinements of simple depth gages, angle gages, and protractors. They cover a range up to 24 in. The squares consist of a square head, which slides along a slot in a blade and may be locked at any position. The square is so designed that it can be used as a 90° square or a 45° mitre. As a depth gage or as a length measurement instrument, it is accurate to $\frac{1}{64}$ in. or $\frac{1}{100}$ in. When this combination square blade is equipped with a bevel protractor head and centering head, it becomes a combination set. These heads have a spirit level for use when set on the zero line. The centering head is used to locate the center of round stock. Figure 5-15 shows a combination set.

Fig. 5-15. Combination set.

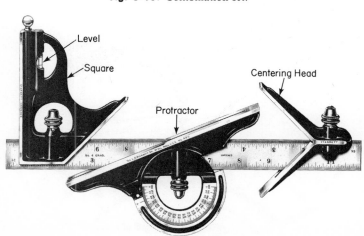

Dial Indicators

Dial indicators fall into two classifications, which may be defined as American Gage Design standard indicators and Dial Test indicators. Both are used in conjunction with a base, fixture, or machine. They are primarily used for comparing workpieces against a master. Dial indicators basically consist of a body with a round graduated dial and a contact point connected with a spiral or gear train, so that the hand on the dial face indicates the amount of movement of the contact point.

American Gage Design Standard Indicators. In the early 1940's the U.S. Government, in conjunction with the major manufacturers of indicators throughout the country, established standards for four basic sizes of indicators. They are available in 0.001-, 0.0005-, 0.00025-, 0.0001-, and 0.00005-in. accuracies. The dial reading may be consecutively graduated, in which case the graduations are normally numbered clockwise from zero to the range included in one complete revolution of the hand. Other dials are known as "balanced dials," in which case the graduations start at zero, proceed to the six o'clock position on the dial face, and then return to zero. The total range may run from as low as three thousandths to a maximum of 12 in. A.G.D. standard indicators have $2\frac{1}{2}$ revolutions. There are many variations in A.G.D. dial indicators. They are provided with or without jeweled bearings and shockproof mechanism. Tolerance hands to indicate maximum and minimum tolerances are available. Indicator backs and contacts can be obtained for adaptation to various uses. Dust guards seal out grinding dust or other foreign matter. Top lift or lever control (see Fig. 5-16) can be furnished for easy removal of the contact from the workpiece. Under normal circumstances, temperature change is not an important consideration. These indicators

Fig. 5-16. American Gage Design Standard dial indicator with lever control.

can most easily be checked for accuracy by gage blocks and surface plate with the indicator attached to an indicator base.

Dial indicators are designed for use on a wide range of standard measuring devices such as dial bore gages, portable dial hand gages, dial depth gages, vibrometers, crankshaft distortion gages, inside dial gages, cylinder gages, out-of-roundness gages, internal groove gages, diameter gages, and dial indicator snap gages.

Dial Test Indicators. One type, known as the toolmaker's indicator, is shown in Fig. 5-17. It is easily recognized by the fact that its dial face is much smaller than the smallest A.G.D. standard indicator. It may be graduated in thousandths, half-thousandths or tenths-of-thousandths. It has a range of approximately 0.030 in. Because of its small size and its thin tapered body, it can be employed in many places not accessible with other indicators. It is also used as an accessory with many machine tools. This type of indicator is very accurate and should be handled delicately. Other dial test indicators are built with more ruggedness and a somewhat larger dial. These are sufficiently accurate for general pupose work and are widely used because of their economy. They are generally known as universal dial test indicators. An assortment of attachments and contacts can be supplied with these indicators.

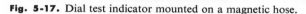

Fig. 5-17. Dial test indicator mounted on a magnetic hose.

Planimeter

The *planimeter* (planekator), illustrated in Fig. 5-18, is a tool for checking the flatness of plane surfaces to tenths-of-thousandths of an inch, or closer.

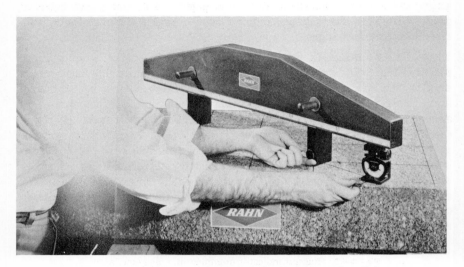

Fig. 5-18. Planimeter (planekator). (*Rahn Surface Plate Co.*)

It consists of a diabase straight edge, an adjustable mounting for the straight edge, and a 0.00002-in. reading indicator. The straight edge is always in the same reference plane at every position on the surface being checked. Readings are taken under the straight edge and recorded directly onto a contour chart of the plane being checked. Points of equal height are connected to form a visual picture of the high and low points in the plane. Extreme care should be taken in handling this gage to retain its accuracy and not to damage the surface being checked.

There are many other tools which can be classified as graduated manual types. However, these would almost definitely be termed as modifications of the more widely-used tools that we have described.

NON-GRADUATED MANUAL MEASURING TOOLS

Calipers

Calipers follow a progression which originates with standard inside and outside calipers. These are non-graduated tools for measuring the distance between two points of contact on the workpiece. This distance then must be transferred to an actual dimension by use of a graduated direct measuring instrument.

Standard calipers, in general, consist of two movable metal legs attached together by a spring joint at one end and with formed contacts at the other, and so designed as to take inside readings (contacts facing out), outside readings (contacts facing in), or readings from one point to another, (straight, sharply-pointed contacts). These are called inside calipers, outside calipers, and dividers, respectively. The most popular designs are shown in Fig. 5-19. These have a fine adjustment screw, and a quick-adjusting spring nut. Accuracy obtained with these tools depends largely on the inherent skill of the user. A fine "feel," a good eye, and patience will give the best results. Care in removing the caliper from the workpiece without disturbing the setting is also important. Finally, the measurement must be carefully transferred to a graduated measuring tool. The degree of accuracy to which this tool is effective is not disturbed by normal temperature changes.

Fig. 5-19. Standard calipers: (A) for inside measurement; (B) for outside measurement; (C) divider.

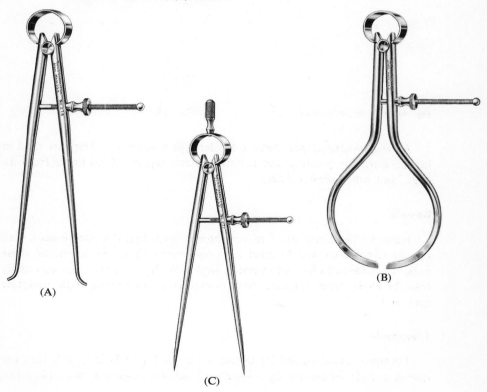

(A)

(B)

(C)

Transfer calipers, one type of which is shown in Fig. 5-20, are used to make transfer measurements from the inside of chambered cavities, over flanges and similar applications where it is necessary to move the legs after setting. The joint is locked, the transfer arm binding nut is loosened, and the leg is swung out or in to clear the obstruction. The arm is then moved back against the stop, and the exact size has been duplicated for transfer to a rule or other gage.

Fig. 5-20. Transfer caliper.

Hermaphrodite calipers have a divider-type pointed leg. They are used in layout work for locating and testing centers, laying off distances from an edge, and other similar work.

Bevels

Basically these consist of two or three non-graduated slotted blades, with one or two screws and knurled nuts connecting them. By loosening these nuts, the blades can be set to varying angles. With such a tool, one can easily transfer angles from a master to a workpiece or vice versa, with moderate accuracy.

Trammels

Trammels are designed for layout work. As Fig. 5-21 indicates, they use inside, outside, or divider legs. Some trammels are furnished with ball points,

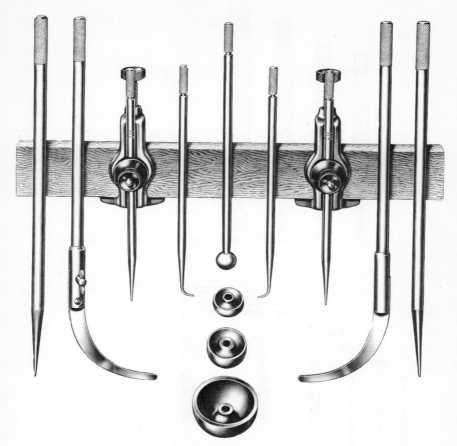

Fig. 5-21. Trammels.

to permit working from holes. Some are also furnished with an adjustable screw on one of the trams, for fine adjustment of the points.

Gages

Small hole gages consist of an expanding ball head which is adjusted to size by a knurled knob to provide an accurate feel for obtaining measurements in a hole or slot. Final size in thousandths of an inch is obtained by measuring over the ball contacts with a micrometer. The measuring range of small hole gages usually runs from $\frac{1}{8}$ in. to $\frac{1}{2}$ in. One set of small hole gages is illustrated in Fig. 5-22.

Telescoping gages have similar uses, but they cover a range from $\frac{5}{16}$ in. through 6 in. There are two styles. One style has a handle with one stationary contact and one spring plunger contact with locking device set at right angles to the handle. The other style, shown in Fig. 5-23, has a handle with two plunger-contacts at right angles to the handle. Both lock simultaneously.

117

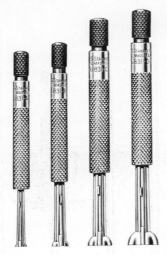

Fig. 5-22. Small hole gages.

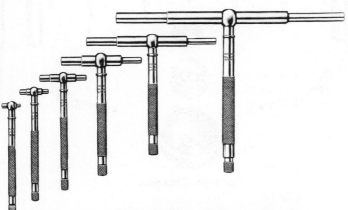

Fig. 5-23. Telescoping gages.

Fig. 5-24. Surface gage.

As Fig. 5-24 indicates, *surface gages* consist of a ground rectangular steel base with a round upright rod and a fine adjustment feature in the base. A universal sleeve holds a scriber which can be set to any position and locked in that position. The surface gage is used in layout work for scribing lines on vertical or horizontal surfaces. It may also be used in inspection work as height or depth gage. A groove in the base adapts the gage for cylindrical work. Accuracies attained with this tool depend upon the care and ability of the user.

Straight Edges

Straight edges are flat lengths of tool steel or stainless steel, ground to extremely fine tolerances, particularly along the edges. They are used for scribing accurate, straight lines and to check surfaces for straightness. Lengths are available from 12 in. to 12 ft. They are available with or without beveled edge and with or without a $\frac{1}{32}$-in. graduation.

Levels

Levels of varying accuracy have been designed for many applications. As seen in Fig. 5-25, they primarily consist of a formed base with a graduated level vial. Some of the more accurate levels have a main vial of 10-second

Fig. 5-25. Level

(one-half thousandth of an inch per foot) accuracy. Many styles of levels have a cross level set at right angles to the main vial. The most accurate ones are used for setting up and testing machinery.

Solid Steel Square

This is one of the most accurate hand tools available for right angle measurement. It consists of a base into which a blade is set. The blade may be beveled or non-beveled. These precision squares are so accurate that when placed against a master square on a surface plate they will absolutely shut out a vertical source of light.

Special-Purpose Measuring Tools

Among the many measuring tools designed for specialized applications are:

Tap and drill gages consist of a flat rectangle of steel with holes accurately drilled and identified according to their size. These cover letter size, number size, fractional size and National Fine and Coarse Thread Series.

Wire gages are round steel plates with slots of ascending width along their edge. As Fig. 5-26A indicates, each hole is numbered according to its size in terms of various standard gages. In both types of gages, the drill, tap, or wire is placed through the hole or in the slot and the smallest hole or slot which will accommodate the piece denotes the size of the measured item.

Screw pitch gages, shown in Fig. 5-26B, consist of a metal case containing many separate leaves. Each leaf has teeth corresponding to a definite pitch. By matching the teeth with the thread on work, the correct pitch can be read directly from the leaf. Screw pitch gages are available in a wide range of sizes for various standard threads.

Radius gages are available as individual leaves as well as with a multiple set of leaves in case. They are designed to check both convex and concave radii (see Fig. 5-26C). Each leaf is marked with its radius.

Fig. 5-26. Special purpose measuring tools: (A) tap and drill gage; (B) screw pitch gages; (C) radius gages.

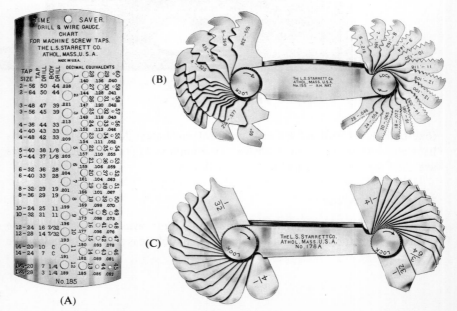

(A)

Thickness gages are furnished in three different forms and cover thicknesses from 0.001 in. through 0.100 in. Through 0.025 in. they can be furnished in $\frac{1}{2}$-in. wide coils. They are also available in 12-in. strips through the whole range. Many are provided in steel cases with a variety of leaves included. They are used in checking bearing clearances, backlash in gears, gaging narrow slots and for many other applications.

GAGE BLOCKS

Linear Gage Blocks

Linear measurement and size agreement of parts, tools, and gages manufactured by various concerns in different locations, is essential to interchangeability. Gage blocks are the master gages providing the elementary law (reference standard) for comparison in linear measurement. They are manufactured in single standard size units in series in both the English and metric system. When combined, they offer a range of sizes in specific increments dependent on the combination of sizes used. Gage blocks act as masters in two basic manners: work masters in the shop or super-accurate inspection masters for final inspection on work parts and gages. The accuracy classification demanded for each is determined by the tolerance limits of the work measured, and by the limitations of the measuring instruments used.

When the required gage blocks are combined to provide the dimension desired, this is called "building a combination." The combination is used to set an indication operating gage to zero. The operating gage is then applied to the work or vice versa, and provides a readout in a plus or minus direction. Sometimes gage blocks are used as actual working gages in the form of slot gages, temporary go and not-go gages, and height gages.

Laboratory master gage blocks are normally used to check inspection-grade gage blocks and are most often used singly rather than in combinations. Their usual purpose is to provide a master reference.

Styles. The Federal Specifications (to be discussed later in this chapter) do not cover the non-gaging overall dimensions such as length and width. However, certain sizes are accepted as standard in industry. The various styles in order of their popularity are:

1. Rectangular—approximately 0.357 in. wide × 1.380 in. long or 1.180 in. long. Thin sizes are 1.115 in. long to keep the block as flat as possible. For accurate readings "thin" blocks should be wrung to larger blocks of more substantial size.
2. Square (also referred to as hoke style)—0.950 in. square with a 0.265-in. diameter center hole, permitting use of attachments and accessories.

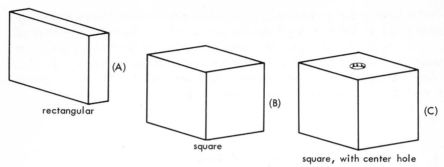

(A)

rectangular

(B)

square

(C)

square, with center hole

Fig. 5-27. Linear gage blocks: (A) Style 1 rectangular; (B) Style 3 square without center; (C) Style 2 square with center.

3. Round, square without center hole, and rectangular style with larger width and length are also in use.

Different styles of gage blocks are shown in Fig. 5-27.

Materials. Requirements include hardness to resist wear, size stability, and the ability to accept extremely fine surface finish. The materials used in their manufacture represent a wide range in these properties. They are:

SAE 52100 tool steel: hardness 65 Rockwell C. The coefficient of expansion is 6.4 millionths of an inch per inch, per degree Fahrenheit (6.4 × 10^{-6} in./in./°F).

Chrome-Plated Steel: the chrome-plating over the basic steel core increases resistance to wear and corrosion. The coefficient of expansion is approximately the same as for steel.

Stainless Steel: annealed and nitrided for hardness to 68–70 Rockwell C. The coefficient of expansion is 5.8 × 10^{-6} in./in./°F.

Tungsten Carbide: with cobalt binder; noted for wear resistance due to hardness (90 to 92 Rockwell A); corrosion resistant. The coefficient of expansion is 3.0 × 10^{-6} in./in./°F.

Chrome Carbide: a sintered material, composed of 85 percent chrome carbide and 15 percent nickel binder. Tests have shown its corrosion resistance to be 10 times that of 18-8 stainless steel. It is extremely stable, has hardness of 88 to 89 Rockwell A, and provides ultra-high surface finish.

Accuracy Specifications. The purpose of gage blocks is to establish a known reference dimension between the gaging surfaces. All gage blocks, regardless of their style or shape, must at least meet Federal Specification GGG-G-15 for each grade of accuracy specified. The degree to which gaging surfaces meet size, flatness, parallelism, and surface finish specifications determine the grade of the blocks. These grades and the corresponding tolerances are shown in Tables 5-1 and 5-2. Both tables are extracted from Federal Specification GGG-G-15.

TABLE 5-1. TOLERANCES ON FLATNESS, PARALLELISM, AND SURFACE FINISH OF WRINGING SURFACES*

| Grade | Tolerances on flatness and parallelism for span of wringing surface | | | | Maximum predominant average surface roughness | Maximum depth of individual scratches | Permissible number of stray scratches per block |
| | ½ inch or less | | Over ½ to 1¼ inches | | | | |
	Blocks to 1 inch in length	Blocks over 1 inch in length	Blocks to 1 inch in length	Blocks over 1 inch in length			
AAA gage blocks..............	1	1	1	1	0.0	0	0
AA gage blocks	3	4	4	5	0.5	2	0
A+ and A gage blocks	4	5	4	6	0.8	3	4
B gage blocks	5	6	6	7	1.2	5	10
Attachments and accessories	5	6	6	7	1.0	4	10

*All dimensions are in microinches (10^{-6} in.).

TABLE 5-2. TOLERANCES ON LENGTHS OF GAGE BLOCKS

| Grade | One inch and less | | | | Each additional inch | | | |
| | English, in. | | Metric, mm | | English, in. | | Metric, mm | |
	Plus	Minus	Plus	Minus	Plus	Minus	Plus	Minus
AAA	0.000001	0.000001	0.000025	0.000025	0.000001	0.000001	0.000025	0.000025
AA	0.000002	0.000002	0.00005	0.00005	0.000002	0.000002	0.00005	0.00005
A+	0.000004	0.000002	0.00010	0.00005	0.000004	0.000002	0.00010	0.00005
A	0.000006	0.000002	0.00015	0.00005	0.000006	0.000002	0.00015	0.00005
B	0.000010	0.000006	0.00025	0.00015	0.000010	0.000006	0.00025	0.00015

Some manufacturers use letter designations other than those of the Federal Specifications, for the various grades, such as *W* for work grade, *I* for inspection grade, and *L* for laboratory or *LM* for laboratory master grade.

Being subject to wear, corrosion, and damage, which effect their size or measuring ability, gage blocks must be checked periodically to verify their accuracy. The frequency of this check depends on the tolerance requirements of the job, the amount of use, and the conditions under which they are used.

Calibration certificates are provided by gage block manufacturers and qualified measuring laboratories who provide traceability to the National Bureau of Standards. These certificates provide a report of the actual size of each block to a degree of accuracy compatible with the corresponding grade specifications.

Effects of Temperature. The universally accepted standard measuring temperature is 68°F(20°C). Each particular gage block and work material has its own coefficient of expansion. If measured and used at 68°F, these differences are not of consequence. By necessity, however, measurements are often made in uncontrolled temperature. In this case, for accurate results, the coefficient of expansion of both gages and the workpiece must be considered. Steel gage blocks used to measure a steel workpiece will usually expand a like amount and produce fairly accurate readings. Conversely, steel work blocks used to measure an aluminum workpiece would require computation of expansion differences through consideration of prevailing temperature, size of work, and coefficient of expansion for both materials. Both metals must be known to have achieved the same temperature. Suitable allowances must then be made in the readings obtained. For example: An aluminum bar is measured with steel gage blocks at 78°F, and is found to be 4.5000 in. long. If the coefficients of expansion for aluminum and steel are 13.1×10^{-6} and 6.4×10^{-6}–in./in./°F respectively, what is the true length (length at 68°F) of this bar?

$$\text{measuring error} = (\text{length}) \times (\text{expansion coefficient difference}) \times$$
$$(\text{temperature deviation from } 68°F)$$
$$= 4.5 \times (13.1 - 6.4) \times 10^{-6} \times 10$$
$$= 4.5 \times 6.7 \times 10^{-5} = 0.0003015 \text{ in. or}$$
$$\text{approximately } 0.0003 \text{ in.}$$

Therefore the length of the bar at 68°F is $4.5000 - 0.0003 = 4.4997$ in. Conversely, if in the preceding example the true length of the rod is 4.5000 in., at 78°F it must measure $4.5000 + 0.0003 = 4.5003$ in. Slide-rule type charts, giving the relative difference in expansion or contraction for different metals temperatures and lengths, are available.

General Manipulation. When individual gage blocks are combined or "built up" to provide a specific measurement, they are to be "wrung" together.

This is achieved by sliding the mating gaging surfaces on each other until they adhere to such a degree that considerable pull must be exerted to break the wring. Factors affecting the desirable wringing effect are: the flatness of the blocks, surface finish, and freedom of foreign elements such as dirt, grease, scratches, and burrs.

The correctness of the wring is a determining factor in the final measurement of the combination, and its importance is in proportion to the results desired or the total tolerance demanded. The general procedure involved in handling gage blocks is that individual blocks and companion tools, i.e., surface plates, comparator anvils, etc., be cleaned free of dirt, grease, and foreign matter (kerosene and Stoddard solvent are used most frequently). They are checked for scratches and burrs which would prevent the wring by lifting the mating surface on contact. This is important to prevent scratching a good block with a burr on the mating block. Occasional burrs are removed by a white Arkansas, sintered aluminum oxide, or granite deburring stone. The mating surfaces are then brought into contact by sliding one over the other to beyond the half-way point and back again until the blocks are felt to be wrung. This can be done either in a unilateral or circular direction; the results obtained should be the same.

The wringing operation is repeated until all the necessary blocks needed to form the combination desired are included. After completing the combination, the blocks should be allowed to lose the heat absorbed. This can be aided by a cooling plate. This problem can be minimized by the use of forceps, gloves, or other insulating factors, making as little contact as possible. Avoid touching the gaging surfaces, since an over-acidic condition can result in etching the steel. Do not leave gage blocks wrung together any longer than necessary to complete the job, since moisture trapped between steel blocks will cause corrosion if the blocks are left together for long periods. This objection can be eliminated if corrosion-resistant material is used. Wipe gages clean with a soft cloth or chamois and apply a light coat of protective oil before returning to their individual inserts in the case. Use of a chamois lubricated with a rust-preventive oil will usually give excellent results.

Building a Combination. The smallest basic gage block set to offer combinations in 0.0001-in. steps is the 34-block set consisting of:

    9 blocks——0.1001 in. through 0.1009 in. in 0.0001-in. steps
    9 blocks——0.101 in. through 0.109 in. in 0.001-in. steps
    9 blocks——0.110 in. through 0.190 in. in 0.010-in. steps
    4 blocks——0.100, 0.200, 0.300, and 0.500 in.
    3 blocks——1.000, 2.000, and 4.000 in.

In selecting the correct blocks for building a combination, start with the smallest increment, i.e., work from right to left of the desired size.

Desired dimension	3.3875
Eliminate the 0.0001-in. digit	−0.1005
	3.2870
Eliminate the 0.001-in. digit	−0.107
	3.180
Eliminate the 0.010-in. digit	−0.180
	3.000
Complete with a 1.000-in. and a 2.000-in. block	−3.000
	0.000

The larger 81-block set employs the same basic system but offers additional blocks providing the opportunity to make two separate buildups to the same size. The 81-block set includes:

  9 blocks——0.1001 in. through 0.1009-in. in 0.0001-in. steps
49 blocks——0.101 in. through 0.149 in. in 0.001-in. steps
19 blocks——0.050 in. through 0.950 in. in 0.050-in. steps
  4 blocks——1.000 in. through 4.000 in. in 1-in. steps

A typical second buildup from this set using the same dimensions as with the 34-block set, without repeating sizes is:

Desired dimension	3.3875
Eliminate the 0.0001-in. digit	−0.1004
(2 blocks)	3.2871
	−0.1001
	3.1870
Eliminate the 0.001-in. digit	−0.137
	3.050
Eliminate the 0.010-in. digit	−0.050
	3.000
	−2.000
	1.000
Eliminate the inches (2 blocks)	−1.000
	0.000

The first buildup of blocks for the 3.3875-in. dimension from the set of blocks would use the 0.1005, 0.147, 0.140, and 3.000-in. blocks.

A good basic rule is to use the largest possible block in each step to reduce the number of blocks used to a minimum.

Angle Gage Blocks

Angle gage blocks are designed for shop and toolroom use, on machines, or in inspection. They reduce setup time and minimize error in grinding both simple and compound angles. The workpiece can be set on the blocks or vice versa, whichever is more convenient.

General Design. Angle gage blocks are to the setting and inspecting of angular measurements what regular gage blocks are in linear measurements, i.e., the masters. Choices of material, grade of accuracy, and style are offered.

Material. Two materials are most commonly used: *SAE 52100* oil hardening tool steel, hardened to 65 Rockwell C, and *chrome carbide*, composed of 85 percent chrome carbide and 15 percent nickel binder, with a hardness of 87.5 Rockwell A.

Available angle blocks are (see Fig. 5-28A):

Degree steps: 45, 30, 15, 5, 3, and 1°——Range 0–99°
Minute steps: 30, 20, 5, 3, and 1′——Range 0–59′
Second steps: 30, 20, 5, 3, and 1″——Range 0–59″

Sets including degree, minute, and second blocks provide a range of 0–99° in 1–second steps or 356,400 angles.

The plus and the minus end of each block is marked. Addition and subtraction from any beginning basic angle block is then made so as to form the desired angle combination.

True Square. Designed as a companion tool for use with angle gage block sets, the true square is available for both tool room and laboratory master angle blocks. All faces of this true square are at precisely 90° to adjacent gaging surfaces with practically perfect optical flatness and parallelism to permit use with autocollimators or indicators. The 90° initial angle, established by the true square, extends the range of the angle block set to 360° in either degree, minute or second steps. The true square is shown in Fig. 5-28B.

Fig. 5-28. Angle gage blocks: (A) complete set; (B) true square.

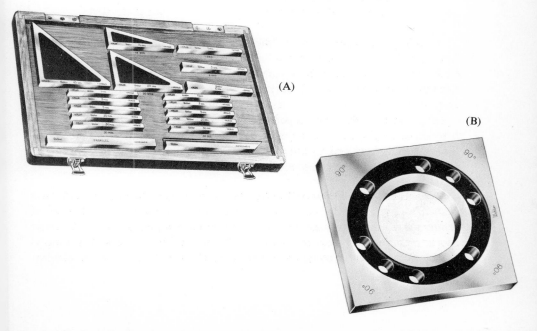

(A)

(B)

Attainable Accuracy. There are two grades of angle gage blocks: toolroom, and laboratory master.

The toolroom grade accuracy classification is designed for use with dial indicators. It is manufactured in tool steel only.

Material: Steel	
Area of gaging surface	$\frac{5}{8} \times 4$ in.
Deviation from marked angle	± 1 sec
Accuracy of optional calibration	$\pm \frac{1}{2}$ sec
Flatness across width	0.000004 in.
Flatness along length	0.000006 in.
Parallelism of sides	0.000010 in.
Squareness of gaging surface to sides	2.0 sec
Surface finish (minimum)	0.6–0.8 μ in. RMS

The laboratory master grade is designed primarily for use in optical tooling or inspection. It provides reflecting surface area more compatible with autocollimators, spectrometers, etc. These blocks are made in tool steel and in chromium carbide.

Material: Steel or chrome carbide	
Area of gaging surface	1×2 in.
Deviation from marked angle	± 0.25 sec
Calibration by optical means	± 0.1 sec
Accuracy of furnished calibration	± 0.2 sec
Flatness across width	0.000002 in.
Flatness along length	0.000002 in.
Parallelism of sides	0.000010 in.
Squareness of gaging surface to sides	2.0 sec
Surface finish (minimum)	0.5 μ in. RMS

Proving Accuracy. Unlike linear measuring, angle measuring, which is actually a division or portion of a full circle, is self-proving. A circle has 360°. Each degree is made up of 60 minutes. Each minute is comprised of 60 seconds. Each portion or value is constant. Therefore, a total aggregate of combined units must equal one unit in its progression. For example: Three exactly equal portions of 90° must equal 30° each, etc. Thus, the "breakdown" system can be employed to create the masters of angle measuring and each combination can be proved by the same method. The calibration of gage blocks is covered elsewhere in this book.

Effects of Temperature Change. Although temperature control is always desirable, angles, set by angle gage blocks, are not altered by a change of temperature, assuming that the change has been completed; i.e., a 30° angle block, manufactured and measured at 68°F, will still be 30° at 80°F as long as the block has been allowed to complete its changes to that higher temperature. Angle accuracy cannot be assured, however, during the transition in temperature changes. Angle gage blocks should be handled in the same manner as described for linear gage blocks.

General Manipulation and Examples. Each angle gage block's measuring surfaces, i.e., those forming the included angle, are flat within their particular grade specifications. When used in combination to form various angles, the individual blocks are "wrung" to each other in the same manner as linear gage blocks. After completion of the wringing operation, the entire complement is then placed on its side on a surface plate or other flat surface and aligned to prevent a compounding of the desired angle. The combination is then ready for use.

Each individual angle block has a plus end and a minus end, which are so marked. Addition or subtraction from any beginning basic angle block is then employed to form the desired angle combination.

Figure 5-29 shows a magnetic chuck, being set for a 38° angle. Three angle blocks, +30°, +5°, and +3°, are combined with the parallel on the top. The accuracy of setting is checked with the dial indicator shown. Adjustment is a matter of seconds. A revolving chuck teams up perfectly with angle blocks in tool grinding.

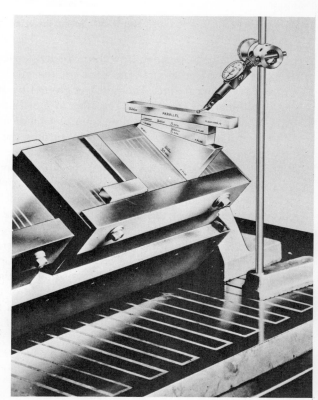

Fig. 5-29. Setting a revolving magnetic chuck.

Fig. 5-30. Set-up for grinding notches.

Figure 5-30 shows how four notches (spaced at 90°) are ground with the aid of the true square. The work and the true square are mounted together on a revolving fixture. The notch is ground by two successive cuts, one at 90° with the true square, and the other at 2° with the addition of two angle blocks (+3° and −1°) mounted on square. An indicator reading is taken before each grind. This process is repeated by turning the true square to successive zero readings.

Figure 5-31 shows a workpiece with a compound angle, the first angle of 14°30′ and a second angle of 8° running at right angles to the first. To check the 14°30′ angle, the work is laid on a parallel which is wrung to the proper combination of the blocks forming an angle of 14°30′. Correctness of this angle is then easily determined by indicating across the top surface of the work. Assuming that this has been found correct, the inspection is continued by wringing together the proper blocks to form 8°. These are laid on the 8° surface of the workpiece. After squaring them and setting them at right angles to the first surface, the correctness of the 8° angle can then be readily determined by indicating along the length of the gage blocks. The work can be placed on the surface plate or on top of the blocks, whichever is more convenient.

An example when angle gage blocks are used with autocollimator in indexing a large rotary table is illustrated in Fig. 5-32. An angle block or

Fig. 5-31. Inspecting a compound angle.

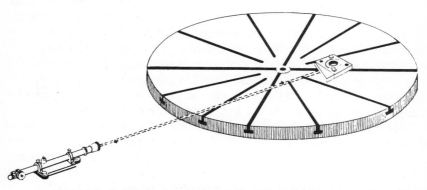

Fig. 5-32. Indexing a large rotary table with the true square and autocollimator.

true square is positioned on the work and a beam of light from an autocollimator is directed against the gaging surface. This becomes 0° or the reference surface. Other angle blocks are then added in proper combination to measure each succeeding angle. The table is rotated and inspected at each position with reference to the light beam. This method permits rapid indexing of large workpieces, with accuracy measured in fractional seconds of arc.

FIXED LIMIT GAGES

Instead of measuring actual dimensions, the conformance of product with tolerance specifications can be checked by fixed (more commonly known as "go" and "not go") gages. These gages represent the limit of size of the workpiece, as per specified product tolerances.

More specifically, a "go" gage represents the maximum material condition of the product (i.e., minimum hole size, or maximum shaft size) and conversely, a "not go" gage represents the minimum material limit (i.e., maximum hole size, or minimum shaft size).

If then, gages made *exactly* to these limits were used, parts being within and outside of the specified limits could be segregated. The attainment of such exactness indeed would be highly desirable, since according to the American Standard ASA B1.4-1955, a part shall be acceptable if its actual size does not exceed the limits of size specified on the drawing. In practice, however, some difficulties arise in fulfilling this requirement with fixed gages. These difficulties arise from the fact that *exact* gages cannot be manufactured. The closer the limits are held, the more expensive the gage is, but variations in size cannot be eliminated. On the other hand, gages wear in use (especially "go" gages), therefore their actual size constantly changes. The latter factor is not a very serious one if wear-resistant material such as caribide is used.

The consequence of gage size variation results in an uncertainty of inspection when parts with actual dimensions close to one of the limits are gaged. Uncertainty implies here that parts being outside of the limits may be accepted, or parts within the limits may be rejected by the gage. This phenomenon is of considerable importance in the manufacture and inspection of interchangeable parts. As the same time, it is a controversial issue that prevented the formulation of a generally acceptable unified gaging policy throughout the United States. In gage design, two major lines of thought are represented by the gage manufacturers and by the U.S. Army Ordnance Department.

Gage manufacturers have a somewhat liberal policy that allows parts exceeding the maximum material condition by as much as one-half of the gage tolerance to be accepted. The philosophical argument behind this policy is that assembly situations in which both mating parts exceed their limits are extremely rare and, consequently, the probability of misfit is negligible.

Ordnance practice is a more conservative one. It incorporates allowances for gage wear ("go" gages only), uses somewhat larger gage tolerances, and does this all within the limits of the work. Consequently, this policy is in complete agreement with the ASA B1.4-1955 criterion for acceptability. Of course, the conformance with the standard mentioned is achieved at the expense of sacrificing manufacturing tolerances, as well as increasing the risk of rejecting good pieces.

Fig. 5-33. Fixed limit gages: (A) adjustable snap gage; (B) plain ring gage; (C) cylindrical plug gage; (D) progressive cylindrical plug gage; (E) cylindrical pin gage; (F) adjustable thread ring gage; (G) thread plug gage. (*DoAll Co.*)

The choice of gage design policy is dependent upon individual product requirements, which should be carefully analyzed and thoroughly understood, before a decision is made. In general, gage tolerances can consume 10 to 30 percent of the component tolerance, and fixed gages are not recommended for part tolerances less than 0.001 in. There is, then, an overlap between gages designed according to the above two systems. The overlap, which is in the neighborhood of the product limits, can give paradoxical results which may be cleared only by the aid of a third, graduated measuring instrument. Figure 5-33 shows fixed limit gages of contemporary design.

SINE BAR

The sine bar is a hardened, stabilized, precision ground and lapped tool for accurate angle setting or measuring.

It is comprised of a bar to which two cylinders of equal diameter are attached. When the cylinders are brought in contact with a flat surface, the top of the bar is parallel to that surface. Starting from this position, if a block of known height is placed under one of the cylinders, the angle by which the top surface of the bar becomes tilted can be determined from the following formula: $\alpha = \sin^{-1} (h/c)$, where $\alpha =$ angle of tilt, $h =$ height of block (combined linear gage blocks), and $c =$ center distance of the two cylinders of the sine bar. Conversely, to set a known angle with the sine bar, the required height of the gage block combination is: $h = c \sin \alpha$.

Fig. 5-34. Sine bar. (*DoAll Co.*)

Example: To set an angle of $\alpha = 14°30'$ with a 10-in. sine bar ($c = 10$ in.), the height of gage block combination must be $h = 10 \times \sin 14°30' = 10 \times 0.25038 = 2.5038$ in. Tables with various values of $c \sin \alpha$ are available. Figure 5-34 shows the principles of angle measurement and setting, by sine bars. Many modifications of this simple device are available for specific requirements.

DIRECT READING MEASURING MACHINES*

The variety of measuring machines available today is extensive, but can generally be divided into categories: special and standard. Special (one-

*By C.E. Blanchard, Superintendent, Gages, Pratt & Whitney Company, Inc.

purpose) measuring machines, employing single or multiple gaging principles, are commonly used in production areas, where their existence on economic basis can be justified. Standard measuring machines (off-the-shelf items), however, owe their existence to the fact that each type must be versatile in its applications. Unlike special measuring machines, the standard machine has not been designed around a particular part requirement. Rather, it is intended to meet general measurement requirements, such as length, diameter, angle, or radius, within predetermined general perimeters.

The following data deal with some of the standard direct-reading machines where accuracies are embodied basically in mechanical, optical, or numerically controlled systems.

The Bench Micrometer

Shown in Fig. 5-35, this instrument provides a single-element horizontal length check between the anvils of a headstock and tailstock. Direct readings through a one-inch range are taken from a precision screw-type headstock by means of a dial readout. Length requirements beyond one inch generally are made by moving the tailstock away from the headstock and zeroing in on standard inch gage blocks, from which direct readings may be taken over the particular inch range required. Standard models generally cover length ranges through 10 in.

Since control of gaging pressure is vital to any reliable contact-type measurement, a good bench micrometer should provide variable pressure settings plus a montitoring readout system of the pressure at the actual time of measurement. A pressure range of 2 through 48 oz should be sufficient for most practical requirements. It should be mentioned here that correct gaging pressures cannot be over-emphasized, and full advantage of the variable setting feature should be taken. If the gage contact surface with the work piece is small, e.g., a line or point contact, excessive gaging pressures can render the resulting measurements virtually worthless.

Fig. 5-35. Bench micrometer. (*Pratt & Whitney Co., Inc.*)

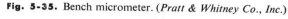

Reliable instruments are available with accuracies of 0.0001 in., when taken as direct reading from the micrometer dial. Instruments of this type may be used as comparators, if a comparative reading suits the job application. When used as a comparator and read off a calibrated gaging pressure meter, the accuracy of this instrument is approximately 0.00002 in.

Direct-measuring mechanical instruments should have a guaranteed accuracy that is traceable back to the ultimate standard at the National Bureau of Standards in Washington, D.C. A good bench micrometer should not be more than one step removed from the NBS through the media of precision gage blocks.

This instrument can be very versatile and is widely used at workshop, inspection, and laboratory levels. It is especially useful in checking cylindrical taper plugs, work thread plugs and pitch diameters by the three-wire method, and highly accurate workpieces.

The Measuring Machine

This instrument, illustrated in Fig. 5-36, provides a single-element horizontal check between the anvils of a headstock and tailstock. Direct readings over a one-inch range are taken from a precision screw-type headstock by means of a dial readout. Length requirements beyond one inch are made by moving the headstock away from the tailstock and zeroing in over a precision inch bar at even-inch intervals by means of a microscope. From these even-inch settings the headstock is then used for measurements over the particular inch range required. The total range of any particular instrument depends on the model selected. Standard available models cover ranges up through 120 inches.

Fig. 5-36. Measuring machine. (*Pratt & Whitney Co., Inc.*)

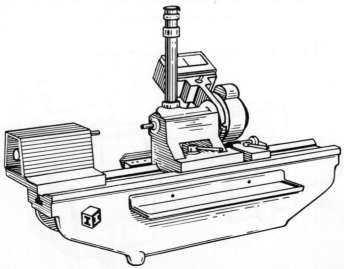

This instrument should be supplied with a variable-pressure tailstock, 2 through 48 oz (see "Bench Micrometers").

Direct readings are obtained from the micrometer dial to 0.000010 in. If desired, the instrument may be used as a comparator and read off a pressure tailstock calibrated meter.

The measuring machine (a name that has long been associated with this instrument) is really a sophisticated version of the bench micrometer, differing principally in the fact that it is direct reading over its entire length, and that the workmanship built into it is commensurate with its accuracy.

The accuracy of the micrometer head and the inch bar are traceable to the National Bureau of Standards.

The measuring machine is a highly versatile instrument whose reliability is of long standing. It is widely used at inspection and laboratory levels. It is especially useful in checking end measures, measuring rods, large cylindrical plugs, pitch diameter of thread set plugs by the three-wire method, master cylindrical plugs, and highly accurate workpieces.

Helical Path Analyzer

As shown in Fig. 5-37, this instrument provides a direct reading of thread helix (or lead) angle through the application of a precision tangent bar. Using the centerline of the workpiece as a datum, the tangent bar is swung to the required helix. A stylus then tracks the helix along the pitch diameter of the

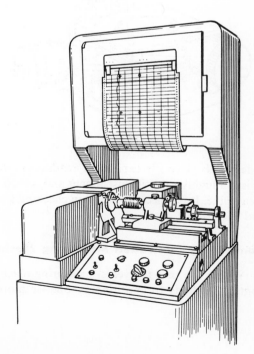

Fig. 5-37. Helical path analyzer. (*Pratt & Whitney Co., Inc.*)

thread flank. Variations from true helix angle are recorded on a chart read-out. Instruments of varying accuracies are available, but if it is required for inspection of setting thread plugs the machine should be capable of accuracies in the order of 0.000010 in. This machine is basically an inspection and laboratory instrument.

Toolmaker's Microscope

As Fig. 5-38 indicates, this instrument provides direct-reading measurement by means of moving two right-angle slides, on which the work is mounted, under a target-type microscope. To determine the positions of the

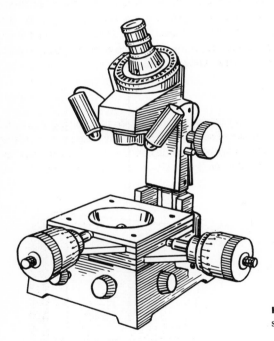

Fig. 5-38. Toolmaker's microscope. (*Brown & Sharpe Mfg. Co.*)

slides, dials generally capable of readouts in the order of 0.0001 in. are used. This is a highly versatile instrument and is used in work shop and inspection areas alike. It is especially useful in checking shoulder distances, radii, angles, and form tools.

Numerically Controlled Measuring Machines

Within the past ten years, measuring machines which employ numerical control methods for positioning one or more axis slides have come into prominence for inspecting multidimensional parts. These machines are especially advantageous when checking free contours, as on nose cones. Although these machines were originally developed to meet requirements on specialized parts, they are now being produced as standard items and their application is becoming more widespread every day. At first it may appear that inaccuracies on a numeric machine would be considerably greater than those on a completely mechanical machine (due to the replacement of manual input by electrical input for positioning the slides), since the electrical system has some inherent errors which tend to add to the mechanical errors. However, through the use of a computer, it is possible to correct for setup errors which cause the workpiece to be out-of-square, non-parallel or eccentric to the measurement datum surfaces, and thereby discount error factors which could very well be considerably greater than the error in the electrical system.

In short, by using a computer in conjunction with the numerically controlled machine, the optimum part axis (or true datum) can be determined, after which subsequent dimensions are related to the true part axis.

Advantages such as printout of a statistical inspection for future record, reduction of mounting fixture costs, elimination of human error, and major time saving, can be particularly rewarding on parts of a complicated nature.

6

OPTICAL PROJECTORS*

The optical projector is a versatile instrument widely used in many phases of quality control and production and has become almost a necessity in the well-equipped toolroom. It has made possible the effective measurement of great numbers of components which, because of size, material composition, or dimensional characteristics, pose serious difficulties to other measurement methods.

The term "optical projector" is here used as a generic term to describe what have been variously called contour projectors, optical comparators, shadowgraphs, lanterns, microprojectors, etc. No generally accepted nomenclature exists for this basic type of measuring equipment.

All optical projectors, as above defined, are fundamentally alike. They all display magnified images on an appropriate viewing screen, as an aid to more precise determination of dimension, form, and, occasionally, physical characteristics of sample parts.

*By Wayne G. Norton, General Manager, Optical Gaging Products, Inc.

Optical projectors possess a special capability, that of being able to display a two-dimensional projection of a part rather than a single linear dimension as with most other gaging devices.

Industrial use of optical projectors involves three basic elements: (1) the projector itself, (2) a screen layout (or chart-gage) for the comparison or measurement of parts, and (3) some form of holding device (staging fixture) to locate the part in the projector.

As a matter of historic interest, the optical projector was first introduced in the U.S. about 1900 by Bausch & Lomb Optical Co. Just prior to World War I a projector was introduced by Jones & Lamson Machine Tool Co., intended primarily for the inspection of screw threads. Use of optical projection methods gained some prominence during World War II, but projectors remained limited in use and design until 1949 when Eastman Kodak Co. introduced a completely new optical system for projectors and, with the assistance of the author's company, led the way to a greatly expanded use of inspection by optical projection. The term "optical gaging" is now generally applied to inspection by the use of optical projectors.

GENERAL DESIGN OF OPTICAL PROJECTORS

For precision measurement, the optical system must project images which are clear, sharp, and dimensionally accurate. The mechanical design and function of the projector must also be compatible with the precision of the optical system.

The design must provide ample working space for the positioning of parts. The viewing screen, on which the image is formed, must be located in a position convenient to the operator at normal eye level. Operating controls must be convenient and accessible.

To satisfy these requirements, all optical projectors incorporate in their design several essential features. These are:

1. A light source.
2. A condenser or collimating lens system to direct the light past the part and into the optical system.
3. A suitable workpiece staging table, movable or fixed.
4. The projection optics, including both mirrors and lenses.
5. A viewing screen to receive the projected image.
6. Measuring devices where required.

The arrangement of these elements varies in different projectors, but their function is the same in each.

In the simplest form, an optical projector is constructed according to the schematic diagram shown in Fig. 6-1. By contrast, Fig. 6-2 illustrates a

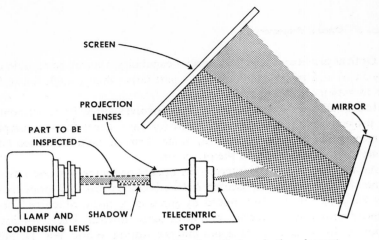

Fig. 6-1. Schematic diagram of basic optical projection elements. (*Jones & Lamson Machine Co.*)

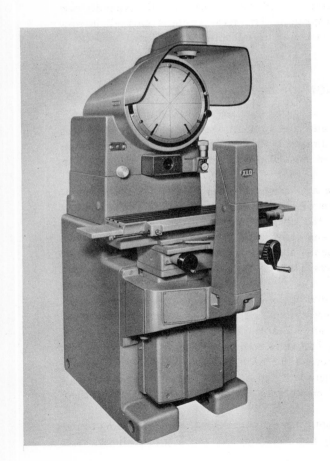

Fig. 6-2. Model 14–814 optical comparator. (*ExCell-O Corp.*)

modern measuring-type projector of high precision and considerable versatility.

While screen sizes of 14-in. and 30-in. diam are by far the most widely accepted by American industry, there are projectors available in sizes from 6-in. diam to as large as 40 × 60 in. Projectors over 30-in. screen diam have not proved popular in the U.S. and are foreign made. The comparators shown in Fig. 6-3 indicate the variety of equipment available.

To provide a clear understanding of the capability and usefulness (as well as the limitations) of the optical projector in metrology, it is important to review in some detail the purpose and function of the various components which make up a projector. It is likewise important to offer some criteria by which the performance capability of projectors and their accessories can be determined.

The exact physical arrangement of a projector is a matter of manufacturer preference as to operator comfort and convenience. The details of any specific projector are readily available in the catalogs of the various manufacturers. It is here intended to discuss only the overall concepts which bear on the proper selection and use of projection equipment.

Two basic uses of optical projectors must be differentiated.

First is the use of a projector for so-called toolroom applications and single-piece inspections. Such a projector requires precision in the staging table mechanism and in the measuring devices associated with it. Since measurements are made with reference to a cross line on the center of the projector screen, just as in a toolmaker's microscope, there is no prime requirement for a completely accurate image over the entire screen. A clear, well defined image will suffice.

Second is the use of a projector for comparison measurement. In this usage the projected image of the part is compared with an enlarged layout placed directly on the screen, and may be spread over the entire screen area. In such applications, accuracy of the image in all areas of the screen is very important.

Thus, for toolroom applications prime emphasis is placed on mechanical measuring, while for comparison applications prime emphasis is placed on the accuracy of the optical system.

Since in most industrial plants, projectors are frequently used for both types of inspection described above, it is generally accepted that equipment must have both a precise optical system, and means for precise mechanical measuring.

Over-all Performance

The over-all performance of any optical projector is dependent on several factors:

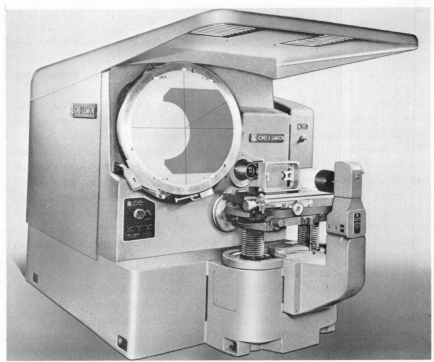

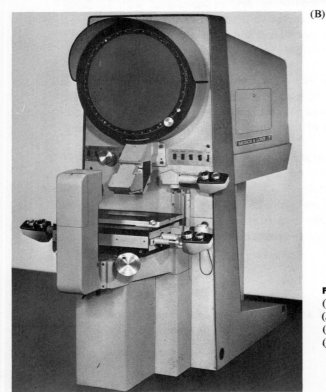

Fig. 6-3. Optical comparators: (A) Epic 30, 30-in. diam screen (*Jones & Lamson Machine Co.*); (B) Model 20, 20-in. diam screen (*Bausch & Lomb, Inc.*).

(B)

(A)

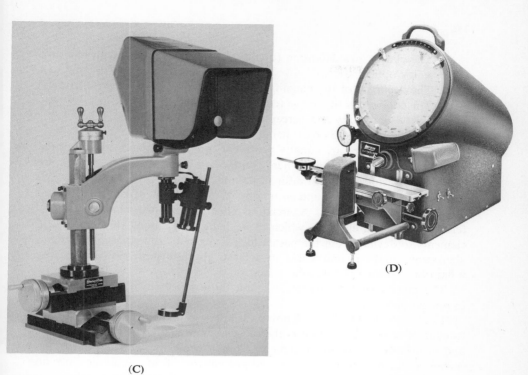

(C)

(D)

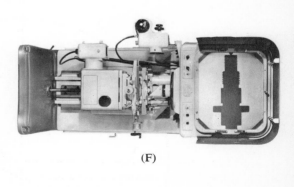

(E)

(F)

Fig. 6-3 (Cont'd.). Optical Comparators: (C) bench model (*Stocker & Yale, Inc.*); (D) Ultrascope (*The Lufkin Rule Co.*); (E) pedestal type (*Scherr-Tumico, Inc.*); (F) Model 5-A (*Nikon, Inc.*).

1. The clarity and definition (quality) of the image formed by the projector optical system.
2. The accuracy of the magnified image (freedom from distortion).
3. The contrast in the image (dark shadows, bright background).
4. The visual acuity and perceptiveness of the operator.
5. The nature of the object being projected.

Not all operators are equally proficient, nor are all parts ideally suited to optical gaging. Attention is here confined to items 1, 2, and 3 which are directly the result of optical design, manufacture, and assembly.

Both individual lenses and entire optical systems suffer from what optical designers call aberrations. Aberrations can be described as those characteristics of optical elements which cause light rays passing through optical elements to deviate from the path which is desired. In a projection system, aberrations make it impossible to achieve absolute perfection in imaging a flat object onto a flat viewing screen.

The most common aberrations, and those most obvious when present in optical projectors, are:

1. *Distortion.* This term denotes variation in magnification from center to edge of screen. Distortion is the most obvious source of projector error, and is usually expressed in percent. Thus a projector with a 14-in. diam screen, and a distortion error of 0.10 percent (half field) would produce an image 0.007 in. off true position at the edge of the field.

Fig. 6-4. Typical distortion curve of projection lens, showing departure from true magnification from center to edge of screen.

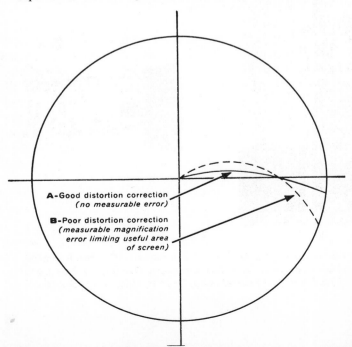

A-Good distortion correction
(no measurable error)

B-Poor distortion correction
*(measurable magnification
error limiting useful area
of screen)*

Distortion does not increase gradually from center to edge, but follows a typical curve as shown in Fig. 6-4. Note the "node" or zero point approximately seven-tenths of the way from center to edge. This 0.7 zone embraces the useable area in many projectors, with increasing error beyond this point. Distortion can be controlled within acceptable limits clear to the edge of the screen by proper optical design and manufacture.

2. *Field Curvature.* The image plane of a projection lens is not actually a flat plane, but is spherical in shape. Thus, an object perfectly focused at the center of a flat screen may appear progressively "out of focus" as the object shifts from center to edge of the field. Field curvature is especially noticeable in simple lens systems, and directly contributes to distortion errors, as well as deterioration of image sharpness.

3. *Chromatic Aberration.* This is caused by a dispersion of white light within the optical system and evidenced by the inability to focus all colors simultaneously in the plane of the viewing screen. (A lens system corrected for color aberrations is said to be achromatic, or apochromatic, depending on the degree of such correction.)

4. *Lateral Color.* A further problem in color correction of the optical system shows up in distinct red or blue fringes of color at the edges of the image, which is caused by unequal magnification of these two colors in the image.

5. *Image Quality.* The sharpness or definition of the image depends not only on the items mentioned above, but also on control of several other factors, such as spherical aberration, coma, and astigmatism. For gaging it is important that the shadow image be sharp and unmistakable, for accuracy in setting to target lines on the screen.

6. *Contrast.* This is defined as the brightness ratio between the image and the background illumination. Shadow images in projectors tend to be somewhat less than dead black. Background illumination is a function of the aperture of the lens system, and the type and efficiency of the light source.

Mechanical mounting of the optical elements to reduce flare and stray light, and the coating of lenses also helps to enhance contrast and insure more reliable observation of the image.

A number of other factors influence projector performance, which are not aberrations of the lens elements. They include such items as the viewing screen, mirrors, "wall effect," telecentricity, etc., which will be considered later.

While perfection in projector optical systems is never achieved, it is possible, through careful and competent design and manufacture to reduce aberrations to very small residuals.

Much has been said and implied regarding the potential accuracy and reliability of optical projectors, but it is generally conceded that there are theoretical as well as practical limits for over-all performance. The figure

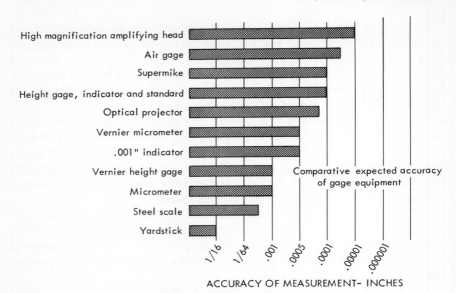

ACCURACY OF MEASUREMENT- INCHES

Fig. 6-5. Comparative expected accuracy of various types of gaging equipment.

usually expressed in terms of error at the part is in the order of 0.0001 in. for good equipment under good conditions. Figure 6-5 gives some idea as to the position of the optical projector among various kinds of measuring devices.

The means by which the various aberrations described above are evaluated are:

1. *Distortion.* This is most critically measured by projecting a calibrated reticle scale onto the screen and comparing with a master scale at the required magnification. This procedure is followed by most manufacturers. A simpler, but effective, method involves projection of known size balls or pins. Figure 6-6 illustrates a standard magnification checker and scale in widespread use.

In testing by means of balls or pins, it is very important that the projector collimator be properly adjusted to avoid the "wall effect," discussed later.

2. *Field Curvature.* Excessive field curvature is not only a source of error, but is an annoyance because operators must refocus from center to edge of screen. The amount of curvature in any projector can be determined by focusing a sharp object at both center and edge of screen and observing the amount of table movement involved. Since the plane of sharp focus of most projection systems does not greatly exceed 0.010 in., curvature in excess of this amount will be readily apparent.

3. *Image Quality, Contrast, and Chromatic Aberrations.* All these factors

Fig. 6-6. OGP magnification checker in use on optical projector. (*Optical Gaging Products, Inc.*)

affect what is generally known as the "definition" of the image at best focus. Good definition is essential to reliable and repetitive observer performance.

Definition is best determined by projecting a resolution test pattern, such as shown in Fig. 6-7, and as approved by the National Bureau of Standards. This pattern is numbered, and the resolution, in terms of lines per millimeter, is easily determined for all areas of the screen.

Fig. 6-7. Reproduction of typical National Bureau of Standards test pattern. Resolution test target consists of progression of line spacings by sixth root of two per step. Span of total series is 36 steps, or a total range of 64 to one line spacing.

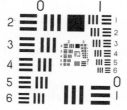

If color is present in the image, the introduction of color filters may improve definition. Some projectors incorporate color filters as standard in order to compensate for any lack of color correction in the optical system.

Lighting System

To put an optical projector system to use, a beam of light is required. The light beam is the medium by which a measurable image of a test part can be presented on the screen for examination.

The light sources most generally used in optical projectors are tungsten filament lamps, with a recent trend in some units to high-pressure mercury or zenon arc lamps. Ideally, a projector lamp would be one producing within itself a concentrated bundle of parallel light rays. In addition, the bundle or beam would need to be of sufficient diameter to illuminate a significant area of a test part for projection. An approximation of this ideal is achieved by optical means.

An achromatic collimator lens system is placed in the path of the beam as it leaves the lamp. Sufficient light rays are thereby collected into a parallel beam of large enough diameter to provide coverage on the test piece and adequate illumination intensity at the screen.

Projectors are designed to use a specified type of lamp, and manufacturers' recommendations should always be followed when making replacements. The mounting and adjustment of the lamps is critical to assure proper positioning of the filament with respect to the optical axis. A protective housing for the lamp and collimator assembly prevents any careless jarring and dislocation in the alignment. Exhaust fans are commonly incorporated to remove excess heat from the area.

Several considerations influence the selection of a light source for any single projector. Collimation can collect only a limited number of the total rays emitted by the source, and within the beam itself as it passes through the optical system there is a continual loss of light due to scattering, reflection from lens and mirror surfaces, and absorption within the system. More important, however, in projector usage is the matter of magnification.

In any projection system the amount of light produced at the screen will vary inversely with the square of the magnification of the system. The light on the screen at 10X, for example, is 100 times brighter than at 100X. An adequate lamp, therefore, should produce clear images with appreciable contrast between shadow and background light at the higher magnifications. While such a lamp may be too brilliant at the lower magnifications, dimming devices can be used to control the intensity of the illumination to a comfortable viewing level.

There are many occasions when it is desirable to have greatly intensified illumination for the projection of nonreflective materials, irregular surfaces, and extremely small components at very high magnifications. For this purpose there have been developed high-pressure arc units of great intensity. These sources are very effective in producing good contrast between shadow image and background light for comparative purposes. Their effectiveness for accurate measuring operations is sometimes overestimated, however, as brightness alone is not the only criterion for proper performance. Source size, magnification, and other factors also play an important part.

Light Beam Systems

Three arrangements of light sources are used in optical projectors: (1) horizontal, (2) vertical, and (3) surface.

Horizontal and vertical systems are both designed to produce a shadow image on the screen. Surface illumination, as the name implies, produces a reflected image of the face of a part. Most projectors have been designed to utilize a single type of shadow projection, although some manufacturers have incorporated both horizontal and vertical systems in the same unit. Surface illumination is in most cases optional equipment on a projector, and may be externally or internally mounted.

Horizontal System. Projectors equipped with horizontal beams provide great flexibility in operation and are used widely in industry. Their basic arrangement permits them to have a generous and open work area. Figure 6-8 shows in cross section a projector of this type.

Vertical System. Vertical light systems may have the light source located above the work area or below it. A mirror is introduced in the path of the vertical beam after it has passed by the test piece to direct it into the projection system. Figure 6-8 shows schematically how this is accomplished.

The work tables used with vertical systems must necessarily incorporate a glass plate or cutout for the passage of the light beam. Test pieces can be placed on the glass plate for inspection quickly and easily. They do not, however, afford the flexibility found in the work tables on horizontal units, and vertical systems are used mainly for inspection of flat pieces.

Fig. 6-8. Schematic view of 14-in.-screen optical system with relay lens and built-in direct-on-surface illumination.

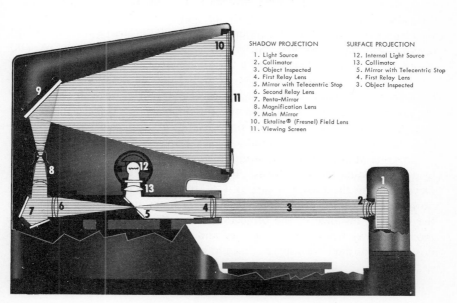

SHADOW PROJECTION	SURFACE PROJECTION
1. Light Source	12. Internal Light Source
2. Collimator	13. Collimator
3. Object Inspected	5. Mirror with Telecentric Stop
4. First Relay Lens	4. First Relay Lens
5. Mirror with Telecentric Stop	3. Object Inspected
6. Second Relay Lens	
7. Penta-Mirror	
8. Magnification Lens	
9. Main Mirror	
10. Ektalite® (Fresnel) Field Lens	
11. Viewing Screen	

Surface Illumination. The surface illumination system differs from the two systems discussed above in several respects. To be effective in projecting surface characteristics, the light must be more intense than that needed for direct projection. High-intensity sources which converge available light in a concentrated beam on a part have made possible the projection of such dull and non-reflective materials as ceramic and carbon.

The surface illumination assemblies are generally accessory equipment added externally to projectors. The light beam is directed by mirrors onto the test piece and thence reflected back into the regular projection system of the projector. Some projectors have the surface illumination system incorporated as an integral part of the projector, and the light source is located inside the housing cabinet. The beam is directed squarely to the part and reflected back into the projection system. While both "oblique" and "direct-on" surface illuminators have their place, the latter is most generally preferred because it is more efficient, and does not foreshorten the part being projected.

Staging Area

The light beam passes from the collimator across the working or staging area of the projector. It is here that the test pieces are staged on the work table so as to intercept the light beam.

Of prime importance is sufficient room for the operator's hands while positioning test parts, and also the amount of space in which parts can be staged. This space is controlled largely by the focal clearance or working distance of the optical system. Working distance is defined as the distance from the plane of sharp focus to the nearest surface of the projection lens, or projector housing. In most projectors the measurement approximates the actual focal length of the projection lens. Working distance may vary with lenses of different magnification, and as the latter increases, the working distance generally becomes shorter. A considerable reduction in working distance may result when changing from a low to a high magnification.

The sectional contour of a test piece that can normally be projected to the screen is the contour lying in the focal plane. The working distance of the projector thus determines the maximum size of a test piece that can be staged. The lack of adequate working distance often presents serious limitations to the flexibility and usefulness of a projector.

In some projectors this variation in working distance has been overcome by the introduction of a "relay" lens as a part of the projection system. Developed by the Eastman Kodak Co., the relay lens assembly is an important contribution to projector design. Its function is to extend optically the working distance of the projection lenses. Its use permits lenses to be mounted away from the staging area and, among other advantages, makes possible a constant working distance at all magnifications

Projection System

The beam passing the test part passes into the projection system. The lenses and mirrors which comprise the system must be held in accurate alignment on rigid supports. The lenses provide the desired magnification, while the mirrors serve both to direct the beam of light to the screen, and to assist in forming an image there in the same relative position as the operator sees the test part in the staging area (i.e., correctly oriented top to bottom, and right to left).

One of the advantages of the projection method of inspection is the ability to select the magnification best suited to the requirements of the operation. To accomplish this, interchangeability of lenses in many projectors has been made positive and accurate. In some projectors the lenses are changed manually. A faster and more satisfactory method employs a turret or slide in which several lenses can be mounted. By means of an external control convenient to the operator, the turret can be indexed to bring a lens of the desired magnification into the projection system.

Magnification must always be considered when planning an inspection operation. A good rule to follow is to use the lowest-power lens that will show the smallest part tolerance limits clearly on the screen without strain to the operator.

Low-power magnification offers certain definite advantages over high power, in both toolroom applications and in measurement by comparison. Images on the screen are sharply delineated with clean-cut edges. There is a positive contrast between shadow and background light which greatly simplifies the making of settings to reference lines on the screen. For comparison measurements, a larger portion of the test part can be projected at a single setting.

The critical limits with which projection methods satisfactorily operate range from 0.010 in. to 0.0001 in. Within this range the larger tolerance limits can be readily seen when using either 10X or 20X lenses. As the tolerance limits grow smaller, a higher magnification is required so that the limit lines on chart layouts can show a definite separation. It is generally conceded that the desirable tolerance spread *at the screen* should be at least 0.015 in. But it must be kept in mind that as the magnification is increased, the sharpness and contrast of the projected image suffers. Shadow edges tend to become fuzzy and accurate readings more difficult.

Most frequently used magnifications are 10X, 20X, 25X, 50X, and 100X. They all furnish a convenient multiple of the unit increment of 0.001 in. Magnifications of 31.25X and 62.5X based on a relationship to the fractional $\frac{1}{32}''$ have lost their significance as fractional scales have become obsolete in critical measurement.

In addition to these magnifications in common use are some of a more special nature. These include very high-power lenses ranging from 200X up to 2500X. Such lenses are useful mainly for comparison purposes. It is quite debatable as to whether these extra high magnification lenses offer any real advantage in measuring accuracy. One manufacturer offers a 5X lens which has found a limited number of applications. Although such a lens offers large coverage of a test part, the magnification of dimensions is not significant except for rather large tolerance limits.

The Screen

The light beam after passing through the projection lens is directed by mirrors to the viewing screen, where the image of the test part is formed. Screens are made of glass with the surface facing the operator ground to a very fine grain. The location of this surface is critical in relation to the rest of the projection system, inasmuch as it determines the position where accurate magnification is achieved. Original equipment screens are referred to as "replacement screens" to distinguish them from "overscreens" frequently used as accessories.

It is important that the ground surface of the replacement screen be flat. Waviness can result in distortion of an image in different portions of the screen. Plastic materials are often subject to waviness and should not be used for the replacement screens although they can be used for "overscreens" as mentioned above.

Because of the critical importance of the ground glass surface in the projection system, the thickness of the glass must be held to close limits. By so doing, screens may be interchanged without affecting true magnification on the surface. (In one standard 14-in. projector system, a change of 0.005 in. in screen location will introduce a measurable magnification error.)

Mechanical Features

The mechanical features of optical projectors are largely centered in the staging or work area. Principal among them is the work table. It serves as a support for the test piece that is to be examined. It may be stationary or equipped for movement. Its choice depends largely on the type of inspection for which the projector is intended.

Tables that provide movement generally have provision for the attachment of measuring devices. Many are equipped with an angular adjustment for positioning to the helix of threads and worms.

Protractor rings mounted with the viewing screen simplify the determination of angular measurements.

The design and manufacture of all mechanical elements in a projector requires the same care and attention as the optical systems with which they are to be used.

Work Tables

Projector work tables can be classified under three types: (1) stationary, (2) moving (non-measuring), and (3) moving (measuring).

Stationary Tables. These are generally found on projectors used for production inspection. Such inspection is usually accomplished with a setup of staging fixture and coordinated with chart-gage. Stationary tables provide a good surface for the mounting of the fixtures which are clamped in position for the duration of the inspection run. Most projectors are equipped with keyways or T-slots for fixture mounting.

As these tables do not move, they do not require any appreciable mechanical understructure. This is an advantage as it permits design of simple bench-type projectors and the space in the work area accommodates quite large fixturing setups. If repositioning of parts is necessary in the inspection, movement can be incorporated in the fixture itself. Because of their rigidity, stationary tables make possible the addition of auxiliary equipment to fixturing such as automatic loading and unloading devices.

Moving Tables (non-measuring). Almost all non-measuring moving tables can be converted to measuring units by the addition of suitable attachments. However, for many production purposes, using chart-gages and fixtures, a measuring device is not needed and a simple moving table is sufficient for the inspection involved.

Tables are designed to travel in one or more directions. First is generally a focusing movement. On a projector with a horizontal beam, the focus travel is an in-and-out movement parallel to the axis of the light beam. The table usually moves on friction or ball slides, and is controlled by a conveniently placed handwheel or knob.

The focusing movement on a vertical beam projector must be vertical. Tables are usually mounted on dovetail or box-type slides which are rigidly controlled and aligned. To permit the passage of the light beam, this type of table has an optically flat glass set into the top. This glass surface provides a good surface for the positioning of a variety of flat parts without any other special fixturing. The metal portion of the table is often fitted with standard keyway slots for mounting centers and other devices to hold parts over the glass and in the light path.

In addition to focusing travel, tables may have movement in at least the other two planes. These compound tables are precisely machined and all surfaces and slides are held to close tolerances. The assembly must be carefully controlled to assure accurate travel in relation to the axis of the optical system. Ease and precision of movement and adequate control and adjustment are very important.

The tables on a number of projectors are similar to the stages of a toolmaker microscope. They are not intended to stage large parts but are well adapted to handle very small and fragile components. They are found principally on projectors having rather small viewing screens, or on larger projectors employing a vertical light beam. Travel in the majority of these tables is limited, seldom exceeding a very few inches.

Larger tables are much more sturdy in their construction because they are intended to support larger and heavier parts. They are found principally on projectors equipped with horizontal-beam light systems and their construction permits large bearing surfaces for full load-carrying capacity. Vertical travel on these larger tables is often power controlled for the convenience of the operator.

The size of work tables varies considerably from one manufacturer's product to another. Some of the small bench projectors are equipped with larger tables than units having much larger screens. In the popular 14-in. screen projectors the tables may vary from approximately 12 in. to over 30 in. in length. The 30-in. screen projectors are usually equipped with the largest and heaviest compound tables of all. These tables provide horizontal travel up to 10 or 12 in. and greater, and vertical travel of 9 in. and greater.

Although the larger tables are provided on projectors arranged for horizontal beam lighting, they can (on some manufacturers models) be used with a vertical beam by means of an adapter and accessory lamphouse (Fig. 6-9). The accessory consists of a staging unit with a glass plate which is positioned in the vertical light beam. There is a mirror below the glass which reflects the beam from the overhead lamphouse into the regular projection system of the projector.

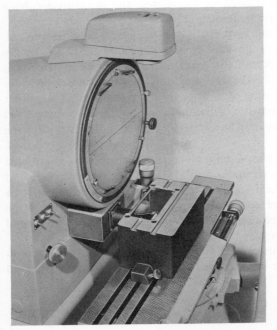

Fig. 6-9. Vertical beam system for staging flat parts which are best inspected on a horizontal surface.

Moving Tables (measuring). These tables generally offer travel in three planes: focus, horizontal, and vertical. Construction is quite similar to that of the non-measuring units and they generally incorporate the same amount of travel. It is essential that each direction of travel be carefully coordinated for true alignment to the optical axis.

There are various types of measuring devices for reading the amount of travel. They are almost always installed on the movements controlling X and Y travel. Some projectors also provide micrometers for reading the focusing travel, a convenience when using a vertical beam adapter on a horizontal beam table. When so used, the focusing movement becomes the travel in the Y plane.

The measuring attachments are usually micrometers alone, or in combination with dial indicators. Generally provision is made for using gage blocks or end measures for long travels. Micrometers and indicators graduated for readings to 0.001 in. are sufficient for many inspection purposes. For more exacting work, instruments graduated to 0.0005 in. and 0.0001 in. are employed.

The micrometers used on some of the smaller projector tables are similar in size to the ones found on measuring microscopes. On larger equipment the micrometers are also larger in diameter and provide clearly visible readings. All measuring devices should be located at positions convenient for operator control and viewing.

Newer projector tables are being equipped with direct read-out digitizers. The digitizer displays positive measurements regardless of direction, and has a "zero anywhere" feature.

Current development also indicates a trend to electronic digital display, optical digital readout, and optical readers with scales. While such devices are perhaps available on special order, they are not, at this writing, generally available.

Helix Rotation Provision

Helix rotation is provided by an attachment to give angular positioning to a work table. It is used primarily when inspecting such parts as threads, worms, and hobs. It is generally desirable, when inspecting this type of part, to bring the helix into parallel alignment with the optical axis of the projector. By means of the helix rotation the table is turned through an arc corresponding to the helix angle of the part.

The effective rotation is about $15°$ both to the right and to the left. The measuring is graduated, usually in $\frac{1}{2}°$ divisions and, with its accompanying vernier, readings can be made to one minute of arc. Refocusing is frequently necessary when projecting parts have a large helix, as often only one side of a tooth form may be in sharp focus from side to side, or from top to bottom. Under these conditions it is necessary to refocus in order to complete the inspection.

Some projectors are designed with the helix adjustment installed *under* the focusing travel of the work table and some with it installed *above*. When *above* the focusing table, the refocusing described above can be accomplished *without* a lateral shift of the screen image.

Some vertical beam projectors can be equipped with special attachments for making helix adjustments, but the arrangement proves awkward and is rarely incorporated in standard models; they are generally accessory equipment.

Protractor Rings

Protractor rings provide the means for making accurate readings of angular values on projectors. The rotational feature also serves as a useful tool in some inspection procedures not directly concerned with angular measurement. Protractors must be as carefully designed and machined as any other part of the projector.

Protractors are standard equipment on most measuring projectors and are available as auxiliary equipment on many others. The rings serve as the holder for the viewing screen. Adjustments are provided in most projectors for exactly centering the screen in the ring although one manufacturer machines rings and glass to avoid this operation. Once assembled, both the protractor ring and the screen should be concentric with the optical axis of the projector.

Degrees of arc are usually marked directly on the rings. Readings are made with correlated verniers bearing scales readable to one minute of arc. Some of the rings used on very large projectors are marked for every 10° and are used with a continuous-reading dial vernier from which the intermediate degrees and minutes can be read. These vernier dials are readable to one minute of arc also.

The protractor rings are usually ball bearing-mounted for smooth and easy rotation. Positioning is done by means of a hand knob. Reed-type locks hold the protractor in set position without danger of shift or misalignment.

MEASUREMENT TECHNIQUES

There are three basic techniques for measurement generally employed in optical projection usage. The inspections performed on many parts are concerned not so much with actual part dimensions as to whether the parts are within permissible tolerance limits. These are essentially go, not-go inspections made by comparison to a master.

Analytical inspections are concerned generally with the dimensions themselves. It is necessary to make careful measurements of each of the dimensions, and this is usually a slower operation than that which compares a part to a master.

A great many parts contain features that cannot be projected by a light beam directly but whose contours can be measured indirectly. This is accomplished by a combination of tracing and optical projections, to be described later.

Many inspection operations combine the previously mentioned techniques in various ways. The three techniques described above have been designated: (1) measurement by comparison, (2) measurement by movement, and (3) measurement by translation.

All optical projectors are suitable, within the capability of the optical and mechanical design, for making measurements by comparison. To measure by movement requires a projector with table travel and appropriate measuring devices. Measurement by translation requires special tracer accessories.

Measurement by Comparison

The two-dimensional screen images produced by optical projectors provide the means for making measurements by comparison. These images magnify exactly the dimensions of parts positioned in the focal plane of the optical system. It follows that every dimension of the magnified image can be accepted as equivalent to the actual part dimension multiplied by the magnification. A master layout or chart-gage made to represent the high and low limits of the theoretically perfect part at the magnified size can then be compared to the screen image (Fig. 6-10). If the image falls within the limits of the master gage, the part is acceptable. If it does not, the part is a reject.

A chart-gage and an associated holding device or staging fixture is generally used when performing inspections by comparison. The chart-gage serves as a master gage. It may be of replacement or overscreen type. The part contour is laid out on it at the magnification selected for the inspection. A chart that is drawn to one magnification can be used only with a projection lens of the same magnification. Were it to be used with any other magnification the contour lines would in no way conform to the projected image.

The staging fixture serves to support the part in such a manner that the area or contour to be projected is positioned in the focal plane of the optical system. In many instances the same holding device will adequately support a number of different parts. Sets of matched staging centers and V-blocks are frequently used. They are commercially available with bases designed

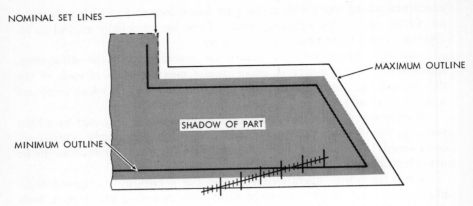

NOMINAL SET LINES

MAXIMUM OUTLINE

SHADOW OF PART

MINIMUM OUTLINE

Fig. 6-10. Spread of tolerance on a part as seen on a contour projector screen.

to fit the table keyways of most projectors. There are also obtainable standard kits consisting of a base into which a number of interchangeable part holders can be inserted. These units will accommodate many different types of parts.

In many instances the nature of the part and the inspection will require a custom designed fixture. Insofar as possible, the part is located in the fixture exactly as it would locate in actual use. Thus part location is *functional*, one of the significant benefits of optical projection inspections.

Occasionally the part may require inspection of only some critical portion, which is all that is necessary to project to the chart-gage. The area may be dimensioned from a reference point such as a hole center which does not itself need to be projected. A tapered pin through the hole can locate the reference point on the fixture. A target edge (or "set surface") is provided in the fixture in order to align the chart-gage contour to the invisible reference point. Corresponding "set lines" on the chart-gage represent the target, and the contour of that portion of the part being measured is laid out in relation to these sets. The inspection is fast and positive once the original alignment has been made.

Charts for measurement by comparison generally are of the envelope type. In such charts, dimensions and manufacturing tolerances are interpreted to produce a double-line outline indicating allowable maximum and minimum conditions of the part. There is usually a reference line for alignment of the part image to the chart. Layouts of this nature have the advantage of indicating all of the contour characteristics such as irregular curves, chamfers, and fillet radii, features which might not warrant separate inspection by other methods. In almost all cases the inspection of an image to the double-line charts can be made rapidly as the eye sweeps over the screen.

For more critical dimensions, additional scales, close tolerance line construction, etc., are used to enhance readability.

Measurement by Movement

Measurement by movement is used primarily for single-piece inspection and for making a variety of non-repetitive measurements. This technique utilizes the travel of the work table in relation to a positive index or reference. The optical axis of the projector furnishes an appropriate reference and is identified by the center cross line on the screen. This "optical reference" is unique in that it has no weight, exerts no pressure, cannot warp, and requires no physical support at the point at which it is used. In making measurements by movement it is convenient to consider the horizontal and vertical cross lines of the screen, or any point in relation to them, as index references. The vertical cross line is referenced when using horizontal travel and the horizontal cross line when moving the screen image up or down.

Practically all projectors are designed with tables whose movement to left or right will cause the screen image to also move horizontally. The movement of the table which will produce a vertical shifting of the image varies according to the manner in which the light beam is directed. On horizontal beam projectors the vertical movement of the image is produced by raising or lowering the work table. If the projector has a vertical beam, the image will shift vertically as the work table is moved to and from the operator standing in front of the screen. To avoid confusion in describing procedures it is convenient to refer to all movements in terms of the horizontal and vertical travel of the screen image.

Although the measurement of any one dimension or part characteristic might be accomplished equally well by other measuring methods, optical projection offers the advantage of handling vertical, horizontal, and angular dimensions simultaneously. A few examples of simple measurement will illustrate the point.

A part to be measured is positioned on the work table, and the edge of the shadow of the part is referenced to the vertical centerline of the screen. The measuring attachments on the table are zeroed and the table is moved until the opposite edge of the shadow is brought to the centerline. The micrometer is then read to obtain the measurement between the two sides of the part. The actual measurement, however, is made of the displacement of the table.

It is not necessary for the entire shadow of a part to be visible on the screen at one time in order to measure its length, provided that the length does not exceed that of the table travel. The visible end of the screen image is referenced to the centerline and the table micrometer is zeroed (Fig. 6-11A). The table is then traversed until the other end of the shadow appears on the screen, as in view B, and is in turn referenced to the same centerline. The length of the part is determined but it is the table travel that has been measured. (Longer parts may be accommodated by relocating or indexing them along the table itself.)

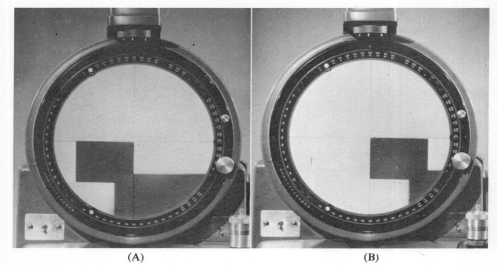

(A)   (B)

Fig. 6-11. Checking length dimension with horizontal micrometer.

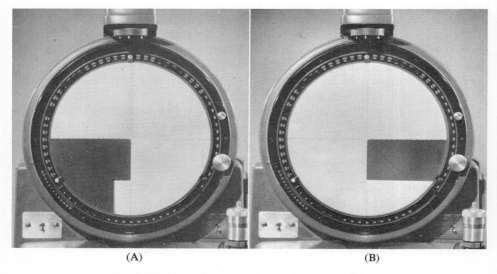

(A)   (B)

Fig. 6-12. Measuring very long pieces by table movement:
(A) measuring right-hand end of piece; (B) measuring left-hand
end.

A slightly more complex problem illustrating how easily an optical projector handles "outside-to-inside" measurements is shown in Fig. 6-12.

Optical projectors are peculiarly well adapted to make measurements
involving dimensions to points in space. A familiar example (Fig. 6-13A)
is one having a radiused corner and a drilled corner relief. The dimensions
on the part drawing are taken from the referenced corners (points in space).

162

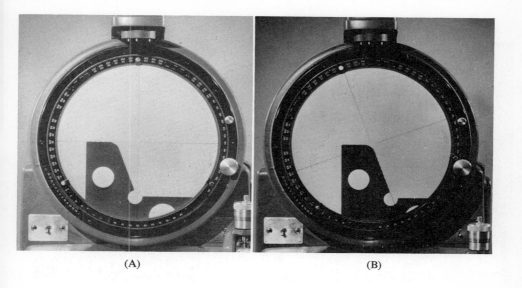

(A)   (B)

(C)

Fig. 6-13. Measuring "points in space" using radiused corner. Horizontal and vertical table motions plus chart rotation permit true location of missing corner on the part.

The radiused corner is referenced at the centerline intersection of the screen by sequential movement of the table and by rotation of the screen until both centerlines can be made to touch both edges of the shadow image (Views B and C). The same procedure is followed with the drilled corner relief. At the final position, when rotation of the screen will bring both centerlines to touch both edges, the actual centerline intersection will coincide

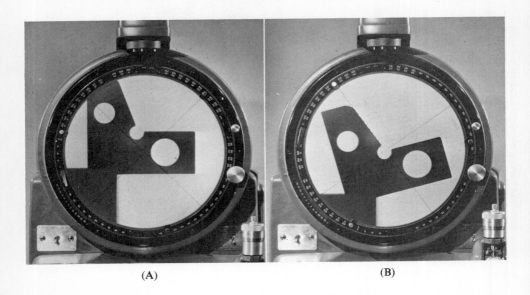

(A) (B)

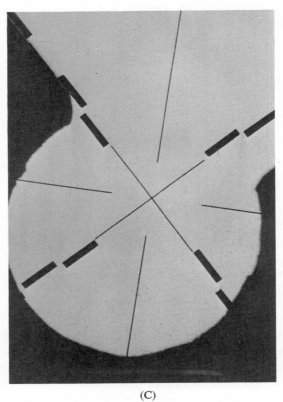

(C)

Fig. 6-14. Measuring "points in space" using drilled corner relief.

with the theoretical intersection of the two edges (Fig. 6-14). With this "point-in-space" established on the screen, measurements can be made from it exactly as if it were a definite physical point.

The same part presents another inspection problem, namely, gaging of dimensions taken from centers of holes. The procedure is simple. The screen is rotated so that the centerlines are at 45° to the horizontal (Fig. 6-15). The screen shadow is shifted by table movements to position one of

Fig. 6-15. Measuring "points in space": (A) and (B) lines at 45° to horizontal act like V blocks; a hole set tangent to the sides of a V has its centerline at same height as the centerline intersection of the screen. (C) and (D) holes are placed tangent to the top or bottom V quadrants for reading horizontal measurements.

(A)   (B)

(C)   (D)

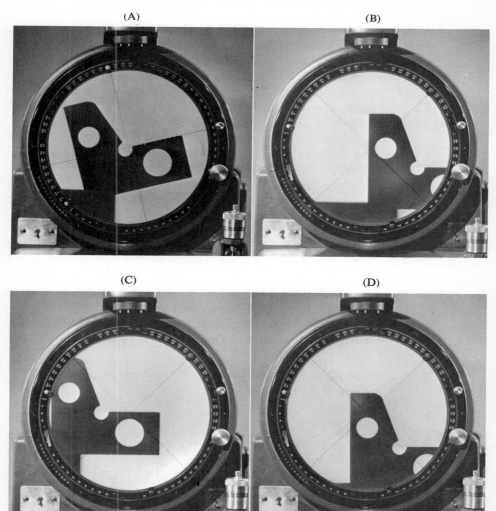

the holes tangent to the V formed by the centerlines. As the center of radius of an arc tangent to an angle must lie on the line which bisects the angle, the center of the hole has been established as being on the line passing through the centerline intersection. The measuring attachment for horizontal travel is set at zero, and the table is shifted to bring the second hole tangent to the same set of angle lines. Its center must lie on the same line as the first one. The reading of the horizontal micrometer is the true distance between the centers of the two holes in the X plane. The Y dimension can be measured by the same process of centering the holes tangent to the V's at the side, and reading the vertical movement micrometers.

Measurement by Translation

Many parts can be successfully gaged on optical projectors, even though the part configuration cannot be projected by the light beam. Parts having recessed contours such as actuator cam tracks, ball sockets, and the internal grooves of ball nuts can all be gaged by means of tracer techniques. A tracer, as the term is used in projection gaging, is a one-to-one pantograph. On one arm of the pantograph is a stylus which traces freely over the part contour in a given plane. The other arm carries a follower which is projected by the light beam as it moves. Three types of followers are used (Fig. 6-16):

1. Probe follower (View A): an exact duplicate of the stylus tracer in size and shape.
2. Dot follower (View B): a glass reticle having an opaque dot of the same diameter as the stylus tracer.
3. Reticle-gage follower (View C): a glass reticle having an exact one-to-one actual size reproduction of the part profile.

The choice of follower for a given gaging problem depends upon the size of the part and the magnification to be used. In general, the probe or dot is used if the size of the part is less than the field of view of the projector at the given magnification. In some cases larger parts are gaged by using two followers suitably spaced to correlate with a special type of chart in which one section of the contour is superimposed on another section. For some purposes the dot follower is preferred to the probe because it provides a complete circle shadow unrestricted by the shadow of the supporting stem.

Fig. 6-16. Projector tracer followers: (A) probe type; (B) dot type; (C) reticle-gage type.

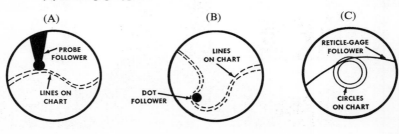

(A)

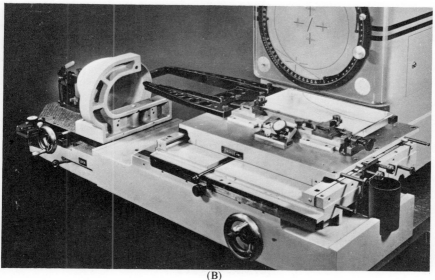

(B)

Fig. 6-17. (A) Standard tracer projector unit with ball-type follower. An automotive ball joint component is being checked for
internal groove contour and concentricity. (B) Tracer projector
with two probe arms for checking internal and external profiles
and wall thickness of missile components.

The reticle-gage follower is more versatile in its application since it is not restricted by part size or magnification. Very large parts can be gaged with reticle-gages, using high magnification. The reticle-gages must be of a very high order of accuracy because any error in them shows up directly as an error in the part. To achieve the necessary accuracy, the contours should be laid out on precision scribing machines at a magnified size. Precision cameras can then be used to reduce them photographically to the one-to-one size for the reticle.

Tracer units equipped with either probe or dot followers are used with chart-gages having a contour layout of the part. The layout may be a single-line profile or it may be a double-line profile showing the permissible limits of the part. As the stylus traces across the part, the projected image of the follower moves across the screen. If a single-line chart is being used, the follower shadow must stay tangent to the line throughout the transit for a part to be without error. Using the double-line chart, the edge of the follower shadow should always remain between the two lines.

A different type of chart-gage is used when tracing with a reticle-gage follower. This chart has a circle on it representing the diameter of the stylus tracer at the magnification being used. The projected reticle-gage contour moves past this fixed circle as the part is traced and, if the part is perfect, will always remain tangent to it. If the tolerance limits on the part are uniform throughout, it is convenient to put two circles on the screen to represent the tolerance spread. The projected reticle contour then should fall between these circles as it passes across the screen. If the part tolerance varies from point to point along the contour, the tolerance lines can be put on the reticle follower and projected to a single circle on the screen.

Standard tracer units are available as accessory equipment and can be used on many projectors. Their coordinate slides operate on precision preloaded balls to provide uniform motion without play or backlash. They can be fitted with special stylus arms for specific purposes such as the tracing of internal contours and checking for concentricity (Fig. 6-17). Some tracers are designed to be used with horizontal light beams and others are for use with a vertical beam. The standard units can provide coordinate movements up to 4 × 9 in., but special tracers of considerably greater travel have been built.

CHART-GAGES

The effective use of all optical projectors relies upon a chart-gage. It furnishes the point of reference for the operator when making measurements by comparison or by movement. Some projectors are furnished with plain ground glass viewing screens without markings of any kind. They are intended simply as a surface on which an image can be formed. Before any measurements can be made of the image, however, a chart-gage with reference lines must be mounted over it.

Most projectors are equipped with viewing screens which are also chart-gages. They usually have horizontal and vertical centerlines only, although many also include one or two angular lines as well. Chart-gages of this type are essential for making measurements by movement of the projector table. The axis of the light beam of a projector terminates at the center of the viewing screen and this point can be utilized as a positive index from which measurements can be taken. The centerlines passing through this point provide suitable reference lines to which part shadows can be set. Chart-gages for comparative measurement are of many styles, generally being specially designed for a specific part.

Most chart-gages are processed on glass or plastic. They are classified in three types: (1) replacement chart-gages, (2) overscreen chart-gages, and (3) overlay chart-gages.

Replacement Chart-Gages

These are intended to be used as a substitute for the standard viewing screen of a projector. When such a substitution is made, the new replacement chart-gage becomes an element of the projection system. It should have the same physical characteristics as the original viewing screen with respect to thickness, flatness, and surface texture.

Thickness is particularly important. Normal tolerance for a 14-in. diam screen is ± 0.005 in. of nominal. Variation outside of stated tolerance is measurable in terms of magnification error.

Glass should always be used for these chart-gages because of its stability. Care should be taken when installing a replacement chart on a projector that it has been positioned properly in its holding frame to assure that the image surface falls in the plane of true optical magnification. The layout lines on these charts are always placed on the ground surface facing the operator. The layout is called "right image," i.e., the relationship of all contour elements is exactly the same as they appear in the projected image.

Overscreen Chart-Gages

These are placed over the projector viewing screen and fastened in place. They are usually rectangular, although they may also be circular with diameters somewhat smaller than the viewing screen. The layout lines *must be on the surface which is placed in contact with the viewing screen.* The layout is always mirror-image when viewed on the surface. When placed over the viewing screen, it presents the necessary right image to the operator as he looks through the chart. This arrangement puts the layout in intimate contact with the plane of true magnification in which the image is formed. Overscreen chart-gages should never be used with the outline on the surface towards the operator because parallax can easily distort a comparison of the outline to the image.

The placement of overscreens in this fashion eliminates the effect of the thickness of the chart material. The principal factor is that the material be free from waviness and rest perfectly flat against the viewing screen. Both glass and plastic can be used for these overscreens. Vellum is also occasionally used but presents certain problems. Glass used for these chart-gages is generally about 0.125 in. thick. Plastic can be much thinner, the usual thicknesses being from 0.010 to 0.050 in. Anything thinner is apt to introduce objectionable waviness.

Clips are usually installed on the viewing screen frame by which overscreen charts can be held in place. Chart holders are also available for installation on most projectors which furnish a flat bar on which the chart can be seated. Adjustments on the bar allow the chart to be squared to the centerlines of the viewing screen.

Overscreens, once they are aligned, offer the same permanency for repetitive inspections as do the replacement chart-gages. They are much simpler to mount than the replacement charts. Overscreen chart-gages are also used where frequent changes of setup are called for or where a small chart will suffice on a large screen.

Overlay Chart-Gages

These differ from overscreens in their method of use. They are hand held and positioned by the operator on the part image. They are exactly the same in having mirror image layouts which are placed in contact with the viewing screen surface. In many instances they are equipped with knob handles for ease in positioning. As a rule they are smaller than the average overscreen chart. They are made of either glass or plastic.

Overlay chart-gages are not intended to be used for permanent setups. They offer advantages in simplified staging in that they can be quickly oriented to the part. Many standard overlay chart-gages are available for checking specific features such as fillets and radii, small diameters, and protractors for checking angles.

Chart-gages can be obtained in many ways. Specialists in optical gaging offer an enormous number of standard chart-gages of many types. They also provide facilities for preparing custom chart-gages to customer specifications. Some users of projection equipment prefer to make their own.

Several methods can be used to make chart-gage layouts. Hand layout methods comprise a variety of techniques but they all depend to some extent on the skill and experience of the draftsman. The greatest source of inaccuracy is in the placement of lines, but uniform line weight, constant line width, and accurately true radii also present problems which may limit their application.

Hand-drawn layouts can be made with pencil, ink, or scribing tools. The layouts are made on many materials such as paper, vellum, and plastic sheet. Most of these materials are subject to distortion by changes in temperature and humidity. They do not offer the permanent stability of glass layouts. Some plastic materials, however, are sufficiently stable for all but the most demanding accuracy, and are widely used.

Special machines have been developed for scribing chart layouts with a high degree of accuracy. The scribing is done on specially coated plates and very fine lines of controlled and uniform width and reliable location can be obtained. From these master layouts any number of duplicate chart-gages can be reproduced. The originals are frequently preserved in case of

Fig. 6-18. Aristo coordinato-graph for precision layout work. (*Courtesy Optical Gaging Products, Inc.*)

future engineering changes which can be incorporated on the layouts with very little difficulty. Some of the machines which perform this work are available only to specialists in chart making, although a machine, called a Coordinatograph, is commercially available in this country and is an excellent and reliable unit for making accurate layouts (Fig. 6-18).

Choice of Chart Layout Method

The choice of a method of chart layout should be determined by the requirements of the inspection involved. Table 6-1 shows the relationship between layout accuracy, magnification, and part tolerance for various layout methods.

Effective error is the layout error divided by the magnification and is the equivalent of a gagemaker's tolerance. Effective error should not exceed 10 percent of the part tolerance. The high-precision method of layout is reserved for work demanding exceedingly accurate layouts. It requires tooling available only to specialists and only unusual requirements can justify the greater cost in using this approach.

TABLE 6-1. EFFECT OF LAYOUT METHOD AND MAGNIFICATION ON GAGING TOLERANCES*

	Chart-gage tolerance	10X		50X	
		Effective error	Part tolerance	Effective error	Part tolerance
Hand drawn	0.010	0.001	0.010	0.0002	0.002
Hand scribed	0.005	0.0005	0.005	0.0001	0.001
Machine scribed	0.002	0.0002	0.002	0.00004	0.0004
Machine scribed	0.001	0.0001	0.001	0.00002	0.0002

*All dimensions are in inches.

Magnification provides a favorable factor in making chart layouts. They are always made at some enlarged scale of known magnification. This may be 10X, 20X, or any one of the standard magnifications. A magnification should be selected that will furnish clear and definite separation of the tolerance limit lines for positive readings. For example, a tolerance of 0.002 in. or less would seldom be projected at 10X magnification. It could be read far more easily at 20X or 31.25X magnification.

All layout dimensions when related to the subject part must be divided by the magnification used. This is equally true of any possible error which may occur in the layout itself. Precision machine-scribed layouts can be guaranteed to an accuracy of at least 0.002 in. If the magnification were 10X, 0.002 in. on the chart, can be considered an acceptable gage tolerance of 0.0002 in. At higher magnifications this relationship becomes practically insignificant.

Micro-Gage Bridge Lines

Measurement by comparison involves the gaging of the shadow of a part against lines on a chart representing the maximum and minimum limits of the dimensions. As tolerances grow smaller, the chart limit lines draw closer together, and it becomes more difficult for an operator to see and decide whether the shadow edge actually falls between them.

The micro-gage bridge line is of material assistance to an operator in making such readings. The principle of the micro-gage bridge is based on

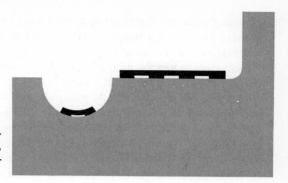

Fig. 6-19. OGP micro-gage custom design, combining bridges, micro-gage lines, and conventional chart limit lines.

the ease of viewing lighted gaps or apertures. The construction of the line resembles a bridge (Fig. 6-19). It consists of a heavy band from which evenly spaced blocks extend. The inner edge of the heavy band between the blocks represents the maximum limit of the dimension and the bottom edge of the blocks represents the minimum. When the shadow of a part is projected against the bridge, alternate gaps of light and darkness indicate that the part is within permissible limits. No light, or continuous light, shows that the part is outside of tolerance. Micro-gage bridge lines can be used on curved as well as straight contours and, in addition to contributing to the accuracy with which close tolerances can be determined, they enable an operator to read much faster and with far greater ease.

Chart Design

Good chart design should provide a layout which permits an operator to quickly, easily, and accurately decide whether a part projected to it is within its dimensional limits. It should furnish appropriate notes as to magnification of the layout, setting locations and, if several resettings are necessary, the order of sequence for making them should be clearly indicated. It is always desirable to include on a layout a magnification check. This is usually a pair of lines representing a convenient pin size at the magnification of the layout. On many charts having a multiplicity of dimensions being checked, it is helpful to have the pertinent dimension noted adjacent to its tolerance lines. Line weight should be uniform and of sufficient density or blackness to be clearly visible without strain on the part of the operator.

Tolerance limits are most frequently shown as parallel lines denoting maximum and minimum. If the tolerances are so small that no workable separation is possible at the magnification being used, then other methods such as the micro-bridge line should be introduced and the intended function clearly indicated.

Almost every part drawing includes some reference surface or point. These reference dimensions should be used in a chart layout of the part exactly the same way and their location indicated. These references generally provide the means for aligning a chart-gage to the part in its holding device. If there are no such specific reference points on the part, it is then usually necessary for a reference target to be built into the holding device to which the chart-gage can be aligned. In a few cases it is possible to align a part shadow directly to the chart contour.

Chart-gage layouts usually resemble part drawings except that they have a double-line contour in place of the single-line contour of the drawing. The manner in which the engineer's drawing is dimensioned influences all chart layouts. This may occasionally result in a chart-gage being laid out in accordance with all print specifications and yet permitting the acceptance of some imperfect parts or rejection of others which are actually within tolerance. This occurs most often in checking the size and location of holes which are dimensioned on centers. This and kindred problems of questionable dimensioning are being solved by the introduction of true-position dimensioning as a standard in engineering design. Chart layouts prepared from drawings based on true-position dimensioning are simple in design and offer no problem of interpretation of true limits.

Many chart-gages are made to check parts which cannot be projected completely in a single setting. Fixturing is usually designed to provide for shifting the part to various positions for viewing. These shifts are carefully controlled and are used as the basis for breaking the chart layout into a series of segments. These segments do not need, however, to be placed on separate charts. One segment is superimposed upon another on a single chart-gage. Suitable setting lines are placed on the chart for alignment of chart and fixture. Proper placement of the superimposed contours permits the shadow of each section to fall into proper position as the part is shifted in the fixture.

Occasionally chart-gages are made showing only a mean-line contour. These layouts are simpler to make since no provision for handling tolerance limits needs to be considered. However, such chart-gages are more difficult to use because they depend upon auxiliary means for reading deviations in the screen shadow. They are used principally for statistical sampling in quality control to establish percentages, usually with a view to reducing tolerance limits. Generally, they are used only when go, not-go charts cannot be used.

FIXTURING

The function of fixturing in optical projection is to provide the means for supporting a part for projection and to orient the part with respect to the chart-gage. This is usually accomplished with only a few closely held dimensions. These might be reference sets for coordinating the chart-gage to the fixture or surfaces to locate a part in a fixture. Frequently the shadow

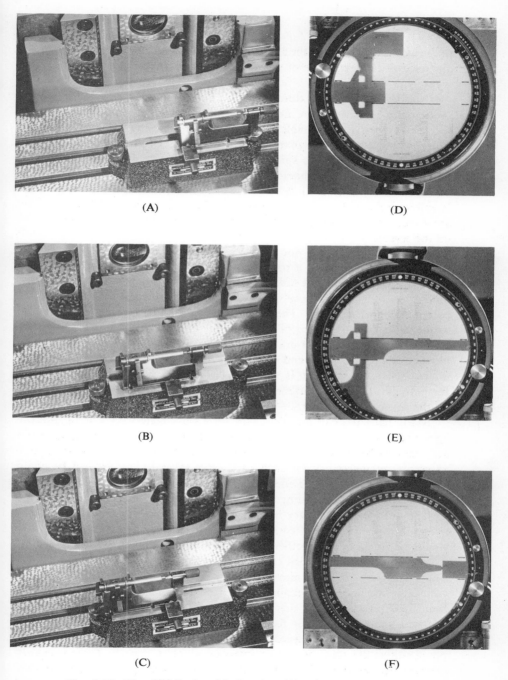

Fig. 6-20. Use of "shift plates" in fixturing: (A), (B), and (C) show the shift-type fixture in various positions; (D), (E), and (F) show the corresponding screen images.

of the part is sufficient for the alignment of fixture and chart-gage, eliminating any necessity for reference or set surfaces. Contact wear in a staging fixture is rarely critical.

One of the simplest fixtures that can be employed is a V-block, either singly or in matched pairs. Equally useful are matched centers fastened in the keyway of the work table of the projector. They can be used to stage a large number of axially symmetrical parts of various diameters and lengths. A single Vee fitted with a spring clamp is ideal for positioning many small screw machine parts. Commercially available is a multi-use staging kit which offers a number of holding devices which can be mounted on a single base. It will accommodate parts with diameters from $\frac{3}{32}$ up to $\frac{3}{8}$ in. Such devices are useful chiefly for supporting parts small enough to be seen at one position on the screen.

Length of parts does not necessarily restrict inspection on projectors. One means of inspecting a part whose length exceeds the field of view of the lens is to stage it on a shift-type fixture (Fig. 6-20A). This fixture incorporates a shift plate to move the part along to bring successive areas of the part profile to the screen. The shift plate is positioned laterally in relation to the chart-gage by means of an index bar and plunger. View E shows the screen image with the part in its first staging position. The shift plate is then moved to bring the other end of the part into position (View C). The screen image in this last position is seen in View F. The same chart-gage is used for both positions, the outlines for the second station being superimposed on the contour of the first.

Many flat parts can best be staged on a glass plate with a vertical-beam light path. A variety of sizes and shapes of motor laminations up to 8-in. diam can all be staged in this manner on a single fixture. Individual chart-gages are not necessary for each part, since several contours can be combined on a single layout. Differences in patterns are easy to distinguish and no difficulty results in relating a part image to its proper contour.

The automotive industry has taken the advantage of optical projection methods to inspect many components faster and more economically than would be possible using other procedures. Figure 6-21 shows an indexing fixture which was developed to check long automobile transmission shafts. The inspection requires measurement of shoulder lengths and fillets of various spline and gear sections as well as diameters. Template gages had been used previously for this inspection; but they are costly and require constant surveillance. This fixture with a chart-gage replaced them. It is a sliding-type fixture, coupled with an accurate index spacing bar, which pre-positions the shaft at known intervals along its length. These intervals are carefully coordinated with reference lines on the chart-gage. The operator has only to compare the shadow of the part to the chart reference lines at each successive station to make a rapid and accurate gaging of the entire shaft.

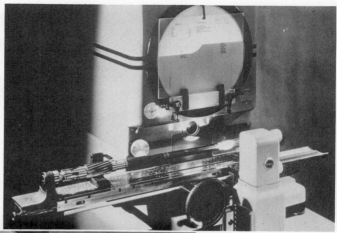

(A)

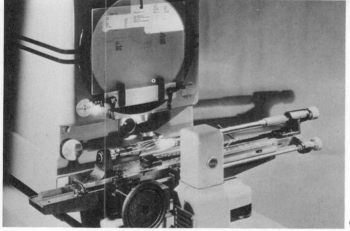

(B)

Fig. 6-21. Principle of the shift-type fixture extended to check rather long parts. Shoulder lengths and fillet condition of an automobile transmission shaft are being checked.

Another part shown in Fig. 6-22 has five equally spaced detents. Inspection is required of their depths, angular positions, radii, and location to datum. These features cannot be projected by ordinary methods. The use of a tracer unit and staging fixture and chart-gage permits the complete multiple inspection to be made in a minimum of time. A five-position index fixture with a hydro chuck arbor locates the part on the pitch diameter of the thread. The probe is shown inserted in one of the detents and the corresponding projection appears on the screen. The inspection rate for this entire operation, including loading and unloading, is six minutes. Any other method would be extremely time-consuming, if not almost impossible.

An interesting development in the use of optical projection methods is illustrated in Fig. 6-23. Shown are a number of parts with some of the staging

Fig. 6-22. OGP projector tracer checking five equally spaced detents for depth, angular positions, radius, and location to datum.

Fig. 6-23. Staging fixtures and associated chart-gages for gaging an entire family of automotive transmission component parts from rough to finish machining.

fixtures and chart-gages used to check them. In this instance the manufacturer presented to a specialist in projection methods an entire family of automotive parts for recommendations for their inspection. The gaging was to cover all operations from the rough machining to the finished machining. The purpose was to provide a package operation which could be installed in a new plant abroad. The projection specialist, by having the entire operation to consider, designed the necessary fixturing with each step coordinated to the next, resulting in the most efficient and economical method that could be devised for a series of so many different components.

Surface illumination has simplified the inspection of many critical conditions such as helical parts, rifling in bores, face cams, and impellers. A three-dimensional cam track, internally located, presents a difficult inspection problem. A drum carrying a stainless steel sleeve on which the master helix outline can be accurately plotted, is inserted in the part (Fig. 6-24). A follower in the fixture engages in the cam track and slowly rotates and elevates the drum. The reference circle on the chart-gage is coordinated to the cam follower. Surface illumination reflects an image of the master helix outline to the screen as it passes by the reference circle, and an extremely difficult inspection is performed in a matter of minutes.

Fig. 6-24. Inspecting an internal three-dimensional cam track on a gun ejector casting.

Figure 6-25 shows an indexing fixture which gages a bearing retainer assembly. It incorporates a mechanism made up of sixteen fingers which close simultaneously to hold the part round for checking the control diameter. The index head is actuated by a ratchet to provide a rapid check of the spacing and profile dimensions of each segment of the part.

Fixturing frequently combines several projection techniques. Figure 6-26 shows a two-station staging fixture which utilizes both measurement by comparison and tracer technique. It is a setup designed for the inspection of internal gears and splines at the station on the right and the mating external contoured parts at the left. A tracer and probe gages the internal contours. The external gear forms are projected directly to the same screen at the left.

It is frequently desirable to make inspections of certain types of parts by reference to a sample part rather than to a chart-gage. This often occurs in operations in which it is necessary to make adjustments to the part being inspected to have it conform to the sample. Optical projection makes this a simple operation. The technique used is dual image projection. An assembly of two lamphouses replaces the single horizontal-beam lamphouse. An optical box containing special mirrors and a combining glass to superimpose the two images is installed at the opening to the relay lens of the projector. The fixture which provides two stages for the parts is mounted on the projector table.

Filters are placed over the lamphouses, one red and the other green. When the images of the two parts are exactly superimposed, the screen image is black. If red or green fringes can be seen around the part profile it is an indication of an undersize or oversize condition or a deformation of the part. Adjusting tools can be used to correct deformation to bring the part into alignment with the master sample. A standard grid chart-gage can be used on the projector screen to measure any differences in size between the two images.

Another example of the versatility offered by projectors involves both a gaging and an adjustment operation by means of surface illumination. The assembly is a photoelectrically controlled iris for a camera. The iris leaf is fragile and not suitable for ordinary handling which might produce mechanical distortion. The projected image of the assembly can be readily gaged by comparison to a chart-gage and the part adjusted and balanced at the same time.

Optical gaging methods have been helpful in solving troublesome inspection problems in the typewriter industry. The inspection of the characters on a type wheel utilize surface illumination. The size, position, and alignment of the characters can be compared rapidly to a chart-gage. Individual rows of the characters are positively indexed into position by means of the rotary indexing fixture.

Fig. 6-25. Indexing fixture used to gage ball bearing retainer assemblies. Sixteen fingers of the mechanism close simultaneously to hold the part round for checking control diameter.

Fig. 6-26. The tracing station of a two-station fixture checks profile of internal gears and splines. External gear profiles are checked by direct projection at the second station (not shown).

A double inspection is performed by seeing simultaneously both the face and side view of the type on individual type bars (Fig. 6-27). This fixture holds an entire type carrier. The fixture incorporates special optical components for projecting across the face of the type as each type-bar is raised to its normal striking position. The face itself and the cross view are imaged on the screen by means of surface illumination.

In many instances it is necessary to inspect two or more planes, or views, of an object such as a radio tube grid. In such a case, a fixture incorporating a "free block," on which the grid is located, can be used (Fig. 6-28). Guide rails are installed on the base fixture against which the block can be moved to the desired positions. The block can also be positioned on end. Steel anvils support the delicate windings of the grid and the entire delicate component is magnetically held to the block (View A). High magnification can be used for the inspection because the free block can be shifted from side to side (View B) to cover the entire length of the grid. The oval-shaped grid is viewed across the minor diameter by placing the free block on its side. The block is provided with a relief hole for the light beam to pass through (Views C, D).

In the OGP Gear Analyzer fixture for observing and analyzing involute gear form and action, a basic rack form is used to initiate gear action and a similar form is used on the chart-gage for image comparison. Operating

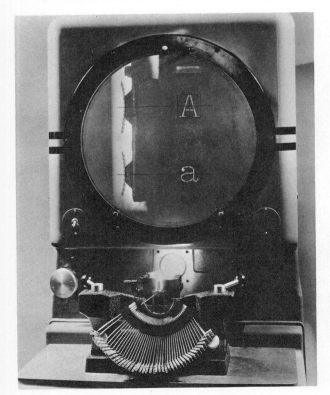

Fig. 6-27. Fixture holding an entire type carrier. As each type-bar is raised in turn to its normal striking position, the operators see both the face and the side view simultaneously, due to addition of special optical components.

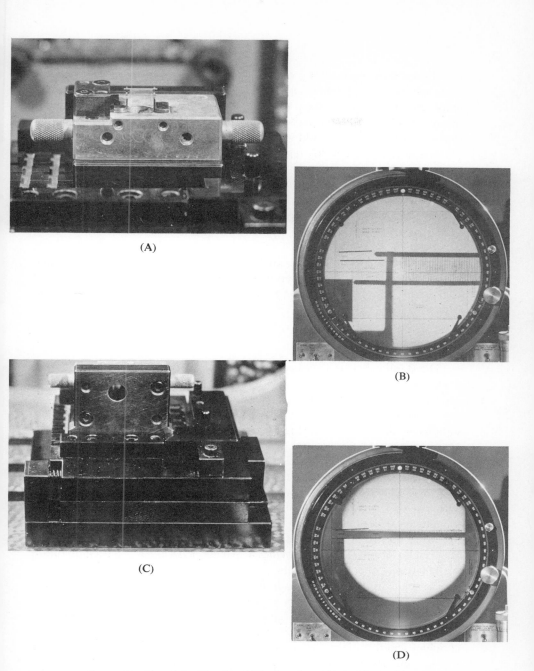

Fig. 6-28. Use of the "free block" in fixturing: (A) the block; (B) image when block is shifted to one side to accommodate an entire radio tube grid length at high magnification; (C) free block placed on its side so as to view the oval-shaped section of grid, by (D) light passing through the hole.

conditions are simulated by traversing the work support fixture laterally with one gage tooth profile in contact with a fixed half-rack pin. The gear is free to rotate about its axis. Lateral movement of the work support causes the tooth adjacent to the half-rack pin to move through the arc of action precisely the same as it would with a mating gear. The gear is checked against the master rack involute by regeneration of its involute profile.

STANDARD ACCESSORIES

Standard accessories are available for use on optical projectors which greatly increase their general utility. The accessories include both standard chart-gages of many types and a number of devices for staging parts conveniently.

Standard Chart-Gages

The standard chart-gages are designed for use on all projectors. They are available in all standard magnifications and as either replacement or over-screen charts. They simplify the measurement of many parts and their use can convert even basic projector models into measuring machines. The most familiar of these standards (Fig. 6-29) are the radius chart-gages, grid chart-gages, protractors, toolroom chart-gages, thread chart-gages, and many scales.

Radius chart-gages offer a choice of several useful patterns. Some of them are concentric circles whose radii are spaced in equal increments. The spacing varies usually with the magnification. At the 10X magnification, increments are usually 0.010 in., while at 50X it may be only 0.0025 in. There are other radius chart-gages laid out in steps of 0.001 in. The arc for each step is a 90° segment which provides a spacing between arcs in each quadrant of 0.004 in. Other charts contain arc segments so arranged that readings can be made at any of the standard magnifications. All arcs on these radius charts are clearly numbered for easy reading.

Grid chart-gages provide coordinate measurements for a variety of operations. Simultaneous horizontal and vertical measurements of contours, shoulder lengths, diameters, hole locations, etc., can be quickly made using them. Increments at 10X are usually 0.005 in. and at the other standard magnifications 0.001 in. Lines are numbered for convenient reading of measurements.

Although angles themselves are not affected by magnification, protractors are very useful projector accessories. They provide accurate reading of chamfers, tapers, and angled parts. The markings are at 1° intervals and they may be had for 90°, 180°, or the full 360°.

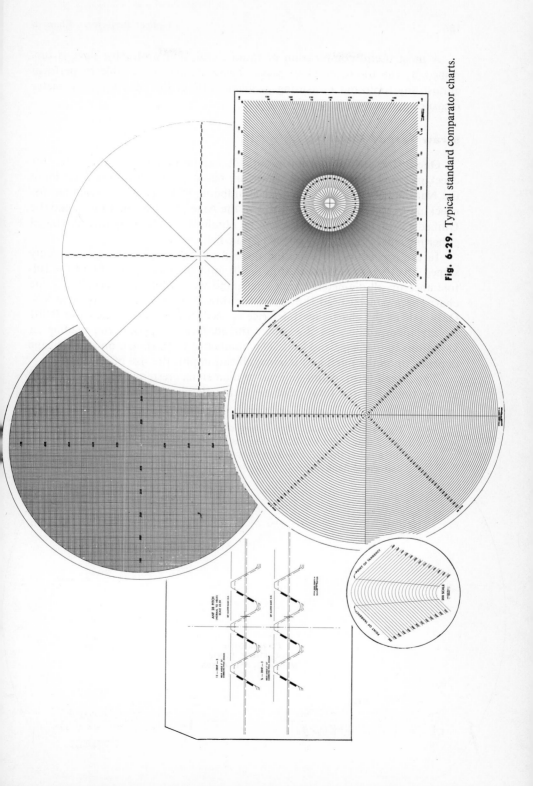

Fig. 6-29. Typical standard comparator charts.

A most useful combination of radius, grid, and protractor lines is furnished by the toolroom chart-gages. These standards are able to perform almost any toolroom measuring problem without the need for micrometer measuring attachments.

Screw Thread Checking

One of the most important groups of standard chart-gages are those for checking screw threads. These charts are based on specifications as set up in the National Bureau of Standards Handbook H28. They are available for checking both fine and coarse forms of the American National Form and the Unified Form. The chart-gages can be obtained for checking threads staged either normal to the axis or normal to the helix.

In the procedure for checking normal to the axis, the thread is usually staged on the pitch diameter (Fig. 6-30), and the chart-gage shows the full tolerance on all diameters, flank angle, and worn tool allowance. The same chart-gages can be used, however, for threads staged on centers or in V's. Only half of the chart-gage tolerance is used. Scales in increments of 0.001 in. are incorporated on the center thread form to permit the reading of variations in diameter and lead. The number of teeth shown on a chart-gage depends upon the pitch and the magnification plus the size of the chart.

The thread form, major and minor diameters, crest, and root are checked at one time over the total number of threads visible across the screen. All

Fig. 6-30. Normal-to-axis thread chart-gages are available for all NF 2 and 3 and NC 2 and 3 series. Chart-gages include, for each thread size, the *full tolerance* for pitch diameter, major and minor diameters, flank angle.

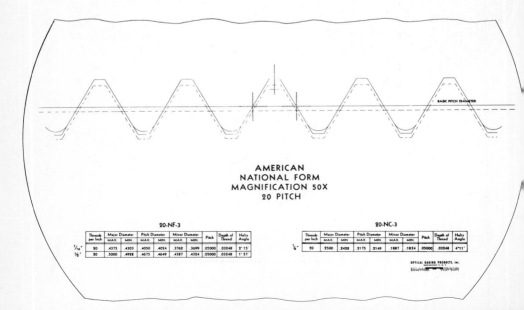

AMERICAN
NATIONAL FORM
MAGNIFICATION 50X
20 PITCH

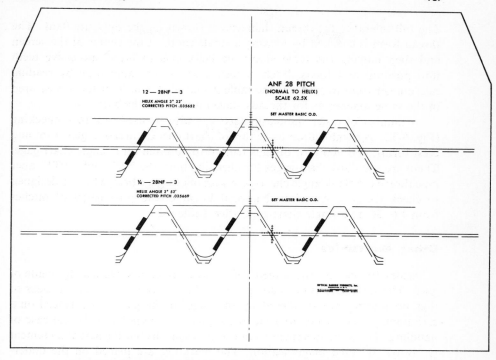

Fig. 6-31. Normal-to-helix thread chart-gage, available for the entire NF and NC series, and for classes 2 and 3.

right or left flanks are simultaneously in focus, although not both right and left at once. Pitch can be measured by comparison to the chart-gage profile, or it can be measured by traversing the table and reading from the measuring micrometers.

Pitch diameter is measured by fitting the tooth form into the chart-gage profile. The table is then moved to fit the opposite space into the same profile and the amount of the table travel is measured. The thread angle can be checked directly from the chart-gage. Some refocusing from one flank to the other may be required, depending upon the helix angle of the thread. Focus is not generally a problem in threads of small diameter.

Threads staged normal to the helix require a different procedure (Fig. 6-31). A measuring table equipped for helix rotation is used. The projected image of a thread staged normal to the helix is foreshortened and only a single tooth is in sharp focus. The chart-gage profiles are corrected for both pitch and flank angle to correspond to the foreshortening. A notation of the corrected pitch appears on the chart-gage.

The chart-gage design for these threads employs a micro-gage line consisting of heavy blocks on one thread flank angle for positive alignment.

The full tolerance for thread thickness is shown on the opposite flank. The thread form is checked by viewing a single tooth at the center of the screen and then moving the table along the helix axis to bring successive teeth into position and focus. Pitch is measured at the same time by reading micrometer measurements as the table is moved. Pitch diameter is measured in the same manner as for threads staged normal to the axis.

A number of other standard charts can also be used in thread checking (Fig. 6-32). A combination basic thread chart checks thread angles, root and crest forms, and depth of threads from 4 to 80 pitch on a single chart-gage. There are standard chart-gages for checking both the NPT and NPTF taper pipe threads. A flank angle chart-gage with micro-gage bridge lines is designed to check Class X American National Form thread plug gages of pitches from 4 to 80 on a single chart-gage. (See Table 6-2.)

Other Accessories

Scales for use on the screens of optical projectors are usually made of glass. The scale itself is normally positioned in the center area of the glass so that no interference is offered by the edge of the glass when placed on a screen image. The scales are generally supplied with knob handles for ease of handling. The scale increments read in thousandths but the actual increment is always at some magnification. The markings are placed on the under-surface of the glass so that when used on the projector they are in intimate contact with the screen image and parallax does not distort the readings.

Reference has been made to the use of such accessories as matched staging centers, matched pairs of Vee blocks, and the do-it-yourself type of kits for holding parts for projection. As a further aid to users of projector equipment there are standard fixture bases which fit all projector tables having standard keyways. These bases come in a number of sizes and can be machined by the user to meet his own specifications.

Projectors with fixed stages can be equipped for limited table travel by auxiliary stages. They can be mounted on the fixed stage and provide horizontal travel with micrometer measuring devices graduated to 0.001 in. Elevating stages can also be mounted on the fixed tables of basic machines. These tables provide horizontal as well as vertical travel of about 2 in. in each direction. They also have a focusing movement of approximately $\frac{3}{4}$ in. They are especially useful where frequent fixture changes are necessary. They are designed principally for use with horizontal-beam projectors but can be used also on some vertical-beam units.

Still another type of stage provides assistance on projectors with fixed tables. This is a unit for fast focusing, providing about an inch of in-and-out travel. The stage incorporates a standard keyway for the attachment of fixtures.

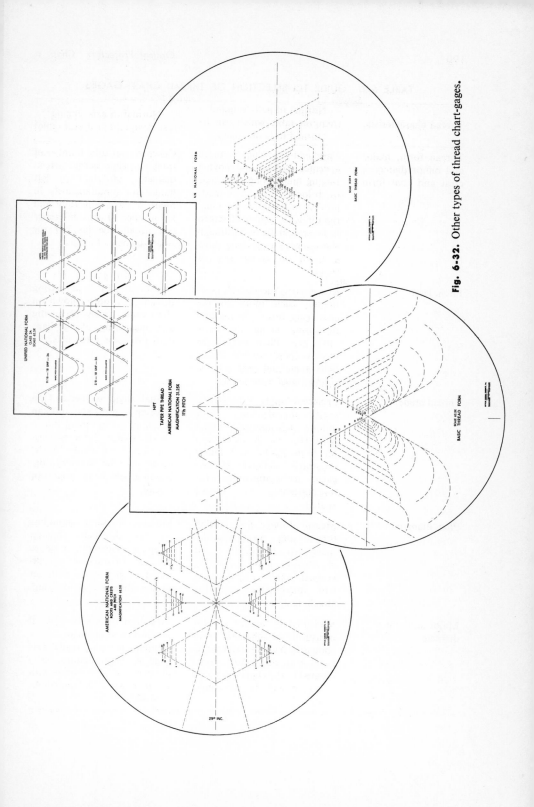

Fig. 6-32. Other types of thread chart-gages.

TABLE 6-2.   GUIDE TO SELECTION OF THREAD CHART-GAGES

Thread characteristic	Normal to helix staging (requires table which can be turned to helix angle)	Normal to axis staging (uses standard projector table)
Thread form, major and minor diameter, crest and root form	Checked by viewing one tooth at center of screen and moving staging table along helix axis to bring successive threads into positions and focus. Only the thread at center of screen is in critical focus, although chart-gages customarily show a tooth on either side of center.	Checked over total number of threads visible across screen diameter, all right or left flanks are simultaneously in focus, but not both right and left at once. (Focus difference can usually be ignored for small diameter threads.)
Pitch, lead	Measured by successively positioning each tooth to the chart-gage form, moving and measuring along the helix table axis. Pitch over three teeth is foreshortened due to helix angle and chart-gage is compensated accordingly.	Measured by comparing threads to profiles shown on chart-gage, or by traversing and measuring along standard projector table axis.
Thread angle	Projected angle is foreshortened approximately four minutes depending on thread helix. However, focus is sharp on both flanks and image accurately defined. (Chart-gages are compensated for foreshortening of thread angle.)	Actual angle as specified on drawing is projected and can be compared to thread shown on chart-gage. Some refocusing from one flank to the other may be required, depending on helix angle of thread.
Pitch diameter	Measured by first fitting thread and then opposite space into thread form on chart-gage, and measuring vertical table displacement with micrometer measuring attachment.	Measured by same method as for normal-to-helix staging. In an alternate method, stages on special fixture are coordinated to chart-gage with set master thread gage or plug.
Major and minor diameter	Measured by use of vertical measuring attachment, or in comparison with thread chart-gage. A staging fixture, coordinated to the chart-gage with a set master, is sometimes used.	Measured by use of vertical measuring attachment, or in comparison with thread chart-gage. A staging fixture, coordinated to the chart-gage with a set master, is sometimes used.

Projector tracer adapters can be added to many projectors to perform the measurement of contours by means of translation. They can be obtained for use with both horizontal and vertical-beam units. Their function has been described in the section on measurement by translation.

Riser blocks frequently are used to increase work diameter capacity or to place fixturing in a more desirable position. They are made in a number of different sizes and have keyways for the attachment of other standard units.

SPECIAL GRINDING APPLICATIONS

The unique advantage of enlarged, two-dimensional images provided by optical projectors has resulted in several interesting applications in grinding operations. Projectors have been mounted on grinding machines to check and control the entire grinding process.

In one application, machine tools were ground to specification on a universal grinder. The procedure required about ten steps, not including repeated checking on a projector shared with other workers and located at some distance from the machine. A small projector was mounted on the machine with the screen directly in front of the operator where he could follow every step of the operation. It was reported that with this control, an average of three man hours per job were saved.

Another company mounted a projector on a converted grinder in a special convoluting fixture. In the operation, the first and last imperfect threads of precision gages are removed at the root diameter and blended into the adjacent thread. Because of the tolerances to be held, the operation had previously taken 60 minutes per gage. Despite care, scrap sometimes resulted. With the projector to guide the work, scrap was no longer a problem. The convoluting time now averages about six minutes to remove the imperfect threads.

Still another company engaged in making electrodes uses a surface grinder with a unit called Visual Grind to control the shaping of its product. A master chart at some magnification is made of the proper form and placed in the projector viewing area. Once the initial alignment of workpiece to chart is made, the grinding wheel is manually operated to follow the master chart form. Surface illumination is used in this setup. The light is reflected from the end view of the electrode blank and the grinding wheel, and a reflected image is projected to the screen. The entire optical system moves with the workpiece, insuring continuous focus. Any excessive heat which occasionally develops and discolors the workpiece can be immediately detected.

A unit called the Projecto-Form grinder also incorporates a projection system. It is a direct projection system with the light source on the opposite side of the workpiece. It produces a shadow image on the screen. The grinding operation is controlled by following a master chart placed in the viewing area.

COST ADVANTAGES

The price of any individual projector is not exclusively a measure of its value to the user. More important is a consideration of the many different types of parts that can be checked on it as compared with the other types of gages which might be used.

Optical projectors are in no sense specific to a single part or even family of parts. The same projector can generally gage any part that can be staged in its work area regardless of size, shape, or contour.

A survey of comparative costs for the inspection of a single part should start with an examination of the dimensioning of the part and its tolerance allowances. This will determine appropriate measuring tools for consideration. The number of parts to be manufactured is important. Next is the amount of inspection time, including setup time, that will be required. For a simple part, needing a minimum of setup time to check a few dimensions, projection methods and mechanical gaging might well show comparable times. But for parts of increasing complexity, optical gaging is almost invariably faster. Many parts can be staged in a single position with no need for rehandling, and all of the dimensions can be checked at a glance on the screen. With other gages these parts would probably require considerable handling and a multiplicity of separate readings.

The wear of fixed gages is a continual problem and frequent checking and repair are necessary in order to maintain tolerance requirements. The effect of wear contributes greatly to the cost of mechanical gaging. Since there is no wear to a light beam, less surveillance is required for optical gaging equipment.

When high volume and long production runs are involved, heavy use of fixed gages requires the manufacturer to maintain several sets in order to keep up full-volume operations. With optical gaging, duplicate gage sets are seldom required. Sometimes duplicate chart-gages are required for repetitive inspection operations on a part at different locations, such as often occurs between prime and sub contractors. These duplicate charts can be supplied by reproduction from the standard master layout at a fraction of the original cost.

Engineering changes sometimes cause extensive modifications to be made to mechanical gages and occasionally the entire original cost must be reincurred. Such design changes rarely require any alteration in fixturing for the projector, and only a simple change in the chart-gage. The necessary change is made on the master layout by blocking out old dimensions and entering the new ones. New chart-gages are reproduced from the revised master and can be in use in a relatively short time.

With optical gaging, the part contour and all of the interrelated dimensions are seen simultaneously on the screen. In addition, it furnishes what might be termed "bonus information." Mechanical inspection rarely provides information other than what is specifically sought. Optical projection offers the operator the chance to view all characteristics of the part outline including such things as fillets, undercuts, chamfers, and radii.

7

PNEUMATIC COMPARATORS*

GENERAL FEATURES OF THE PNEUMATIC COMPARATOR

A pneumatic comparator or air gage utilizes a pneumatic circuit to measure dimension or condition individually or in combination.

Essentially it consists of an amplifying indicating instrument and pneumatic gage head with one or more air escapement orifices, nozzles, or air jets, and setting masters. It checks dimensional accuracy by determining the flow or pressure of air escaping between the gaging element and the part being gaged.

The design of the gage head or the tooling is appropriate to the configuration of the part, dimension, or condition to be checked. Figure 7-1 shows a setup for checking gear rack teeth. It can be an open-jet spindle to

*By Henry L. Boppel, Works Manager, The Sheffield Corporation, a subsidiary of The Bendix Corporation.

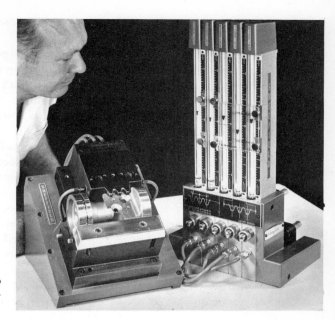

Fig. 7-1. Multiple-column air gage with engineered fixture to check gear rack teeth of automotive part.

check a bore without contact, a non-contact air snap or air ring for an external diameter, or an engineered fixture using contact-type air gaging cartridges and sensors as well as open jets.

The gage head can be presented to the part or the part to the gage head.

Basically, an air gage is a comparator that measures size by variation of flow or pressure in its pneumatic circuit. It compares an unknown dimension or condition on a part to a preset flow or pressure value in the gage, and indicates whether the dimension is within tolerance or the amount that it is out-of-tolerance.

Some air gages indicate the inspected dimension by the position of a float in an air column; others show it by a dial and pointer, and a third type by the height of a column of water in a glass tube.

The known value in a pneumatic comparator is determined with setting masters, subsequently discussed. Maximum- and minimum-size parts or master rings and disks are used to set the high and low tolerance limits within the instrument's gaging range.

Air gages with true linearity of gaging range can be used for variable inspection (measurement of size) as well as attribute inspection (go and not go) gaging to limits.

Air gaging is recommended for tolerances of 0.002 in. or less, and for checking multiple dimensions and conditions on a part simultaneously, often in less time than it takes to check one dimension with conventional gages. It is the most practical bore gaging method there is, spanning a bore diameter range from 0.020 to 36 in. and more.

In addition to its initial and still basic function as a single- and multiple-

195

dimension inspection tool, air is used as the gaging medium in many types of automatic gaging, classifying, and segregating machines.

Pneumatic circuitry can be integrated with machine tool circuits to automatically bring parts to size, to initiate turn-on of maximum and minimum warning lights when size trend is toward out-of-tolerance, or to stop the machine if faulty parts are produced.

Today, air gaging possesses all of the qualities necessary to modern indicating gaging systems, namely, accuracy, speed, reliability, and economy. It can be used to measure practically any dimension or condition of a part or relationship of one part to another.

Dimensions of length, diameter, squareness, parallelism, concentricity, taper, center distance between holes, and other geometrical conditions are inspected with air. And, where air gaging is used to inspect a bore, the complete story of size, taper, straightness, camber, and bellmouth can be revealed.

Other inherent advantages of air gaging are:

Non-contact inspection. In theory, an air spindle or air snap gage does not touch the part, but is protected by a cushion of air. For this reason, air spindles and air snap gages regularly last more than 100 times longer than fixed gages made of the same steel and used under the same conditions.

Self-cleaning. The jet of air provides a self-cleaning action which helps to eliminate errors due to dirt and foreign matter on the inspection surface.

No marring or distortion of thin walled, highly polished, and easily deformed parts.

No special skills. Unskilled operators can gage parts without having to develop a sense of touch or feel or make a decision. A glance at the float or dial shows whether the part is acceptable, or is over or under specifications.

Multiple dimensions can be inspected as quickly as one.

Remote gage head location. Some air gages permit the gage head to be separated from the base instrument by as much as 100 ft. without loss in speed of response or accuracy.

Interchangeable tooling. The basic air gage does not become obsolete when a job runs out or there is a change in part design. A wide variety of quick-change tooling is available as standard stock items.

Interchangeable amplification. Standard free-flow air gage amplification covers a range from 62.5:1 to 200,000:1 to accommodate a large range of dimensional tolerances and accuracies.

Variable (size measurement) or *attribute* (go and not go gaging to limits) inspection is interchangeable on some air gages.

Simple circuitry provides low maintenance and surveillance costs.

Time Savings. In a typical multiple-dimension inspection gage application, for example, 13 dimensions are checked simultaneously in a fraction of the time previously required on 13 hand-type functional gages.

AIR GAGE CIRCUITS

There are two general types of air gage circuits: free-flow and back pressure. Each type of gaging circuit has individual advantages and areas of performance. Although the back pressure gage was developed first, the free-flow gage is in greater use.

Free-Flow Gage

This is the simplest type of pneumatic circuit (Fig. 7-2). Compressed air from the factory line, filtered and reduced to 10–20 psi passes through the tapered glass tube containing a small metal float, and then through a plastic hose to the gage head, which in this case has two diametrically opposed orifices for air escapement.

Placing a part on the gage head restricts the flow of air and changes the position of the float in the tube. Thus, the amount of clearance between the part and the gage head determines rate of air flow and relative position of the float. The greater the clearance, the greater the flow of air and vice versa.

The total escapement of air from the two orifices is the same and gives the same reading for a certain diameter regardless of how the gage is held. Orientation of the gaging member in the piece part normally is not necessary.

If the spindle is moved to one side, the air flow is decreased; however, the air flow diametrically opposite is increased an equal amount so the indicating device in the instrument does not change (Fig. 7-3). Gage readings from operator to operator will be uniform because they do not depend upon a high degree of operator skill or sense of feel.

The air escapement orifices in an open-jet spindle are recessed below the cylindrical surface so that they never contact the part being gaged. Spindle wear from continuous use will not affect accuracy until the spindle is worn down to orifice level.

A typical flow-clearance curve is illustrated in Fig. 7-4. As clearance between part and orifice increases, so does flow. The straight portion of the curve is where both clearance and flow are constant or linear, and it is this portion that is used for the measuring range.

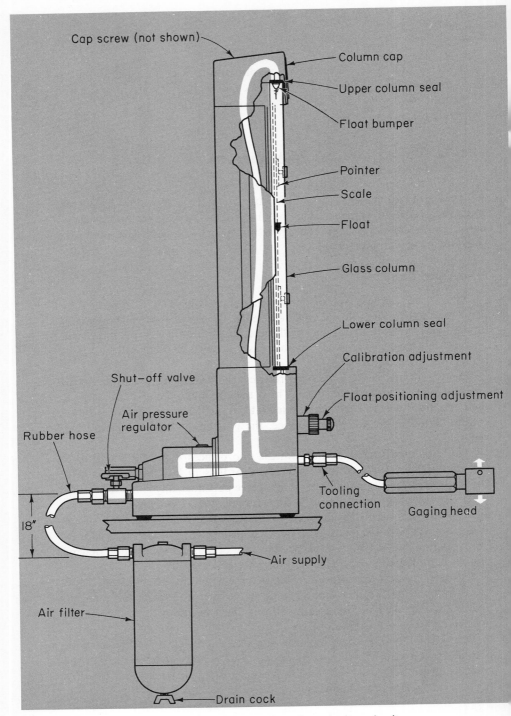

Fig. 7-2. Schematic of free-flow air gage circuit.

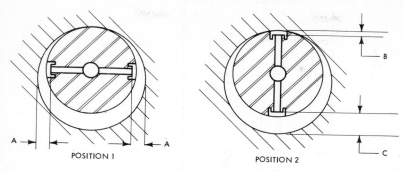

POSITION 1   POSITION 2

Fig. 7-3. When an air spindle is placed as shown in position 1, total flow from each metering orifice must equal flow with spindle as shown in position 2 to obtain rotational accuracy.

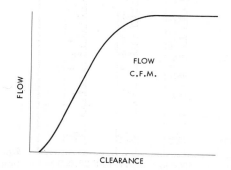

Fig. 7-4. Typical flow-clearance curve.

True linearity within the gaging range permits the dimension to be read in thousandths, ten-thousandths, or millionths of an inch, depending upon the amplification and scale that are used.

A pneumatic comparator circuit should give linear readings within the full length of the recommended usable scale to within 1 percent of the total range. The type of tooling, and accuracy to which it is made, may somewhat increase this figure.

Important design and application features of the free-flow gage are its unlimited amplification, up to 200,000:1, long scale range for classifying sizes quickly and accurately, and instantaneous indicator response no matter how far the gage head is from the base instrument.

High amplification and long scale range of the free-flow air gage permits easier and more accurate readings. Where 10,000:1 amplification is used, a variation in size of only 0.0002 in. will cause the float to move two inches in the column (Fig. 7-5).

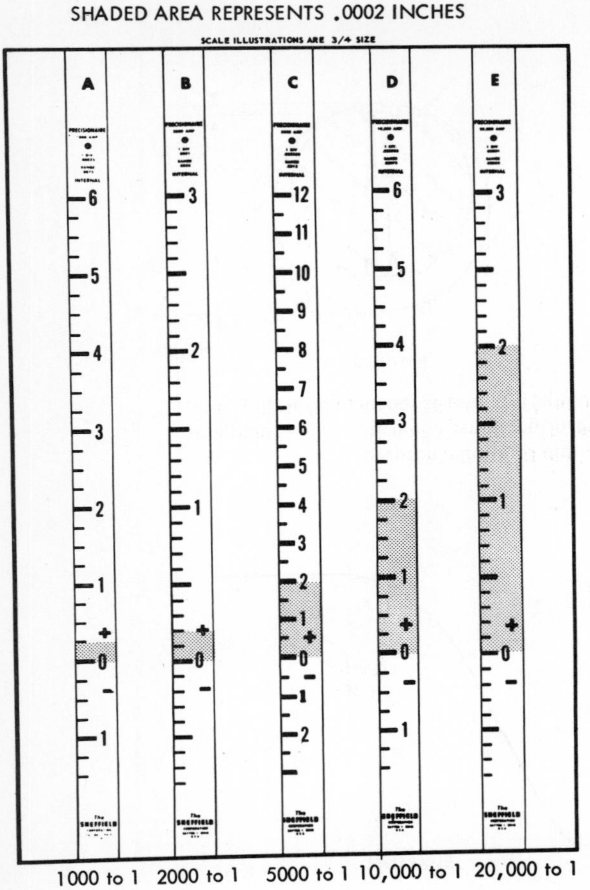

SHADED AREA REPRESENTS .0002 INCHES

SCALE ILLUSTRATIONS ARE 3/4 SIZE

1000 to 1   2000 to 1   5000 to 1 10,000 to 1 20,000 to 1

Fig. 7-5. At 10,000:1 amplification, 0.0002-in. equals two inches.

Free-flow column-type gages can be assembled one to another or mounted to a common base to save space and to permit single-glance panoramic viewing of multiple dimensions.

Back Pressure Gage

Several types of back pressure circuitry are used in pneumatic comparators. They include basic back pressure, differential back pressure, and the Venturi circuit, a combination of both back pressure and free-flow circuits. Normal gaging pressure is 20–25 pounds.

Basic Back Pressure. In the basic back pressure circuit (Fig. 7-6), a bourdon tube, or it can be a bellows or diaphragm, deflects according to back pressure changes built up in the circuit when the part is placed over the air escapement nozzles. The deflection is amplified by lever and gear arrangement and indicated on a dial.

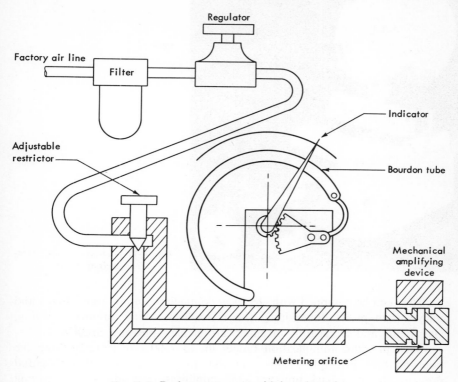

Fig. 7-6. Back pressure gage with bourdon tube.

Water Column Back Pressure Gage. Restricting air escapement at the gage head with a part builds up back pressure that actuates a relay whose output is read by a well-type water manometer or dial indicator.

Differential Back Pressure Gage. Regulated air passes through two channels, one going to the bellows cavity and gage head and the other partially exhausting to the atmosphere for zero setting and terminating in the bellows. Restricting air flow causes a pressure differential that is registered by a dial indicator.

Venturi Back Pressure Gage. The regulated air passes into a Venturi tube and on through the gage head. Restricting air flow causes a difference in the pressure in the two sections of the Venturi tube, a consequence of the higher rate of flow in the narrower channel. The pressure difference actuates the bellows which operates a mechanical dial indicator.

Characteristics of Back Pressure Gages. Back pressure gages provide a type of pneumatic comparator (Fig. 7-7) for low-amplification production checking in many shop operations.

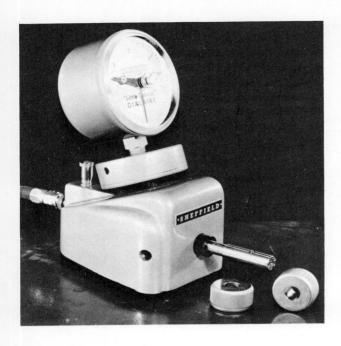

Fig. 7-7. Dial-type back pressure air gage comparator.

They can be equipped with electrical contacts to initiate signal lights and relays when preset dimensional size is reached. Many automatic gaging, classifying, and segregating machines are of back-pressure circuitry.

Back pressure amplification ranges up to 7500:1 in systems using the bourdon tube principle (Table 7-1) and up to 20,000:1 with differential pressure circuitry. Back pressure gage amplification is adjusted by varying the down-stream pressure.

TABLE 7-1. DIAL TYPE AIR GAGE AMPLIFICATION AND RANGE

Amplification	Tolerance range—3.75 in.	Graduations, in.
62½:1	0.060	0.002
125:1	0.030	0.001
250:1	0.015	0.0005
500:1	0.0075	0.0002
1000:1	0.00375	0.0002
1250:1	0.003	0.0001
1500:1	0.0025	0.0001
2000:1	0.001875	0.0001
2500:1	0.0015	0.00005
3000:1	0.00125	0.00005
5000:1	0.00075	0.00002
7500:1	0.0005	0.00002

Response speed of a back pressure system is not as fast as free-flow, since there is some time lag while pressure builds up. Although this is of no practical effect when the gage head is separated from the base instrument

202

by only a few inches, it does become troublesome when they are separated by several feet such as in gaging gun barrels, cylinder bores and crankshafts.

To speed up back pressure response, the bourdon tube can be oil-filled, which has a dampening effect, restricting the pressure from dropping to zero when the part is removed, or by using a booster.

The moving parts in back pressure gages are subject to wear.

AIR GAGE TOOLING

Non-contact-type and contact-type gaging elements or tooling are used mostly in metal working. In another type of non-contact air gaging the air escapement orifice is the same as the bore being measured, such as a carburetor jet.

Non-Contact Tooling

Non-contact tooling, "open-jet" or "airejet," uses the direct flow of air from the air escapement orifice to contact the part. The rate of flow depends upon the cross-sectional area of the jet and the clearance between the jet and the part (Fig. 7-8).

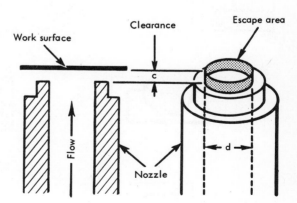

Fig. 7-8. Air flow depends on orifice diameter d and clearance c.

A non-contact gage head may have a single jet, dual jets, or multiple jets. Single-jet applications are shown in Fig. 7-9. Dual-jets are used in air spindles for internal diameter inspection and in air snap and air ring gages for outside diameters. Figure 7-10 illustrates some dual-jet applications.

A dual-jet spindle measures true diameter. It has diametrically opposed jets to eliminate the need for precise placement of the part.

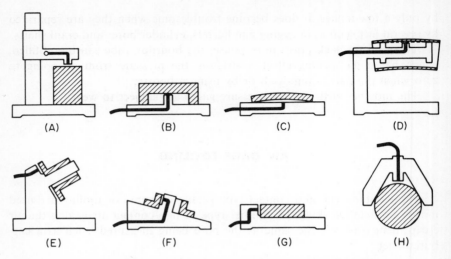

Fig. 7-9. Single open-jet tooling checks: (A) height, (B) depth, (C) and (D) straightness, (E) and (F) squareness of long and short bores, (G) face squareness, and (H) outside diameter.

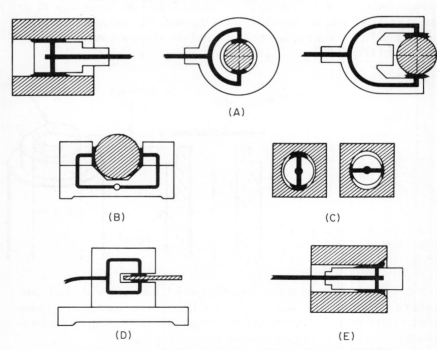

Fig. 7-10. Some dual-jet applications: (A) true diameter, (B) OD in vee, (C) out-of-round, (D) thickness, and (E) bellmouth.

The gaging orifices are "balanced" for complete rotational accuracy. Thus, the reading is the same when a gaging spindle is presented to the part with the orifices either in a horizontal or vertical position, or at any intermediate degree.

Out-of-round is detected by rotating the spindle 90°. When traversed through the bore it detects hourglass or barrel shape; as it enters and leaves the bore it will reveal bellmouth.

Multiple-jet elements have three or more evenly spaced jets for measuring average diameter of a bore or OD.

Air Ring and Air Snap Gages. These are two of the most used non-contact gaging elements. They inspect true and average outside diameter of a cylindrical part and reveal any conditions of cloverleaf, taper, or out-of-roundness. They are manufactured in many different types, shapes, and sizes and may be designed for presenting the part to the gage, the gage to the part, or for use in automatic gaging machines.

Non-contact tooling is ideal for automatic gaging because the free-flowing air helps to blow away oil or foreign matter from the gaging area.

Contact Tooling

Contact tooling has a mechanical member between the air escapement orifice and the part. It can be a ball, a lever, a plunger, or a blade, the displacement of which, when it is in contact with the part, changes the rate at which air flows from the jet. Spindles are shown in Fig. 7-11. The functioning of an air cartridge is diagrammed in Fig. 7-12.

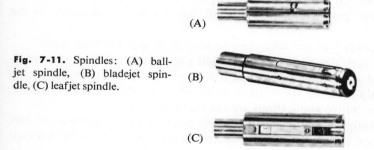

(A)

Fig. 7-11. Spindles: (A) ball-jet spindle, (B) bladejet spindle, (C) leafjet spindle.

(B)

(C)

Fig. 7-12. Basic parts of an air cartridge.

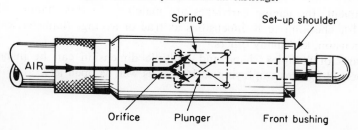

Spring   Set-up shoulder

AIR

Orifice   Plunger   Front bushing

This type of tooling is generally used for surface finish rougher than 65μin, RMS, where open jets would be subject to error because they would be measuring a combination of size and surface finish. They are used to measure porous metals, where actual surface absorption or leakage might tend to introduce error. They offer a means for providing a greater measuring range than can be realized with open jets ranging as high as 0.100 in.

Ball-type gaging tooling gives a point reading, rather than the average over a small area as given by open-jet tooling.

Air Cartridges. Small plunger-type air gaging cartridges (Fig. 7-12) are highly efficient size-sensing elements for a wide range of gaging, tooling, fixturing, and machine control applications.

Essentially, the cartridge consists of a spring-urged plunger that acts as a precision valve stem to regulate the amount of air flowing through an orifice. Any change in the plunger position changes the air flow and reading on the air gage. The maximum and minimum limits of plunger travel are set with leaf masters.

There are models for gaging tolerances as small as 0.0001 in. to as wide as 0.100 in. or more. Generally 2000:1 amplification is used and the type of scale is determined by application.

One type of cartridge, called *normal*, decreases air flow as the plunger is depressed, causing the float to fall in a column-type gage. This is best for gaging internal diameters, since a plus part will cause the float to rise while a minus part would cause it to fall, a logical sequence to the operator.

To provide for opposite float actions in the gage column there is a *reverse* cartridge. This allows air to flow only during the gaging action. As the plunger is pushed in, the flow of air increases and the float rises. This type of cartridge is best for external gaging jobs, since a plus part will cause the float to rise, while a minus part will cause it to fall, again a logical sequence to the operator.

Most plunger-type cartridges can be used with back pressure gages.

A single cartridge mounted to a height gage stand makes an ideal comparator, and a cartridge inserted in a surface plate so that the gaging tip extends slightly above the surface plate gives accurate flatness reading. Some representative applications are shown in Fig. 7-13.

The cartridge is secured in its gaging position by set-screw-urged jam plugs, position clamps, special clamps and receptacles, or it can be threaded into a jam nut.

When more than one air cartridge is connected to the same indicating instrument, the gaging cartridges are matched. In this manner, they are used for checking such dimensions as true or average diameter, calipering a dimension, and many others.

Parts of complex shape and multiple dimension can be inspected in engineered fixtures employing cartridges as well as open jets.

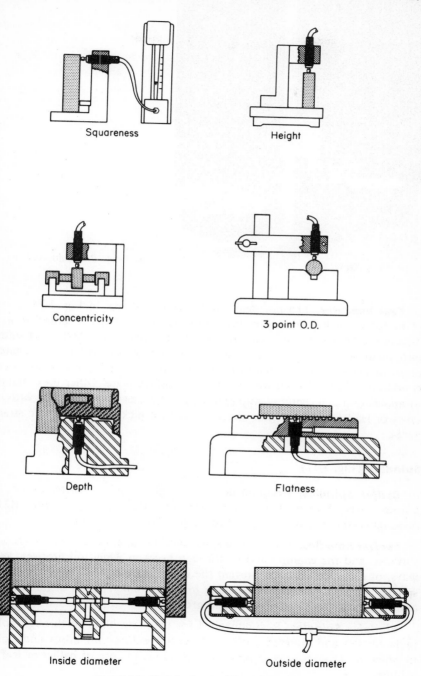

Squareness

Height

Concentricity

3 point O.D.

Depth

Flatness

Inside diameter

Outside diameter

Fig. 7-13. Simple air cartridge applications.

Fig. 7-14. Pneumatic test indicator.

Test Indicator. The pneumatic test indicator shown in Fig. 7-14 is free of hysteresis or lag or drag in indication when the stylus is moved in any direction across the workpiece. Its slim design makes it efficient for entry into small holes, keyways, slots, etc. It may be used as a height indicator or to determine flatness, parallelism, concentricity, and other geometrical conditions of parts, when working from a surface plate. Other uses include its application as a center pickup unit in jig borers, as an indicator on various types of lead testers and gear checkers, or as a pickup unit in static strain gages.

Spindles (Fig. 7-11)

Balljet Spindles. Recommended for gaging inside diameter in soft or porous parts. Also recommended when ID surface finish is 65μin. RMS or rougher, for narrow lands, and for gaging ID to hole edge.

Leafjet Spindles. Recommended for checking laminated bores and rough surfaces, and for gaging blind or through holes in which oil grooves, keyways, or cross-drilled holes prevent the use of open-jet spindles. The leafjet spindle can also be used for checking to the extreme bottom of blind holes and to the extreme edge of holes and grooves.

Bladejet Spindles. Recommended for checking blind or through holes in laminated and sintered parts, and for inspecting gun bores and holes in which oil grooves, keyways, or slots preclude the use of balljet or leafjet spindles.

Adjustable Tooling

The need for air gage tooling to handle new designs, short runs, or altered dimensions is met immediately and economically through adjustable air snap gages and contact-type adjustable spindle kits.

Data Recording

Automatic recording of dimensional data simultaneously with manual, fixture, and automatic air gaging is obtained with a pneumatic strip chart recorder.

The instrument automatically records plus or minus deviations from nominal part size. It uses back pressure circuitry and open-jet tooling and air cartridges. Chart travel is continuous or intermittent with single or two-pen units available.

Non-Contact Thickness Gage

An air gage can be used to measure thin, fragile materials such as semi-conductor wafers, germanium and silicon dice, plastic film, sheet rubber, thin glass, metal and foil without gage point pressure.

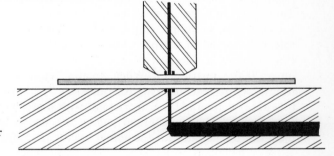

Fig. 7-15. The flowing air calipers the part.

The pressure-free gaging is obtained by means of opposed air jets, one in the head and one in the anvil (Fig. 7-15). Air flowing from the jets calipers the part and thickness is read by the position of the float in the air column.

The controlled air flow also helps to "clean" the part to insure positive thickness measurement.

AMPLIFICATION SELECTION

Amplification selection depends on the gaging application, tooling, and how much "spread" the tolerance must cover on the scale to provide a clear display of dimensional information.

Figure 7-5 illustrates how different amplifications spread a 0.0002-in. tolerance over a column-type scale. At 1000:1 amplification, the 0.0002-in. tolerance is spread over 0.2 in.; at 20,000:1 it covers four inches.

Amplification change in free-flow circuitry is obtained by quick change of tube, float, and scale. Column-type amplification conversion kits up to 40,000:1 are available as standard items.

Air gage amplification and range are based on the tooling and instrument standards of the manufacturer. Table 7-2 shows the tolerances and ranges for the standard 9-in. column instruments of one manufacturer. It is based on standard air spindles having approximately ⅛-in. diam orifice and within the range of 0.296 to 4.000-in spindle diam.

Air gage tooling with special smaller-than-standard-size jets for use in gaging special conditions such as narrow lands, shallow holes, extremely small diameters, etc., may provide fractional amplification. However, in most cases, full amplification can be obtained by using a supplementary pneumatic amplifier.

In this manner, open jet spindles check 0.020-in. diam holes to +0.0002 − 0.0000-in. tolerance with repetitive accuracy of five millionths.

A super-amplification long-range 15-in. column instrument with a pneumatic amplifier is available with tolerances and ranges as listed in Table 7-3. Only the scale is changed to obtain the various amplifications.

To select the amplification and instrument to use, determine the total tolerance spread of the parts and choose the model that covers that range. For example, a tolerance of ±0.001 in. has a total spread of four inches on a 2000:1 instrument. When greater "come-up" (the amount the float travels before reaching part tolerance) or "go-beyond" (float travel beyond tolerance) is required, an instrument with a greater recommended tolerance spread should be used. Good gaging practice is to use from two to four inches of the column for the actual tolerance spread.

A ±0.0005-in. tolerance covers two inches at 2000:1 amplification. This leaves a 0.002-in. spread or four inches of the column unused. There

TABLE 7-2. TOLERANCES AND RANGES FOR 9-IN. COLUMN INSTRUMENT

Amplification	Full scale range, in.	Recommended		Each graduation, in.
		Tolerance, in.	Spread, in	
1,000:1	0.0075	0.005	5	0.0002
2,000:1	0.0045	0.003	6	0.0001
5,000:1	0.0018	0.0012	6	0.00005
10,000:1	0.0009	0.0006	6	0.000020
20,000:1	0.00045	0.0003	6	0.000010
40,000:1	0.000225	0.00015	6	0.000005

TABLE 7-3. TOLERANCES AND RANGES FOR 15-IN. COLUMN INSTRUMENT

Amplification	Full scale		Recommended		Each graduation, in.
	Range, in.	Spread, in.	Tolerance, in.	Spread, in.	
5,000: 1	0.003	15	0.0024	12	0.00005
10,000: 1	0.0015	15	0.0012	12	0.00002
20,000: 1	0.00075	15	0.0006	12	0.00001
40,000: 1	0.000375	15	0.0003	12	0.000005
50,000: 1	0.0003	15	0.00024	12	0.000005
80,000: 1	0.000148	15	0.00015	12	0.000002
100,000: 1	0.00015	15	0.00012	12	0.000002

are a number of things that can be done with the unused 0.002 inch. It can be left on the spindle to provide maximum wear life. It can be left off the spindle to provide greater "come-up" for the operator where the spindle is to be used for in-process gaging on the machine, or part of the unused 0.002-in. can be used for wear life and part for approach.

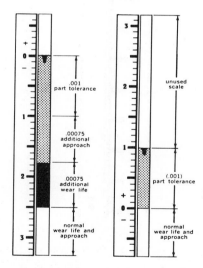

Fig. 7-16. Top Zero (Optimum) process "O."

2.000 to 1 amplification

The name given to this technique is "Top Zero" spindle processing. It is available in three forms: (1) Process "C" for greater "come-up" (maximum clearance) in-process gaging, (2) Process "W" for greater wear life in receiving and final inspection, and (3) Process "O" (Fig. 7-16), an optimum condition of more wear life and greater clearance.

Amplification for In-Process Gaging

Pneumatic in-process gaging on the machine helps to prevent out-of-tolerance parts from being produced.

Figure 7-17 shows the setup that provides the operator with maximum "come-up." Amplification is 5000:1 and part tolerance ±0.0002-in., with the tooling processed to "Top Zero" standards to provide nearly three times more approach than conventional processing.

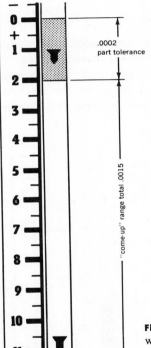

Fig. 7-17. Amplification 5000:1 with Top Zero processing for maximum "come-up."

The operator watches the float come up from ±0.0015 in. oversize and continues to remove stock until the float position indicates that the part is within specified tolerance. The 5000:1 amplification provides a one-inch display of the tolerance and plenty of scale for watching the part come to size. Higher amplification would display the tolerance larger than necessary and reduce "come-up." Lower amplification would increase "come-up" but make it difficult to judge borderline parts. As a general rule, a tolerance display greater than $\frac{1}{2}$ in. should be chosen for easy reading.

With automatic grinding, the need to observe the part coming up to size is eliminated and 10,000:1 amplification would be selected for a two-inch display of the tolerance.

Amplification for Classification Gaging

In selecting the proper amplification for classifying parts, the higher the amplification the greater the spread between size groups. Parts are classified into predetermined size groups when the production machines are not able to hold the desired tolerances or it is not economical to do so.

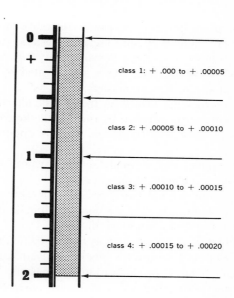

class 1: + .000 to + .00005

class 2: + .00005 to + .00010

class 3: + .00010 to + .00015

class 4: + .00015 to + .00020

Fig. 7-18. 20,000:1 amplification provides one-inch spread for each 0.00005-in. class.

For example, to classify a 0.0002-in. tolerance into four 0.00005-in. classes (Fig. 7-18), each class covers one inch at 20,000:1 amplification—best choice for easy reading—or 0.5-in. scale for each group at 10,000:1. One long-range 15-in. modular air column application provides 12 size classes of 80 millionths per class, with a $\frac{3}{4}$-in. spread between each class. Another long-range instrument application indicated 45 size classifications of 0.001 in. per class in $11\frac{1}{4}$ in. of the 15-in. linear scale.

General Principles for Amplification Selection

In-Process Gaging. Choose an amplification great enough to provide a clear tolerance display, yet small enough to allow generous come-up.

Final Inspection. Choose an amplification about the same as that used in process gaging or inspection. If it is required to verify dimensions with maximum 10 percent error of part tolerance, use a higher amplification.

Classification. Choose an amplification such that the combined mastering and operational error does not exceed 10 percent of one classification.

AIR GAGING MASTERING

The maximum and minimum tolerance limits on a pneumatic comparator are established with "setting masters" or master piece parts.

The column instrument is made ready for inspection by setting the scale pointers to the tolerance limits as indicated by the difference between the minimum and maximum masters.

The masters are placed on the spindle alternately and the float position for each master is adjusted by turning the knurled knobs at the base of the instrument until the top of the float is opposite the corresponding limit pointer.

Air spindles are normally set with rings, and air snaps and air rings with disks or cylindrical plugs.

The use of two masters is preferred in setting an air gage because it gives complete assurance that the gage is functioning at both product limits (maximum and minimum) at all times.

Contact-type tooling such as balljet, leafjet, and bladejet spindles are set with a calibrator and gage blocks, and air cartridges with minimum and maximum "feelers" or calibration leaf masters.

Master setting rings and disks are normally furnished with the gagemakers' tolerance taken bilaterally (tolerance is split plus and minus from nominal size), unless otherwise specified. For example, a Class XX master setting ring of 0.750-in. diam would have gagemakers' tolerance of 0.00002 in. taken as plus or minus 0.00001 in.

Table 7-4 shows the range of standard setting masters available from one manufacturer of pneumatic comparators.

Only master setting rings and disks of Class X or finer should be used. Class XXX and Class XXXX rings and disks permit size classification to increments of less than 0.000,010 in. and 0.000,005 in. respectively.

Masters are steel, hard chrome, carbide flame-plated, and aluminum hard coated. Surface finish should be better than 3μin. RMS. Many are made to American Gage Design styles.

General mastering practice is to set the comparator at the start of the shift and at the half-way point. Major air gage users find that this procedure works well. It gives an even balance between good gaging practice and good wear life on the masters.

Where extremely close tolerances are inspected, mastering should be done more frequently until an adequate history can be developed to determine the exact frequency of calibration required.

Similarly, where high-production inspection is allied to highly abrasive operations, such as sizing at a hone, conditions are prone to cause wear, and calibration frequency should be determined to establish a mastering schedule.

To prolong the accuracy of masters, they should be kept clean, protected from rust, nicks, and falls, and be used only for mastering air gages.

MACHINE CONTROL

Air gaging can be used on external grinders, surface grinders, and centerless grinding machines to locate parts precisely, to indicate wheel infeed, to measure wheel wear, and to measure and control part size.

Figure 7-19 shows an air cartridge mounted to the infeed slide of an external grinder. The cartridge indicates against a fixed adjustable stop attached to the stationary part of the machine. As the part is ground, infeed slide movement is shown by the falling float in the air column. When the

Fig. 7-19. Schematic of air gage machine control.

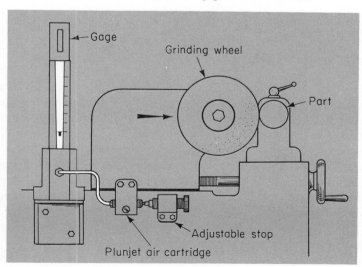

float reaches a pre-set position in the column, the operator knows that the part is at final size.

In setting up the operation, the first part is ground and then gaged on a comparator or air snap gage. The stop is adjusted to correctly position the float in the column. The infeed slide wheel is next manipulated until the float is at "O" in the tube, indicating the correct diameter size. All succeeding parts are ground till "O" float position is reached in the column gage.

Another method of continuous grinding control is to use an air cartridge in a caliper sizing gage. This enables the operator to accurately control stock removal by watching the float action against the large easy-to-read scale.

Automatic machine control gages are described in a subsequent section.

TABLE 7-4.   TOLERANCES FOR MASTER SETTING RINGS AND DISKS

| Nominal size, in. | | Gagemakers' tolerances, classes | | | |
Above	To and including	X	XX	XXX	XXXX
0.059	0.125	0.00004	0.00002	0.000,010	
0.125	0.825	0.00004	0.00002	0.000,010	0.000,006
0.825	1.510	0.00006	0.00003	0.000,016	0.000,008
1.510	2.510	0.00008	0.00004	0.000,020	
2.510	4.510	0.00010	0.00005		
4.510	6.510	0.00013	0.000,065		
6.510	8.010	0.00016	0.00008		

MULTIPLE DIMENSION AIR GAGING

One of the outstanding advantages of air gaging is the ease, accuracy, and speed with which multiple dimensions and conditions can be inspected. Thousands of multiple column and multiple dial instruments are in use throughout the automotive, aircraft, appliance, missile, ordnance, and bearing industries.

In one such application, a multiple column gage checks 59 dimensions and conditions on automobile transmission cases in less than three minutes, including 19 diameters, 7 lengths, 9 parallelisms, 14 combinations of squareness and concentricity, as well as location and flatness of pan face at 10 places. The 17-column air gage in Fig. 7-20 shows the panoramic float pattern across the face of the instrument that the operator reads at a glance.

A schematic of a multiple dimension gage using air cartridges is shown in Fig. 7-21. The gage checks length, width, thickness, and taper dimensions.

Fig. 7-20. The multiple column float pattern is read at a glance.

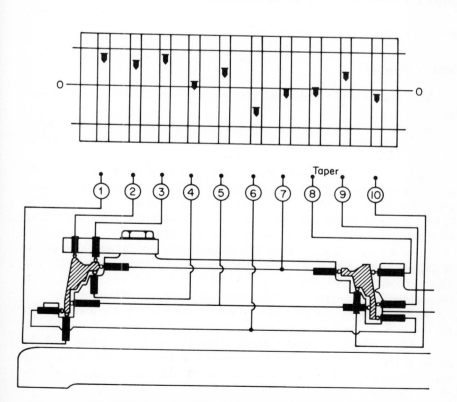

Fig. 7-21. Length, width, thickness, and taper dimensions.

Computation and Match Gaging

Pneumatic circuits are used to determine dimensional differences in a part, such as taper, bore center distance, etc., and to select parts to assemble to predetermined clearances.

Taper is measured by comparing the value of the diameter of a bore at two different points along a part. The flow of each jet is combined in the circuit (added or subtracted) and the change read as taper (Fig. 7-22). Figure 7-23 illustrates the circuitry in which taper is read as a comparison of the two diameters by means of a sliding scale.

One of several types of circuits to check the center-distance between holes is shown in Fig. 7-24. The fixture has two air spindles, each with opposed air jets connected to a two-column air gage. The jets are interconnected so as to allow the floats to move together when there is any diameter change.

If there is a change in center-distance, the floats move in opposite directions. For example, if the centers have moved outward, the inner jets are closed off, and the float in the column representing that circuit falls. The outer jets would permit the air to blow, so the float in the other tube representing that circuit would rise. The amount of spread between the two floats would be the change in center-distance.

Match Gaging

Air gages are used to select parts to assemble to predetermined clearances or interference fits.

A male and matching female part (e.g., piston and sleeve) are placed in a gage which indicates the amount of clearance there will be when they are assembled. Clearances as close as 0.000010 in. can be determined.

Figure 7-25 shows a three-column air gage with air ring and air spindle tooling for selective matching of piston and sleeve. One column of the gage shows the exact OD size of the male part; the second column shows the exact ID size of the female part, and the third column shows the resulting total clearance or interference between the two parts.

There are also single- and double-column selection or matching gages. A single-column instrument shows only the clearance between the two parts. The two-column instrument shows ID and OD size with clearance between them indicated by means of a sliding scale over the face of the column.

Match gaging is used in final inspection to mate random parts, and at the machine to enable the operator to size a part to its mating component.

At the machine, a finished sleeve is placed on the air spindle and the piston is ground to conform to the desired clearance. An open-jet air snap gage can be used instead of an air ring so that the operator can check the part without removing it from the grinder.

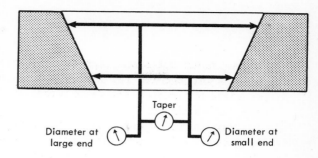

Fig. 7-22. Taper is read on a dial.

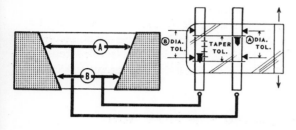

Fig. 7-23. Taper is read by float position thru sliding scale.

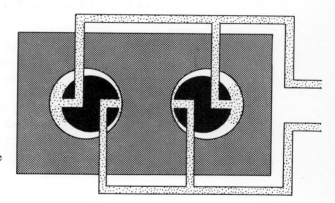

Fig. 7-24. Center distance gage uses two-column air gage.

Fig. 7-25. Three-column matching gage.

On internal operations, such as grinding, honing, or lapping, the procedure is just reversed. The finished piston is placed in an air ring or on a pneumatic comparator. The sleeve is then machined until the desired clearance is obtained.

In final inspection matching, a piston is placed in the air ring, and sleeves are checked on the spindle until one is found that conforms to the clearance tolerance. This procedure can be reversed (selecting a piston to go with a sleeve which is being gaged on the air spindle).

A single-column matching gage has been developed that measures the difference between the two race diameters of a ball bearing simultaneously and indicates one of 13 ball sizes required to obtain an assembled bearing with a predetermined amount of radial play. Each division equals 0.0001 in.

AUTOMATIC AIR GAGING FOR INSPECTION, MACHINE CONTROL, AND ASSEMBLY

Automatic control over machining, inspection, and assembly assures greater productivity, higher quality, and maximum use of machine capability. Control units must be accurate, have high-speed response, and be unaffected by vibration, oil, dirt, and moisture.

Practically all dimensions, conditions, or spatial relationships can be automatically inspected, including internal and external diameters, length, depth, taper, out-of-round, and geometrical conditions such as squareness, parallelism, concentricity, and center-distance.

Automatic Transducers

The back-pressure air-to-electric transducer (Fig. 7-26) is the basic building block of automatic pneumatic dimensional inspection and control systems. It uses non-contact and contact-type air tooling, i.e., air spindles, air snaps, air rings, and air cartridges.

It supplies an electrical impulse when the size being gaged reaches one of two preset size limits. These limits may be designated as either maximum

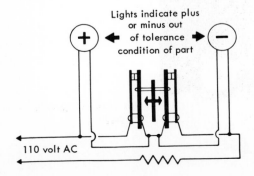

Lights indicate plus or minus out of tolerance condition of part

110 volt AC

Fig. 7-26. Air-to-electric transducer.

or minimum, or as classified dimensions. The electrical impulse may be used to light signal lamps or to actuate solenoids or relays.

The transducer is highly sensitive, signalling a pressure change as small as 0.05 psi. It is unaffected by vibration and has high speed response. It is rated at 120 volts a-c at 10 amps non-inductive at 5 to 25 psi.

Any number of units can be used in the same gage circuit to provide a series of size classifications and to furnish impulses to actuate signal lights and segregating devices. For example, two air-to-electric transducers used to automatically classify parts furnish the following:

1. A *minimum* size *reject* light and segregation signal.
2. Three OK size classes with individual lights and signals.
3. A *maximum* size *reject* light and segregation signal.

Figure 7-27 shows a standard modular package for one or two air-to-electric transducers. The set-up dial serves as a visual indicator as well as a means of setting the simplification of the pneumatic system.

To illustrate a typical application, the ID of a part is being checked in a post-process gage (Fig. 7-28). The maximum and minimum tolerance

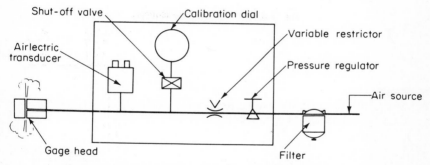

Fig. 7-27. Standard package air-to-electric control unit.

Fig. 7-28. Schematic of post-process gage setup.

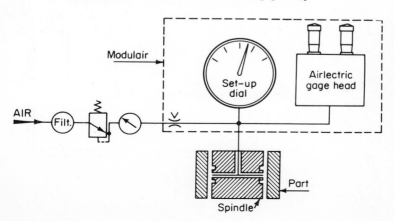

limits are set on the dial face. This is done with the use of minimum and
maximum masters on the gage spindle by varying the air pressure regulator
and using the variable restrictor to secure the calibrated gage readings.
Thus, the amount of back pressure from the gaging point is indicated on the
set-up dial. When the exact limits are set on the dial indicator, the appropriate contacts on the air-to-electric transducer which control the electric
impulses for signal lights and relays are set by external control knobs. If
approach warnings are desired, a second air-to-electric transducer is incorporated in the control unit.

Two additional transducers extend the application of pneumatic circuitry to automation. One indicates the difference between two sizes and
the second the amount of variation in a single dimension.

Differential Transducer. The differential air-to-electric transducer (Fig.
7-29) is used with two gage circuits to give an indication of the amount of
difference existing between two given sizes. It can be used to measure taper,
parallelism of holes, center-distance, and for location gaging. It provides
electrical impulses.

Fig. 7-29. Differential transducer.

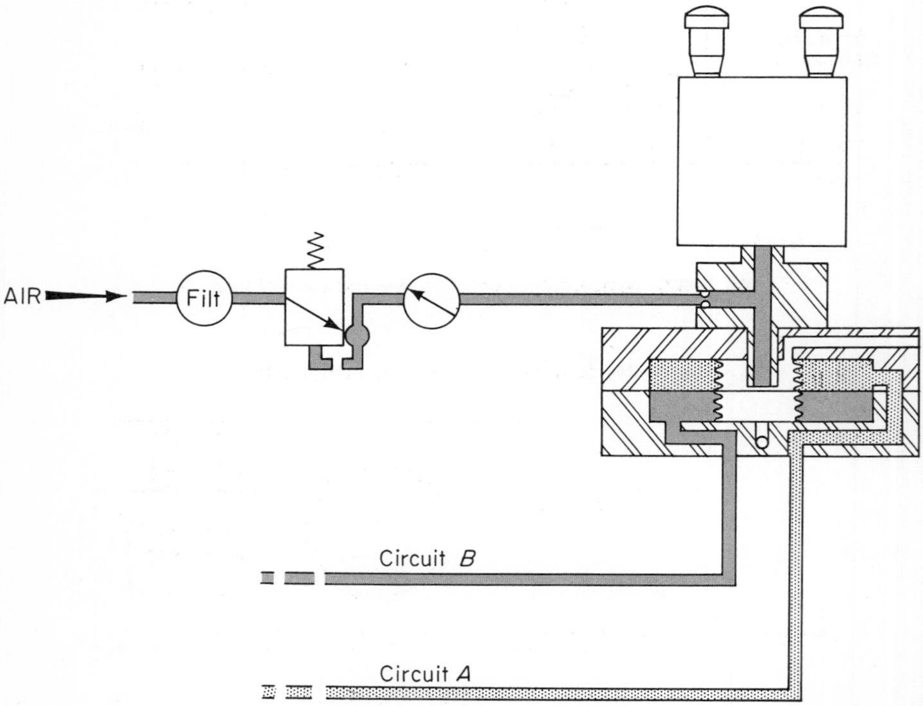

Variation Transducer. The variation transducer (Fig. 7-30) is used with a single gage circuit to measure the amount of variation of a single dimension of a part regardless of the size of the part. It remembers a pneumatic pressure signal and later compares another signal to it and converts the result to an electrical impulse. It is used for gaging out-of-round, cloverleaf, face-to-axis runout, and concentricity.

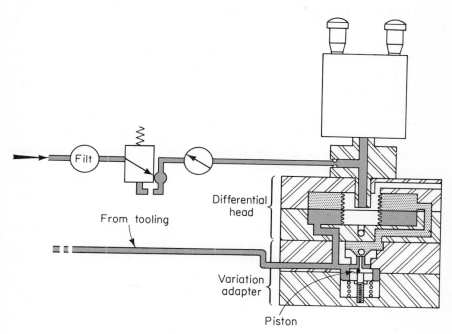

Fig. 7-30. Variation transducer.

In a setup for gaging bore out-of-round, the air spindle is directly connected to the variation transducer. Either the part or the spindle is revolved 360°. Unless the bore is absolutely perfect, the back pressure will build up in the transducer until the minimum diameter of the bore is reached, after which the pressure will gradually decrease until the maximum diameter is passed.

Automatic Inspection

Automatic gaging devices are usually referred to by function or position in the manufacturing process, as

1. Pre-process gages (inspection *before* machining).
2. In-process gages (inspection *during* machining).

3. Post-process gages (inspection *after* machining).
4. Final inspection gages.
5. Assembly gages.

Combinations can provide fully automatic control over dimensional size from the moment the part enters the manufacturing process through assembly.

Pre-Process Gaging. The part is inspected before transfer to machining for excessive or insufficient stock as well as location and completeness of work area.

Pre-process gaging helps to avoid damage to the machine or tooling, eliminates wasting of machining time on parts with insufficient stock, cuts down tool wear, and assures that only good parts are presented to the machine tool.

In-Process Gaging. The gage measures the part during metal removal and indicates when the part is over, near, and at final size. It supplies signals to automatically warn, adjust, or correct for tool or machine wear when size trend is toward out-of-tolerance.

Part shape, type of machining, cutting tool, method of chucking, and the machine's ability to use gaging signals determine the type of in-process gaging to be used.

The standard in-process machine control gage schematically shown in Fig. 7-31 is designed for use on center-type OD plunge grinders having electrical control of wheel infeed and retraction. It has a single air-to-electric transducer. The gage measures the part during grinding and supplies two electrical signals. One signal may be used to change infeed from fast to slow or to stop infeed for sparkout, and the other to retract the wheel at final size.

Fig. 7-31. In-process machine control gage for OD grinder.

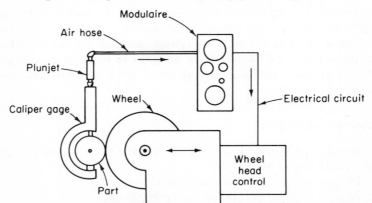

Fig. 7-32. In-process gage automatically controls part to final size, retracts wheelhead.

Where two air-to-electric transducers are used in a single circuit in-process gage, the following is provided:

1. A maximum size *reject* light and segregation signal.
2. A maximum size *warning* light and tool adjustment signal.
3. A minimum size *warning* light and tool adjustment signal.
4. A minimum size *reject* light and segregation signal.

Where the machine does not have electrical control over wheel infeed and retraction, the operator watches the signal lamps to determine when to stop and when to retract the wheel.

The multiform plunge grinder shown in Fig. 7-32 is equipped with automatic in-process size control. The pneumatic "jump-on" gage measures the part OD continuously from a predetermined point (slow feed) and stops wheelhead infeed for sparkout to final size, and then retracts the wheel. The gage is capable of controlling part size to 0.0001 in.

Post-Process Gaging. With post-process gaging, the part is inspected after forming or turning. Signals can be fed back to the producing machine to warn, to adjust, or to shut down the machine if faulty parts are being produced.

Automatic classifications and segregation of parts by dimensional size is featured with this type of gaging, but not always.

Standard pedestal-type gaging units are commonly used to inspect single or multiple dimensions on a part after machining and to segregate it as acceptable or reject. This type of post-process gage is usually located adjacent to the producing machine. The parts are gravity fed into and through the gage station which is adjustable vertically and radially on the column.

The gage utilizes interchangeable tooling enabling it to perform precision inspection over a wide range of internal and external diameters, widths, tapers, and other combinations and part configurations.

This standard-type gage can also be obtained with the following:

1. A signal to stop the producing machine when a predetermined number of consecutive rejects is gaged.
2. Feedback signals for machine compensation when size trend is toward maximum or minimum size limits.
3. Signals to segregate reject parts into salvageable and non-salvageable classes.
4. Signals to classify OK parts by dimensional size.

A pneumatic non-contact gage for a through-feed centerless grinder is shown in Fig. 7-33. The parts are gaged without stopping as they emerge from the grinder. The gage fixture has two air jets for detecting the trend of changing part size either plus or minus from the nominal size. It is adjustable for various sizes and can be used also with a column-type air gage indicator.

Fig. 7-33. Adjustable through-feed gage for centerless grinder.

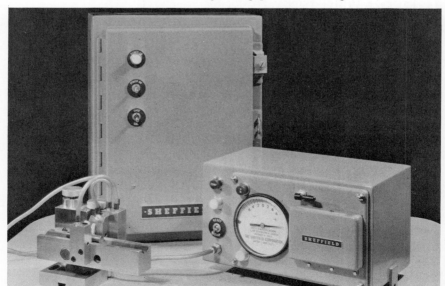

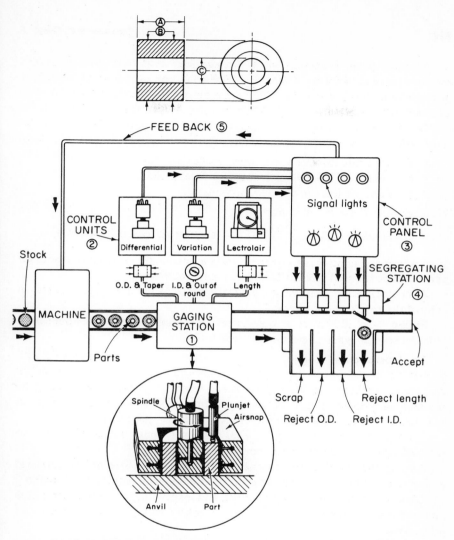

Fig. 7-34. Theoretical automatic inspection job with feedback to production machine.

Chamfers and other interruptions on the surface of the part do not hinder the gaging process because the circuit can be arranged to ignore pressure drop-off when encountered.

The modular control unit provides visual light indication of part tolerance condition and direct reading of part size when a part is stationary. One signal light indicates that the part is above minimum size, and a second light that it is above maximum size. The machine operator watches the lights to see whether size trend is undersize, within tolerance, or oversize. The signals can be used to stop the machine if a predetermined number of consective out-of-tolerance parts is produced.

227

As most parts processed on a through-feed centerless grinder have a tolerance spread of from ±0.0002 to ±0.0005 in., an instrument with 2000:1 amplification is recommended. This provides a full-scale range of 0.0015 in. and individual graduations of 0.00005 in. each on the dial.

The following information must be known to determine whether an application can be handled successfully.

1. *F*: Feed rate through the grinder, inches per minute.
2. *L*: Length of longest interrupted surface, inches.
3. *T*: Time air jets are covered, seconds.

To determine *T* use the formula

$$T\text{(seconds)} = \left(\frac{L - 0.100}{F}\right) 60 \qquad \text{(must be at least 0.75 seconds)}$$

If an automatic control is to be used, then a pneumatic relay is incorporated and *T* can be reduced to as little as 0.25 second minimum.

A compensating unit must be incorporated when the gage is used to control the machine automatically.

Figure 7-34 illustrates a theoretical automatic inspection application utilizing several types of pneumatic gage units.

Final Inspection Gages.   Generally, what can be gaged manually with pneumatic circuitry can be gaged automatically. The gage system of an automatic machine is a high-speed decision making device, performing its function of measuring and indicating a dimension as being acceptable, in a certain size class, or as out-of-tolerance, in a few milliseconds.

Automatic gages check up to 4000 parts per hour; however, inspection rates of 1000 to 1500 parts per hour are more normal.

Among the variables to be considered in automatic gaging are part size and configuration, material and finish, production, tolerances, part handling, cleanliness of part, type of gage element, and inspection rate. Interchangeable and adjustable tooling enable a gage to handle different parts, sizes, and tolerances.

If part size, configuration, etc., prevent its being gaged in one operation, it is better to inspect fine tolerances first. This prevents time from being wasted in checking the broader tolerances first, only to have the part rejected later on fine tolerances.

An automatic gage should have "floating" gaging elements to accommodate slightly misaligned holes or locations. Locating surfaces for the gaging operation should be the same as those used in the machining phase, or they might be from the functional or end use of the part.

A large variety of part transfer devices are used in automatic gages. They include endless belt, gravity feed, indexing chain shuttle bar with pivoting feed fingers, cross-feed, and push movements.

One multiple-dimension automatic gaging and segregating machine performs a total of 25,500 inspections on 1500 automobile pistons in one

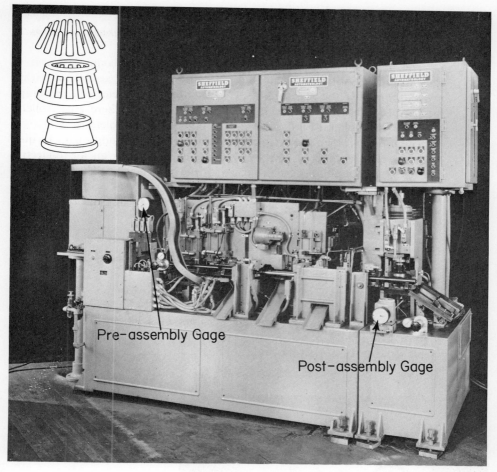

Fig. 7-35. Pre- and post-assembly dimensional gages are used on this automatic assembly machine.

hour. Pistons are automatically sorted into nine skirt diameter size classes of 0.0003 in. per class. The gage also classifies and stamps one of three classes of 0.0001 in. per class on the piston. Groove width and land and groove diameters are checked at three places each, skirt diameter at three places, skirt taper at two places, pin bore diameter at two places, and pin bore taper at one place.

Some automatic gaging and segregating machines require less space than a desk pad, yet can inspect and sort up to 4000 parts per hour.

Assembly Gaging. Pneumatic gaging circuits are used in automatic assembly for both pre- and post-assembly inspection. Parts are inspected for dimensional correctness and selective assembly. Out-of-tolerance parts can jam machines and stop production. Both pre- and post-assembly gaging are used on the automatic taper roller bearing assembly machine shown in Fig. 7-35.

The pre-assembly gage *A* checks the diameter and flange thickness of the inner race to determine the correct roller size to be assembled within a given ring. Then the gage feeds a signal to one of six preselected size storage hoppers to release 18 rollers to the assembly station where race, rollers, and cage are assembled into a bearing of predetermined tolerance.

The bearing is then inspected under a revolving load condition for torque, noise level, and standout, the latter being checked with an air-to-electric transducer *B*. Standout is the distance that the back face of the cone extends from the cup.

Bearings are segregated as acceptable or into reject classes on noise, torque, or standout.

FLUID AMPLIFIERS

Fluid amplifiers or solid state devices are used in dimensional control for inspection and size classification. They have no moving parts. A stream of air flowing through tiny tunnels is used in place of electro-mechanical

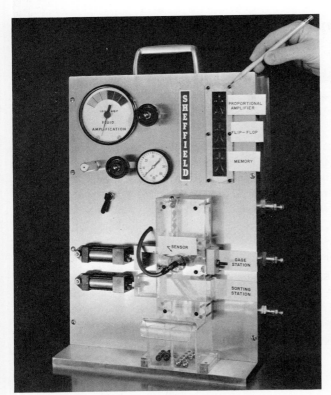

Fig. 7-36. Automatic size classification gage uses fluid amplification gaging circuit.

devices to gage, memorize, sort, switch, and actuate. The configuration used in channeling the air determines the type of operation performed. There are many types and sizes.

Fluid-state devices can be considered analogous to their electronic counterparts and described similarly. For the most parts, the "building blocks" of a system can be divided as follows: oscillator, proportional amplifier, discriminator, memory cell, power amplifier, and actuator.

Fluid amplifiers are used in the gaging circuit instead of conventional electro-mechanical devices in an automatic inspection machine which tests for flow stoppage in hypodermic needles. It uses 25 duplicate fluid-state bistable elements and will check 30,000 units per hour.

Size classification capability is illustrated in Fig. 7-36. This simple automatic gage uses three fundamental forms of fluid state devices. It sorts steel balls into two classes at a rate of 60 parts per minute. Balls are hopper fed to the gage station input and the individual ball is presented to the gage sensor. The resultant pneumatic gage signal is amplified by the upper fluid-state element (proportional amplifier). The output signal may then trigger the bistable flip-flop (switch unit) at an adjustable limit level. The memory unit (lower element) stores the previous signal from the switch unit for controlling the cylinder in the sorting station. Additional switch units and memories can be added for additional classes of part segregation.

8

ELECTRIC AND ELECTRONIC

GAGES*†

Electric and electronic gaging systems are in widespread use in dimensional measurement because their response is virtually instantaneous, and also because their output can be used to perform work. Electronic gaging has the important added advantage of being able to achieve exceptionally high magnifications—as high as 100,000: 1—quite easily and economically.

Generally, the main difference between electric and electronic gages is one of magnification and type of output. Both rely on mechanical contact with the work to be measured.

*By L. O. Heinold, Jr., Manager, Sales Engineering, Federal Products Corporation.
†Except where the figure captions otherwise indicate, all gages illustrated in this chapter are of Federal Products Corporation manufacture.

ELECTRIC GAGES

Typically, the electrical gage head (Fig. 8-1) is quite similar in appearance to the mechanical dial indicator, differing principally in that the indicator rack spindle is equipped to actuate precision switches. These, in turn, can initiate lights to show dimensional classification and/or actuate sorting and corrective mechanisms.

Good switching accuracy is achieved by the electric gage (within approximately 0.000025 in.) because it is derived directly from the spindle rather than from the output of the indicator gear train, and thus does not inherit any errors of the indicator mechanism. In so doing, however, it accomplishes its purpose without the magnification level associated with most gaging systems. Approximately two-to-one magnification is derived from the lever ratio of the switches. Despite this, its speed, accuracy, and relative simplicity satisfy numerous applications. One of the most common uses is on the bench comparator to upgrade operating speed in production work. Not only does the operator save time in observing lights to classify work dimensionally, but is also relieved of dial interpretations and repeated measurements to establish classification of a borderline part. The indicating lights show the true classification instantaneously and accurately. The dial of the electricator shows specific size of the part when such information is needed. This type of instrument is usually set to a master or dimensional standard, just as for a dial indicator, and is available with indicating dials graduated in 0.001 in., 0.0005 in., or 0.0001 in. The single unit provides two switching points, which can be adjusted to coincide with the tolerance extremes, producing three dimensional

Fig. 8-1. Electric gage head. The switching mechanism is spindle-operated. Two independent sets of contacts permit three switching conditions for classifying into "over," "good," and "under."

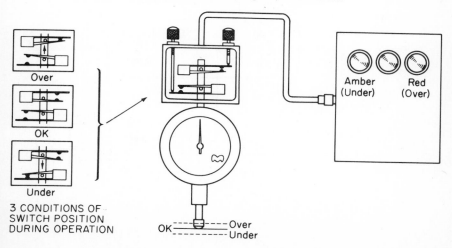

Over

OK

Under

3 CONDITIONS OF
SWITCH POSITION
DURING OPERATION

Amber
(Under)

Red
(Over)

OK ---- Over
---- Under

categories (e.g., *over, good, under*). Double switching units provide two additional switching points for five dimensional categories. The use of the electric gage for automatic inspection will be discussed later.

ELECTRONIC GAGES

In contrast to the electric gage, the electronic gage head produces a continuous output (analog) which, in most cases, is amplified and presented on a moving coil meter, numerical display board or recorder, or a combination of these. Like the electric gage it can also provide switching points. In this instance, the switching is accomplished electronically rather than mechanically. While the electronic gage is more complex, the growing use of solid-state circuitry has reduced both the size and the power consumption of the necessary amplifier, and also has improved dependability so that the burden of complexity is now largely academic.

Continuous output of an electronic gage head can be achieved in numerous ways, but in every case alternating voltage is brought to the gage head and is altered there by action of the mechanical spindle, directly or indirectly, as it responds to the size of the piece being measured. One of the earliest systems (Fig. 8-2) employs a movable, spindle-actuated armature whose change in position unbalances a bridge circuit with a consequent movement of the meter hand. While this system does not employ direct amplification, it does achieve magnification of the spindle movement to 7000X.

Fig. 8-2. Movable armature gage head. Movement of the spindle-mounted arm unbalances bridge circuit, moving meter hand from center (null) position (*Pratt & Whitney Div., Colt Industries*).

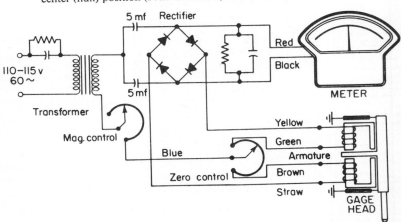

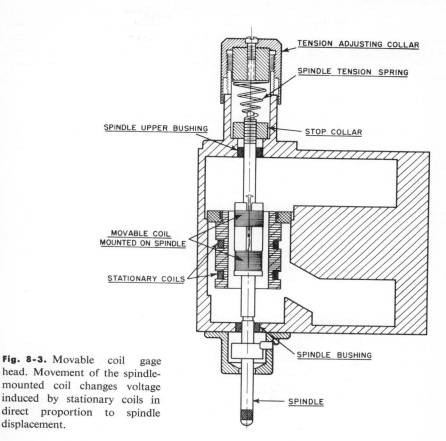

TENSION ADJUSTING COLLAR

SPINDLE TENSION SPRING

SPINDLE UPPER BUSHING

STOP COLLAR

MOVABLE COIL
MOUNTED ON SPINDLE

STATIONARY COILS

SPINDLE BUSHING

SPINDLE

Fig. 8-3. Movable coil gage head. Movement of the spindle-mounted coil changes voltage induced by stationary coils in direct proportion to spindle displacement.

Another system (Fig. 8-3) employs a movable coil. As this coil changes position with relation to two stationary secondary coils in the gage head, they induce a greater or lesser voltage, displacing the meter hand accordingly. This change is amplified to a usable quantity, achieving magnifications as high as 100,000X, which is the practical maximum for most current electronic systems.

Many electronic systems make use of linear variable differential transformers (LVDT) (Fig. 8-4), which can be packaged conveniently in a small cartridge. It produces an output which is proportional to the displacement of a movable core within the field of several coils. As the spindle-mounted core moves from its null position, the voltage induced by the coil changes (one increases, the other decreases), producing an output representing the difference in induced voltages. This type of gage head has the advantage of small size and is thus well suited to mounting in fixtures where space is at a premium.

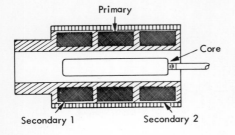

Primary

Core

Secondary 1   Secondary 2

Fig. 8-4. Typical LVDT gage head. For one central position of the core the output voltage will be virtually zero. As core is moved, the voltage induced in the coil toward which the core moves is increased; voltage induced by other stationary coil decreases.

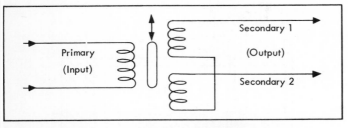

Primary
(Input)

Secondary 1
(Output)

Secondary 2

Schematic Illustration

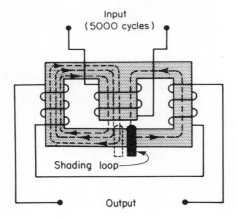

Input
(5000 cycles)

Shading loop

Output

Fig. 8-5. LVDT gage head (variation). A shading loop is used instead of a movable core to vary induced voltages in secondary coils.

Another electronic system (Fig. 8-5) uses a movable shading loop, which produces a proportional differential voltage induced in two coil windings. This LVDT configuration lends itself to establishment of low, uniform gaging pressure.

Quite different in operation is the capacitive type of gage head (Fig. 8-6). It has the advantage of freedom from influence by magnetic fields and produces a relatively high voltage output, eliminating the need for further amplification. It suffers in some applications, however, because the pretravel and overtravel range of the spindle is quite limited. In the capacitive gage head the electrical energy is applied to two metal plates, one of them movable with the spindle. As the small air gap between them changes, the change in capacity upsets the balance of a bridge circuit, producing relatively high changes in output to achieve magnifications of 15,000X or more.

236

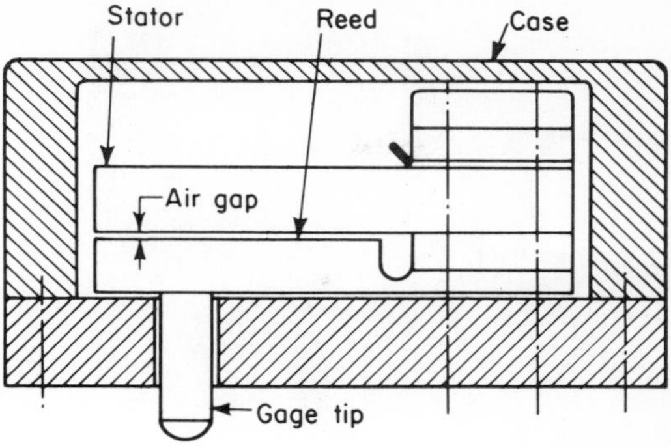

Stator   Reed   Case

Fig. 8-6. Capacitive-type gage head. Movement of the gage tip changes the air gap between plates, thus changing capacitance which alters output of gage head (*Radio Corporation of America*).

Air gap

Gage tip

Fig. 8-7. Typical transistor-operated, battery-powered gaging unit. Three magnifications are available by switching. Unit requires no warmup. Battery produces approximately 1300 hours of operation.

In addition to producing high magnifications, the electronic system can offer a choice of magnifications by switch selection. This advantage becomes important in suiting the gage or comparator to a wide range of tolerance measurements, and facilitates preliminary adjustment in instances where final measurement is made at high magnification levels. Additionally, the electronic gage can incorporate electrical zero adjustment which, in some systems, has a range many times that of the operating range, thus eliminating the need for critical positioning of the gage head.

One of the most common uses of electronic gages is for general measurement work on surface plates. In the typical setup (Fig. 8-7), the gage head is mounted on a suitable height stand, and indication is taken from the meter of a small transistorized battery-powered amplifier. The ease of setup through use of electrical zeroing, and the convenience of selecting several magnifi-

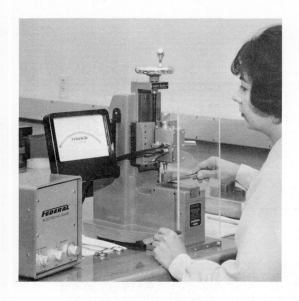

Fig. 8-8. Typical electronic gage block comparator. Checks gage blocks up to 4 inches. Amplifier is transistorized; provides magnifications of 6,000:1 and 60,000:1. Meter graduation values are 0.000,01 in. and 0.000,001 in. Such high accuracy requires extremely rigid frame.

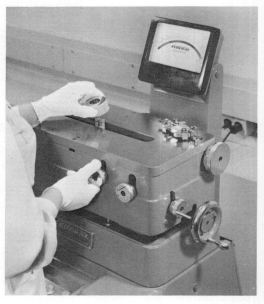

Fig. 8-9. Electronic comparator for ring and disc masters. Transistorized amplifier generates virtually no heat, so is mounted in pedestal without danger of influencing measuring accuracy. Hands are gloved to prevent heat transfer to piece being measured. Meter graduations are 0.000,001 in. on highest scale.

cations, provide greater operating ease and, usually, higher measuring accuracy than is afforded by mechanical means. The amplifier meter unit can, in most instances, be powered by mercury cells, carbon (flash light) cells, or rechargeable batteries. In one system, mercury cell power provides up to 1200 hours of operation. In most gaging units of this type, a small rectifier unit can be installed in place of the battery to permit operation from a power line source, if desired.

The typical gage head in such equipment uses a lever-type contact which is clutch-mounted to avoid accidental damage. This configuration permits a wide choice of mounting positions. Most heads incorporate a reversing mechanism so that contact pressure can be reversed to eliminate the need for reversing the position of the head itself.

Another widespread use of the electronic gaging system is in high-accuracy bench comparators for measurement of very precise production parts and dimensional standards such as gage blocks and ring or disc masters. A typical electronic comparator for measurement of gage blocks is shown in Fig. 8-8. Because of the extreme accuracies involved, the comparator stand must be extremely rigid, a breath shield is placed in front of the comparator, the blocks are handled with insulated forceps, and only after they and the master blocks to which they are compared have been allowed to reach room temperature is the measurement made. This entire environment is closely controlled to assure low humidity and a temperature that remains within a fraction of a degree at the standard reference of 68°F.

An electronic comparator of similar accuracy for measuring master rings or discs is shown in Fig. 8-9. The comparator is set to gage blocks for either type of measurement. On both types of comparators the dial graduation value is one millionth of an inch at the highest magnification.

The continuous output of the electronic gage produces an analog signal which can be recorded—an important advantage in many applications. Typical is the roundness gage (Fig. 8-10) which produces a polar chart record for close examination and comparison. The trace, in this case, represents a profile in which the radial variation is greatly magnified in order that subtle-

Fig. 8-10. Roundness gage. Electronic amplifier actuates recorder which makes profile of the part's roundness in unison with response of gage head as the piece turns on a rotary table.

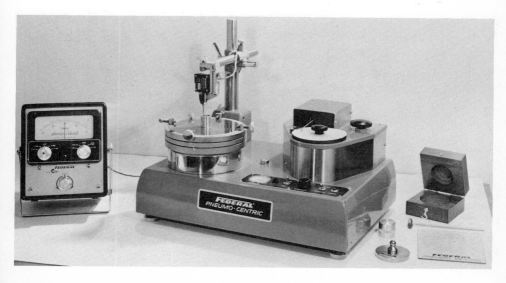

ties of geometrical error can be closely examined. Another electronic gage with recorded output is shown in Fig. 8-11.

The relative ease with which multiple gage heads can be used in an electronic gage is another important operating asset. Whenever comparison is required of two points, such as in taper or parallelism measurement, two gage heads may be arranged to operate differentially (Fig. 8-12). In this way comparison can be made without influence from piece-to-piece variation in size. Opposed gage heads simplify the size measurement of parts which cannot be conveniently positioned against a reference. Several gage block

Fig. 8-11. This machine measures and records change in piston skirt diameter contour to be read to 0.0002 in.; the full 360° measurement is recorded in sixty seconds (*Radio Corporation of America*).

Fig. 8-12. Two gage heads arranged to check lead error of a large screw thread. The outputs are fed to a common amplifier so that its meter displays the difference in reading between the heads.

Fig. 8-13. A gage block comparator which uses two opposed gage heads for measuring thickness. The outputs of the two gage heads are fed differentially to a single amplifier.

comparators use opposed electronic gage heads to obtain point contact on each surface of the block and avoid the need of a critically precise reference plate. A typical comparator of this type is shown in Fig. 8-13. Extending this principle, two or more electronic gage heads may be operated with their output proportioned to suit a mathematical formula, e.g., computing area or volume from measurement of pertinent dimensions. As industry becomes more aware of electronic gaging's capabilities, this principle will see much greater application.

The high speed of the electric as well as the electronic gaging system, plus their abilities to provide outputs which can be used to perform work, make them the popular choice for many automatic gaging applications. Equipment for such applications can be broadly classified into two types: the automatic gage, and the automatic *control* gage.

The typical automatic gage (Fig. 8-14) usually measures one or more part dimensions (the latter simultaneously), and automatically sorts work into a number of size categories. It may also be called upon to feed and position the work automatically, but has no control function. By virtue of its high speed and efficiency it is able to perform constant inspection more dependably than the many gage operators it replaces.

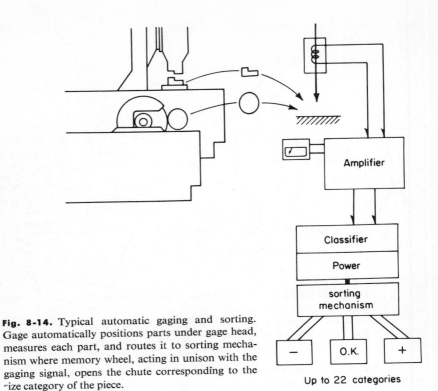

Fig. 8-14. Typical automatic gaging and sorting. Gage automatically positions parts under gage head, measures each part, and routes it to sorting mechanism where memory wheel, acting in unison with the gaging signal, opens the chute corresponding to the size category of the piece.

Amplifier

Classifier

Power

sorting mechanism

—   O.K.   +

Up to 22 categories

Fig. 8-15. In-process control gaging. The simplest and most direct type; involves the least amount of equipment. Gaging takes place as the piece is being machined. The gage, which is part of and master of the machine, measures work continuously as metal is being removed and retracts the tool the instant finish size is reached.

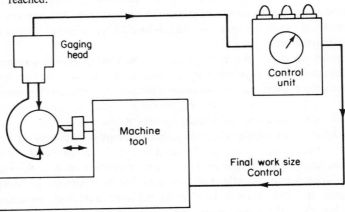

Gaging head

Control unit

Machine tool

Final work size Control

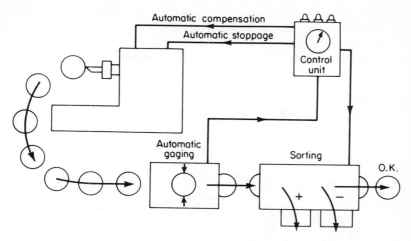

Fig. 8-16. Post-process control gage. Measures the work as it is discharged from the machine, sorts it into "good," "over," or "under," and feeds back signals to the machine so it may correct itself to keep production within tolerance.

The second type of gage (Figs. 8-15 and 8-16) not only measures automatically, but also has means of controlling the operation that produces the work being gaged. Because it is associated with one particular operation, it is normally concerned with only one dimension. The gage may measure the part while it is being machined and control its finish size (in-process), or may check the part *after* machining (post-process) and feed back corrective signals to the machine if the check shows a trend toward out-of-tolerance production. Speed is not an important requirement in the control gage since it must only match the pace of the process. Consequently, the electric or electronic system is combined with air (pneumatic) gaging which has certain advantages in combating machine and work vibrations and facilitates the measurement of internal dimensions.

Figure 8-17 shows a typical automatic gage using the electric system. Separate gage heads are used for each dimension. They feed a three-channel signal unit whose relays actuate gates which direct work to the proper disposal chute.

Generally, the electric gage sorts work into five categories or less, at speeds up to 6000 pieces per hour, and is used for tolerance spreads down to 0.0005 in.

A typical electronic automatic gage is shown in Fig. 8-18. The basic action is similar to that of the electric gage except that there is usually amplification, a continuous signal is produced, and switching action is derived electronically rather than mechanically. A memory wheel coordinates disposal with the switching action which has designated the size classification of the piece. These features enable the electronic gage to sort into more than 20 size categories at speeds up to 24,000 pieces per hour and to discriminate in measurements of 0.0001 in., or less in some instances.

Fig. 8-17. Typical electric gage for automatic sorting. An inner ball bearing race is checked for ID, OD, and width at a speed of 1800 races per hour, and sorted into "good," "over," and "under." Separate electric gage head is used for each dimension. Part tolerance for each dimension is 0.002 in.

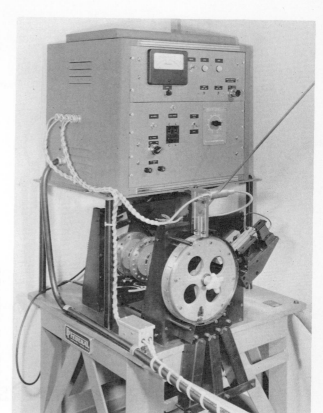

Fig. 8-18. Typical electronic gage for automatic sorting. Roller pins are fed through tube to magazine, and drop into slots on wheel which brings each piece under gage head (2 o'clock) for diameter check. Memory wheels under amplifier housing rotate on same shaft as feed wheel, actuate gages so that each piece will be directed into correct chute (below feed wheel).

9

INTERFEROMETERS AND

ASSOCIATED DEVICES

INTERFEROMETERS*

The Phenomenon of Interference

Light waves are useful for many types of measurement because (1) they constitute an effective unit of measure that is very small, in fact, the smallest used in metrology, and (2) they are capable of the most accurate length definition known. The former attribute is taken advantage of in many applications while the latter has more specialized uses. The wave nature of light, which makes such accurate measurement possible, is ever present but not apparent under ordinary conditions. Only by making light waves interact with each other is the wave effect made visible, and thus made useful for

*By Erwin G. Loewen, Head, Metrology Research, Bausch & Lomb, Inc.

measuring purposes. The phenomenon of interaction is known as "interference" and all instruments designed to measure with interference are known as interferometers, except for testing with optical flats (q.v.), whose widespread and simple application has kept simple flatness testing from being so classified in common usage.

The reason why interference is not observed generally is that it can occur only when two wavefronts, or light rays, come together in a compatible condition known as coherence. By coherence is meant that the two rays that meet at any given point in a field of view must maintain whatever phase relationship they have for an appreciable length of time, and this, in turn, is possible only when the two rays have originated from the same point in the light source at the same time.

As a result, all practical interferometers make use of some type of beam divider that splits an incoming ray into two parts that travel different paths until they are recombined, usually in the same beam divider. An exception to the above, of great scientific interest, is gas lasers whose light output under special conditions is sufficiently coherent to interfere with light from another laser.

As a general rule, the greater the difference in the optical lengths that the two travel between splitting and recombining, the more complex the instrument is likely to be. This path difference varies from just a few wavelengths to one million, or even more with laser light sources. Applications of interference of most interest in metrology are accurate comparison of surface geometry against a master (e.g., optical flats), which can be done with or without microscopic magnification (e.g., interference microscope for surface finish testing), and the relative and absolute calibration of length (e.g., gage blocks). There are many other important applications of interferometry that cannot be considered here.

Fizeau Interference. The most common interference effects are those associated with thin, transparent films or wedges bounded on at least one side by a transparent surface. Soap bubbles, oil films on water, and optical flats fall in this category. Light is usually from an extended "white" light source, such as the sky, but for measuring purposes a single wavelength source, and often only a small part of this, is much preferred. Helium lamps are the cheapest ones that meet this requirement reasonably well, making them the most widely used. The dominant wavelength is $23.4\mu in.$, an orange color.

The mechanism by which interference takes place is most readily described in terms of an optical flat placed over a reasonably reflecting workpiece, Fig. 9-1. Natural irregularities or dust particles can be counted on to provide a wedge angle α, typically 1 to 10 sec of arc, rather than the exaggerated value shown for clarity. The observer's eye looking at a point such as C on the workpiece will see it through the transparent optical flat, illuminated

Extended monochromatic light source

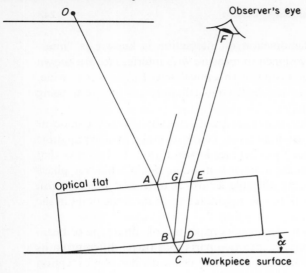

O•

Observer's eye

F

Optical flat   A   G   E

B   D

α

C   Workpiece surface

Fig. 9-1. Simple interference fringe formation—optical flat.

by light along the ray path *OABC*, reflected along path *CDEF*. In addition, a certain amount of light (typically 4 percent) is reflected from both surfaces of the optical flat and some of this also finds its way to the observer's eye. Light reflected from the top surface *AGE* is not interesting under these conditions, but that reflected from point *B* via ray *BGF* is "coherent" with that of ray *BCDEF* and, thus, is capable of interacting with it. Coherence is obtained because the two rays *BGF* and *BCDEF* were obtained from the beam-splitting action of the glass-air interface on the single incoming ray *OAB* at *B*. When two coherent rays come together in this fashion, they interact according to wave theory, giving rise to the phenomenon of interference.

From Fig. 9-1, ray *BCDEF* is longer than ray *BGF* by an optical distance *BCD*. Should this distance *BCD* be equal to one or any whole number of wavelengths, the waves of the two interfering rays will arrive in phase with each other, which causes them to reinforce each other. On the other hand, if distance *BCD* should happen to be $\frac{1}{2}$, $\frac{3}{2}$, or simply $\frac{1}{2}$ plus any whole number of wavelengths, the reverse is true. The two rays will now be just 180° out of phase with each other, and this gives rise to destructive interference. Under these conditions, point *C* appears dark, being covered by an "interference fringe." This discussion is adequate to explain the appearance, but is actually slightly in error. The ray reflected at the glass-air interface *BD* undergoes a 180° phase shift, while at the workpiece surface there is little or no such phase shift. The result is merely to shift the fringe pattern $\frac{1}{2}$ fringe parallel to itself and for that reason the effect is commonly ignored.

The workpiece surface, as it is scanned by the observer's eye, is covered by a pattern of such dark fringes (lines that may be straight or curved), each representing the locus of a constant distance *BCD*. A new fringe is formed

248

everywhere that BCD increases or decreases by one wavelength but, since BC is practically $\frac{1}{2}$ BCD, the fringes repeat every time the wedge has increased or decreased its height by $\frac{1}{2}$ wavelength, commonly written $\frac{1}{2}\lambda$.

It is important to note that an interference fringe is not an entity like a wire, which has a definite position in space. It has no existence except as the observing instrument gives it form. That this is so can readily be confirmed for the system described by moving the head, with everything else unchanged. The fringes will be seen to move around somewhat.

How to interpret such a fringe pattern and derive from it the shape of a surface with respect to that of a reference will be described in more detail under "Optical Flats." Suffice it to say here, that one can try to visualize a sea of imaginary shadow planes, all parallel to the reference surface and separated in height by $\frac{1}{2}\lambda$ of the light source used, whose intersection with the surface being examined gives rise to a contour map with contour lines separated by $\frac{1}{2}\lambda$.

Multiple Reflections. It might be asked why some of the light of ray $CDEF$ is not reflected at D back to the workpiece, and then upward once more to the eye at F. Actually, this is just what does happen. However, as long as only 4 percent of the incoming light is reflected from a glass or quartz surface, the influence of such a double reflection is not visible to the eye.

However, the situation is different when the under surface of an optical flat is given a reflecting coating (50 to 90 percent reflectivity to roughly match that of the workpiece). The rays that combine, as before, at F are no longer limited to the first two but represent a whole series of multiple reflections, 10 or even as many as 100 under special conditions. The most obvious difference to the eye is that the fringes, while still separated by the same $\frac{1}{2}\lambda$ equivalent height, are very much sharper and thus easier to interpret. This comes about because the large number of rays combine destructively only when all are exactly in opposite phase to the directly reflected ray, and this happens only over a very narrow angle of viewing.

The contrast between fringes and their background varies considerably with the reflectivity of both the surface being examined and that of the reference. The better the match between these reflectivities, the greater the fringe contrast, a statement that holds equally well for two-beam and multiple-beam interference. This explains why glass against glass gives good two-beam fringes, but glass against polished steel does not, and why high-reflection coatings on the glass help in the latter case. Multiple-beam fringes demand high reflectivity on both surfaces (at least 50 percent is desirable), which precludes applying the technique to materials like glass unless the surface has been specially overcoated with a thin deposit of metal (silver or aluminum) which may be removed chemically after testing. Semi-transparent films of silver on the reference surface are now generally replaced by stacks of specially-designed dielectric coatings which have the great advantage of absorbing very little light (less than 1 percent) in themselves. This high efficiency makes possible a large number of reflections.

Collimated Illumination and Viewing. Simple visual observation of the Fizeau fringes between two surfaces very close to each other (no more than a few wavelengths apart) as in Figs. 9-1 and 9-2, is quite satisfactory for most applications. However, there are some clear limitations which cannot be ignored if the surfaces are large and if the test specifications are tight, for example, surfaces larger than 3 in. diam, tested to $\frac{1}{10}$ fringe. The limitation arises from the fact that the rays meeting at the observer's eye from different parts of the surface do so at varying angles, so that fringes are formed from rays that view the wedge differently. The result is that two perfectly matching surfaces give rise to slightly curved fringes, when a set of uniformly spaced straight fringes would have been expected.

The theoretically correct arrangement is to illuminate and observe the interference-producing wedge in parallel, or collimated light, as in Fig. 9-3. An additional advantage of such a system is that it is no longer necessary to have the two interfering surfaces touching, except in the important case of multiple beam interference, so that the carefully finished reference surface need never make physical contact with the work surface. A decided disadvantage of a collimated system is its relatively high cost, which increases rapidly with the field of view.

One answer to the high cost of a large-aperture fringe viewing system is to use a small system (1-in. aperture) and traverse it over the stationary reference and workpiece. While it is then no longer possible to judge the shape of an entire surface in a single glance, very precise readings can be made and a very accurate network of surface topography derived. This is

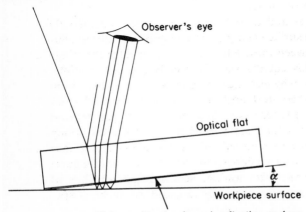

Monochromatic light source

Observer's eye

Optical flat

α

Workpiece surface

High efficiency (low loss) semi-reflecting surface

Reflectivity = 50% to 90% typical
Transmission = 49% to 9% typical

Fig. 9-2. Schematic showing rays for multiple-beam interference (all angles exaggerated for clarity).

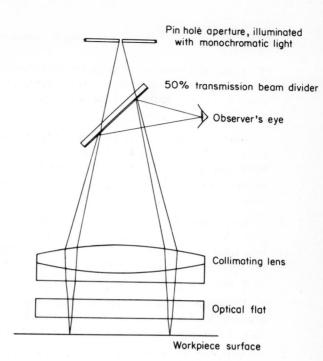

Pin hole aperture, illuminated
with monochromatic light

50% transmission beam divider

Observer's eye

Collimating lens

Optical flat

Fig. 9-3. Collimated light source
—Fizeau interferometer.

Workpiece surface

the method used at the National Bureau of Standards to calibrate master optical flats. The wedge angle is always adjusted so that a fringe is parallel to the direction of traverse. Multiple beam fringes should always be viewed in collimated light in order to obtain the accuracy that goes with the precise, sharp fringes.

Light Sources for Interferometry

Many light sources are used in various interferometers. Choice is based on cost, convenience, and the type of application. The simplest source is a tungsten bulb combined with a filter that transmits only a narrow band of wavelengths. This is adequate for systems where the difference between interfering paths is at most a few wavelengths long, such as simple Fizeau surface geometry testing.

All other sources involve the excitation of atoms of certain elements, which then radiate light at certain discrete wavelengths. Some type of discharge lamp is usually charged with one or sometimes two elements and contains means to vaporize the element, if it is not already gaseous, so that it can then be excited electrically.

Commonly used types of light sources are mercury, mercury 198, cadmium, krypton, krypton 86, thallium, sodium, helium, neon, and gas lasers.

Mercury. It is characterized by its high intensity, and low cost. Green line (5460.72 angstroms) is easily isolated with filters. Maximum path difference is limited because natural mercury contains several isotopes, each one radiating at a wavelength only slightly different from the others. The result is a mixture of wavelengths sufficiently monochromatic only for short path difference.

Mercury 198. Pure isotope, produced by neutron bombardment of gold, is one of the best sources of very sharply defined wavelengths. It is excited by microwave produced electric field and is the international secondary standard of wavelength. Fringes are visible with path difference up to 20 inches.

Cadmium. This is the only natural material producing a spectral line (6440 Å, red) almost completely symmetrical. This caused it to be the source first used to accurately relate light wavelengths to the meter standard. In the form of its 114 isotope, it is an official secondary international standard of length. Its maximum useful path difference is around 8 in.

Krypton. Natural krypton lamps are used in some instruments. They are easily excited and operate with path differences up to 15 in., but the mixture of isotopes makes the lines less monochromatic than krypton 86.

Krypton 86. When excited under specified conditions, and at a temperature of 63.3°K (temperature of nitrogen triple point, which calls for a special cryostat), the orange-red line of the krypton 86 isotope is the new basic International standard of length. The meter is defined as being exactly 1,650,763.73 wavelengths of this source, measured in a vacuum. Fringes can be observed with path differences up to 32 in., the longest possible with any spectral source (except for lasers). This lamp is generally used only in standardizing laboratories, due to the cooling requirement, and because the lamp emits so many different wavelengths (spectral lines) that a fairly elaborate monochromator is required to separate them.

Thallium. Thallium lamps emit over 95 percent of their light at one green wavelength. This makes them unique among lamps operating over a reasonable path difference in not requiring any sort of filter.

Sodium. The yellow sodium light contains two separate but closely spaced lines of equal intensity, which causes interference fringes to wash out as soon as the interference path difference exceeds a few hundred wavelengths.

Helium. This has several wavelengths, but the orange line (5876 Å) predominates and is often used in Fizeau interference where the path difference is not great. For this application it requires no filter.

Neon. Conventional neon lamps are no longer used in practical instruments. They have too many closely spaced lines, all in the red part of the spectrum, and are not as sharply defined as are those of krypton. Neon in gas lasers (see below) has recently assumed a uniquely important role.

Gas Lasers. The high-power, intermittently operating ruby lasers are of no interest to metrology. However, gas lasers constitute a completely new and unique light source. They are capable of producing light that is far more monochromatic than that of even a krypton 86 lamp and at the same time, much more intense. Advances in the field of lasers are currently so rapid that many published statements may be obsolete as soon as they appear in print. Gas lasers up to now have depended on a mixture of neon and helium in a special discharge tube, excited by an electric discharge or a high-frequency field, and located inside a high efficiency Fabry-Perot etalon or a modified version of it. The atomic transitions that give rise to the characteristic red light at 6328Å differ from that in all other spectral sources in that they are all in phase with each other. In addition, the wavelength at any given instant covers an extremely short portion of the spectrum, so it can be said to be much more nearly perfectly monochromatic than any other source. This means that interference fringes can be observed with enormous path differences, up to 100 million wavelengths having already been accomplished. In addition, light intensity is usually at least 1000 times more than any other monochromatic sources.

With so many advantages, it would seem desirable that all interferometers come equipped with lasers. However, suitable lasers are only just appearing on the market. Besides relatively high cost and large size, there are also some present basic limitations. One is that the precise wavelength of a laser is not a quantity completely fixed by the nature of the atom as in other spectral sources, but is influenced to some extent by the mechanical distance between the Fabry-Perot end plates. For longer lasers, there are always several discrete wavelengths called modes, closely spaced, that match the spacing of the end plates. These will change in relative strength as vibration or temperature alters mechanical spacing, by discrete values, called modes. A large amount of research is being devoted to methods for stabilizing lasers, some of it very promising. Very short lasers (4 in.) have been announced that either operate at a single mode or simply go out. Properly stabilized, they may offer new possibilities in long-distance interferometry.

From the point of view of gage block calibration, it is a serious disadvantage to have a source that generates only a single wavelength, since the method of exact fractions (see later) cannot be applied as it can with krypton, cadmium, or mercury sources. For fringe counting devices, such a limitation does not apply, and this makes it the preferred method for applying lasers to length interferometry. The small diameter of laser beams and their natural high degree of collimation is a handicap in that special optics are required to spread the beam over a larger area more suitable for most instruments.

Another source of trouble, not usually anticipated, is that low-intensity reflections from inactive optical surfaces of an interferometer system, which are seldom detectable with ordinary spectral sources, show up sharply and clearly with a laser source. This effect can be very annoying. One solution is to coat these secondary surfaces with multilayer coatings designed for very low reflectivity at the laser wavelength. The high degree of coherence of laser light, important for many applications, is a severe handicap in an interferometer, because it gives rise to diffraction circles from every particle of dust settling on the optics. One awkward, but effective solution is to place a piece of vibrating ground glass in front of the laser. A more elegant method is to use a series of coated, light-transmitting glass fibers (fiber optics).

Types of Interferometers

Michelson Interferometers. The basic Michelson interferometer is shown in Fig. 9-4. Light from an extended source, most often monochromatic or of a single wavelength, falls onto a plane parallel plate BD, which has on its back a semitransparent layer of silver or a more efficient multilayer film. This divides the light into two rays of equal intensity; one is transmitted through compensating plate CP to mirror M_1, the other is reflected through BD to mirror M_2. The rays are reflected back from the mirrors and reunite at the semi-reflecting surface. There they are transmitted to the eye at E, where fringes can be observed.

The only purpose of the compensator plate is to introduce exactly the same amount of glass in each of the paths, which is important mainly when a white light source is used. However, so-called white light fringes can be seen only

Fig. 9-4. Michelson interferometer.

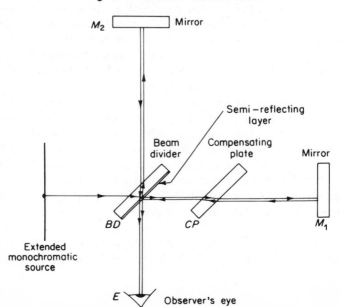

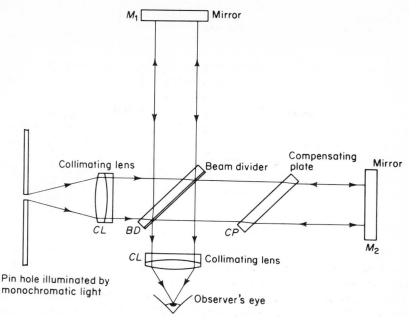

Fig. 9-5. Twyman-Green specialization of Michelson interferometer.

if both ray paths are exactly equal (to a few wavelengths) in total length, glass, and air. The path lengths themselves are not important; only their differences affect fringe formation. Monochromatic sources allow fringes to be seen over a range of path difference that may vary from a few to a million wavelengths, depending on the source.

No currently produced interferometers make use of the Michelson interferometer in the original form just described, although Michelson himself used it with great success in his famous experiments to establish the exact relationship between the meter and the red wavelength of a cadmium lamp. Modern two-beam interferometers are all based on the Twyman-Green specialization of the Michelson arrangement, as in Fig. 9-5. The central rays are seen to describe the same path but, due to the presence of a pair of collimating lenses combined with a pin-hole source diaphragm, all other rays are parallel to the central ray. In the older version (Fig. 9-4) they describe a cone, giving rise to various types of fringe patterns which may be hard to interpret.

Fabry-Perot Interferometers. Fabry-Perot interferometers, or etalons, are made up of two optical flats, flat to $\frac{1}{20}$ fringe or better, coated with a high-efficiency semitransparent film on the two facing surfaces, which must be kept exactly parallel by means of a carefully designed spacer. When illuminated, as shown in Fig. 9-6, a series of very sharply defined bright circles is seen on a screen, which results from interference between rays that are multiply reflected between the two working faces of the etalon.

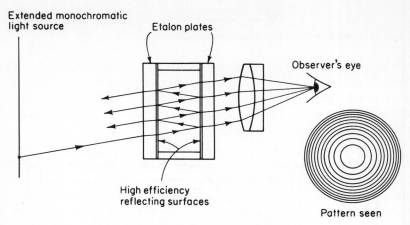

Fig. 9-6. Fabry-Perot etalon.

While etalons are no longer used in any shop metrology, they are of interest because most of the original determinations of the meter in terms of the wavelengths of light were made with this instrument, and all the recent highly accurate (one part in 10^8) intercomparisons of wavelengths depend on specialized versions of the Fabry-Perot etalon. In addition, the operation of lasers is tied to a "cavity" that is a form of the same system.

Spherical Interferometers. The only commercially-produced measuring interferometers that do not measure planes are those that measure spherical surfaces. The problem here, as seen in Fig. 9-7, is that instead of parallel

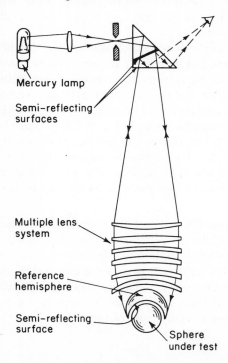

Fig. 9-7. Spherical interferometer optical diagram. (*Courtesy of Engis Equipment Co.*)

collimated light between the interfering surfaces, rays are needed that converge to the center of the concentric workpiece and reference spheres, between which Fizeau-type interference occurs. This is difficult to do with a cone angle large enough to encompass a reasonably large fraction of the sphere, hence the large number of lenses.

Fringe Counting Interferometers. If in a Twyman-Green type interferometer, with both end mirrors perpendicular to the optical axis, one mirror is displaced slowly, exactly parallel to itself, the observer will note periodic changes in the intensity of the field being viewed, from bright to dark. Measurement will show the intensity variation to be sinusoidal, with a period that corresponds to mirror motion of exactly $\lambda/2$, half the wavelength of the light source used. If one of the end mirrors is slightly inclined to the optical axis, parallel fringes will be seen that move parallel to themselves by just one fringe for every $\frac{1}{2}\lambda$ mirror motion. Counting of such fringes by eye, or better, with photo detectors (Fig. 9-8) hooked up to high-speed counters, appears to be a good way to measure linear mechanical motion directly in terms of the wavelength of light. Accuracy of one part in one million should be attainable and has in fact been attained. A number of conditions must be met and understood before such results can be realized.

Bidirectional Counting. For a photoelectric fringe counting system to be responsive to motions both forward and backward, at least two detectors are required to be aligned with respect to the fringes, one located 90 fringe phase degrees with respect to the other. If fringe position is to be detected to less than $\frac{1}{4}$ fringe, then three detectors are required to look at fringe sections 120° out of phase with each other. The most efficient way to do this

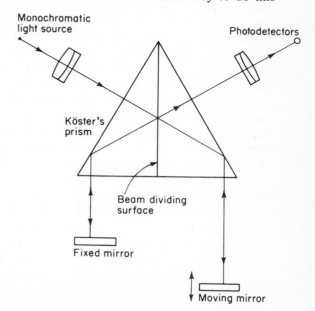

Fig. 9-8. Fringe count system based on Koster's prism.

is to arrange the mirrors perpendicular to the optical axis and coat half (or one-third) of one of them with layers exactly $\frac{1}{8}\lambda$ (or $\frac{1}{6}\lambda$ and $\frac{1}{3}\lambda$) thick. Each photocell is arranged to receive light from just one of the coated areas.

Ways for Mirror Travel. Relatively few instruments or machines have ways sufficiently straight to maintain uniform fringe fields when an interferometer mirror is attached to a moving carriage. One solution to this problem is to use a so-called corner cube reflector which returns an image very much like an ordinary mirror, but is not sensitive to rotation about the point of intersection of the three faces.

Vibration. The high sensitivity of interferometers makes them particularly susceptible to vibrations. Visually, this can either be annoying or, if extreme, may wash out the fringes completely. Photoelectrically, they call for a large reserve in counting speed in order not to miscount a fringe, which would be fatal to accuracy. One of the best optical answers to the vibration problem is to replace the conventional Twyman-Green Michelson system by its much more compact equivalent in the form of a Kösters prism, Fig. 9-8. While difficult to make, this prism has the great advantage that the two interfering paths are conveniently parallel instead of at right angles, so that vibration tends to affect the arms equally, which reduces the problem.

Length of Travel. Until recently, even the most carefully designed fringe-counting measuring systems, using cooled mercury 198 lamps, were unable to function with mirror travel greater than 10 in. At that range the poor signal-to-noise ratio greatly limited the traversing speeds (to 0.0001 in./sec, versus speeds up to $\frac{1}{2}$ in./sec possible when path lengths are nearly equal).

There are two recent solutions to this problem. One is to couple a suitably designed Fabry-Perot etalon with a Twyman-Green interferometer. Fringes up to 20-ft path difference are then attainable with good contrast. The second solution is to use a laser source which should allow even longer path differences to be covered with good signal strengths.

The Effect of Atmosphere. The wavelength of light is fixed only in a vacuum. Since most interferometers must operate in air, the effective wavelengths are modified by the refractive index of air, which unfortunately is not constant. Whether the required correction is important depends entirely on the path difference between interfering rays and the desired accuracy of measurement. It is unimportant in flatness- or most form-measuring systems, but is vital in fringe-counting and gage-block interferometers.

In order to reduce the absolute size of atmospheric corrections, wavelengths may conveniently be specified at standard metrology conditions (note that these are *not* the international wavelength standard conditions):

Pressure:	760 mm mercury (sea level)
Temperature:	20°C (68°F)
Humidity:	57 percent relative humidity
Carbon dioxide:	0.03 percent

Departures from these standard values that correspond to a wavelength correction of one part in ten million are:

Pressure:	0.28 mm mercury
Temperature:	0.108°C
Humidity:	7.5 percent relative humidity

In practice, pressure measurements represent the greatest nuisance, since mercury barometers must be compensated for density of mercury, a function of temperature and local gravity. Temperature effects on density can be quite low with modern temperature conditioning systems. It is quite possible to measure the refractive index of the air interferometrically by incorporating an air cell in one arm of the interferometer and counting the fringes as they move across the field when the cell is hooked up to a vacuum pump. Although straightforward in application, no current commercial linear measuring instrument has provisions for doing this. If the fringe-counting process extends over a period of more than a few hours, as it does for example in continuous feedback control systems for diffraction grating ruling engines, account must be taken of cumulative effects of wavelength changes. This is done with analog computers.

When optical paths become long, the effects of air currents between optical elements become more and more noticeable, requiring careful shielding with insulating, radiation-reflecting enclosures. Unfortunately, such enclosures increase the time required for internal stabilization. The better the surrounding temperature control, the more such enclosures tend to become simple shields against drafts.

Gage Block Interferometers. All gage block interferometers are variations of the Fizeau or Twyman-Green (or Kösters prism equivalent) interferometers. Optical diagrams of two types are shown in Figs. 9-9 and 9-10.

Fundamentally, they measure the length of a gage block with respect to a base plate, to which the block is wrung, by arranging the base plate almost perpendicular to the interferometer axis and determining the number of fringes between the base plate and the surface of the block. Multiplying this number by half the wavelength of the light used should give the length of the block. Since for a 1-in. block the number of fringes is of the order of 100,000 and since all fringes look alike, the exact value is not immediately evident. The only quantity that is readily determined by a glance at the fringe pattern (Figs. 9-9 and 9-10) is whether the block length is an exact integral multiple of the half wavelength, or exceeds it by some fringe fraction. Thus, it is easy to tell that the block is, say, $\frac{1}{3}$ fringe (about 3 μin.) longer than a whole number of fringes, while there is nothing to tell whether this whole number is 100,000, 99,990, 100,010, or some other integral value in the vicinity. Within a range of ten such numbers one can usually arrive at the solution simply by checking the block with conventional equipment (to 0.0001 in.) and

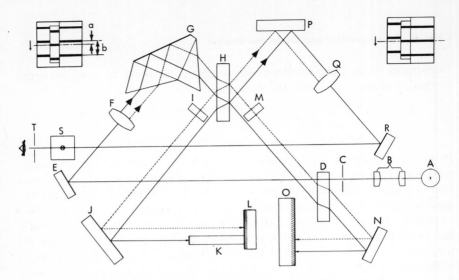

Fig. 9-9. Zeiss gage block interferometer. The light from cadmium lamp (A) is collected on entrance slit (C) by condensing lens (B). It then passes through glass compensator plate (D) and is reflected by mirror (E) through collimator objective (F) which sends a parallel beam of light through the dispersion prism (G) to beam splitter (H). Here the light beam is split, part of the light is deflected by the partially reflecting coating on (H). One side of this beam passes through measuring plate (I) and is deflected by mirror (J) to the surfaces of the gage block (K) and the optical flat (L). After the light is reflected, it retraces its path back to beam splitter (H). The other portion of light passes through (H). One side of the beam passes through the inclinable measuring plane (M). Then the entire beam goes through compensator plate (D) and is deflected by mirror (N) to reference mirror (O). After being reflected, the light beam retraces its path back to the beam splitter (H). Now the two rays from (H) travel together and are reflected by mirror (P) through objective lens (Q) to mirror (R). The light then passes through inverted prism (S) and can be seen by the eye at exit slit (T) as two sets of interference fringes.

dividing this length by the known half wavelength of the light. However, that is not enough. To tie down the missing information, use is made of the "exact fraction" method. This requires observing in fairly rapid sequence the same fringe pattern as before, but at several different wavelengths, usually three to five depending on the spectral source used. The fractional displacement between the base and the gage block fringes is noted each time. Since the wavelengths bear no simple relationship to each other, only one single whole number of fringes can make up the length of the block and at the same time yield the specific fringe fractions observed for each color. Thus, the length is uniquely defined.

In practice, the procedure involved is simplified through the use of tables and special slide rules that save all complicated arithmetic. However, cor-

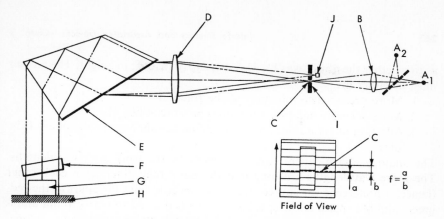

Fig. 9-10. N.P.L. gage interferometer. Light from cadmium lamp (A), or Mercury 198 isotope lamp A_2 is collected by lens (B) and focused on entrance slit (C). Light from (C) is collimated by lens (D) from where it goes through constant deviation prism (E), whose rotation determines wavelength passed, through reference flat (F) to upper surface of gage block (G) and base plate (H) to which it is wrung. Light retraces nearly same path to mirror (J) whose fringe patterns are observed through a telescope not shown. Field of view is shown below.

rections for atmospheric effects on wavelength must be applied, and, even more important, as a rule, are corrections for thermal expansion of the gage block if it is not exactly at 20°C (68°F). To measure to 1 μin. requires that the fringe fraction of the dominant wavelength be determined to an accuracy of better than $\frac{1}{10}$ fringe.

The exact fraction principle can best be visualized with a simple illustration. Place an inch and a millimeter scale side by side, both matched at their zero lines, as in Fig. 9-11. Exact coincidence between the $\frac{1}{2}$-in. intervals and the milimeter intervals occurs only every five inches, although at $1\frac{1}{2}$ and $3\frac{1}{2}$ in. the lines differ in position by only $\frac{1}{10}$ mm. Suppose that an object has to be measured with two such scales, whose numbers have somehow been completely erased. If the object is found to match both scales right on a line, we would know immediately that it must be a multiple of five inches long. A second, very rough measurement is required to decide which multiple of five inches is the correct one. It is also evident that if our ability to determine such scale coincidence is not better than $\frac{1}{10}$ mm, there would be uncertainty

Fig. 9-11. Exact fraction principle.

1/2 INCH INTERVALS

1MM. INTERVALS

as to whether the object was $1\frac{1}{2}$, $3\frac{1}{2}$ 5, $6\frac{1}{2}$, $8\frac{1}{2}$, 10 in. etc., in height. The answer must lie either in:

1. More precise determination of the fraction.
2. More accurate determination of approximate height.
3. Addition of yet a third scale with different subdivisions to either of the others.

The analogy above carries over completely to the work with wavelengths. The more wavelengths are used and the more they differ from each other (hence, a preference for sources that have spectral lines far apart in the red, green, and blue parts of the spectrum), the less one has to worry about ambiguity. In practice, blocks checked interferometrically are so close to nominal size that ambiguity is rarely a problem.

Interference Microscopes. Checking the finish of finely polished or lapped surfaces can be done qualitatively with any good microscope equipped with proper illumination. However, when quantitative information is desired concerning scratch depth and shape, it becomes highly desirable to superimpose interference fringes over the field. Instruments designed for this purpose are called interference microscopes. Fringe patterns are interpreted exactly as in any other case.

Two basic types are available. The simpler one makes use of Fizeau fringes, very often the multiple-beam sharpened fringes that occur between a very small, optically flat reference surface in contact with the workpiece. The flat is not only small but thin, in order to make room for it in the limited space between the microscope objective and the workpiece. Most microscopes of this type are limited in magnification to 150X, sometimes up to 300X, by the presence of the reference flat. Fortunately, this is enough for many purposes, but not for all. Like all such systems, monochromatic light is required, filtered mercury being preferred because very small lamps are available.

It is possible, but much more difficult, to adapt the Michelson Twyman-Green interferometer to a microscope. For very low magnifications (15X) the entire interferometer, in miniature form, fits in front of a low-magnification microscope objective. The only advantage of such a system lies in the ability to use white light fringes, when the interferometer arms are adjusted for equality, which is useful for checking large steps and gives a bright picture. For surface finish testing, it has insufficient magnification. High magnification becomes possible, in both white and monochromatic light, when suitably corrected microscope objectives are placed in both arms of the interferometer, one focused on the reference mirror, the other on the work surface. To get clear fringes, especially in white light, the two objectives have to be balanced to a very high degree. This is difficult to accomplish and, together with other optical requirements not described here, explains the relatively high price of this type of instrument.

Scales and Gratings

The term "scales" is employed when rulings are spaced relatively far apart, requiring some sort of interpolating device to make accurate settings. Vernier height gages are a good example. The term "gratings" is used when rulings are closely spaced so as to produce a periodic pattern without blank gaps. These require special readout systems, usually photoelectric.

Types of Scales. Metal scales in order of increasing accuracy are produced by cutting lines with a V-section milling cutter, etching through a ruled resist or a photoetch resist copied from a glass master, or engraving directly into the polished surface with a sharp diamond.

Stainless steel is the most common metallic material because it takes a good polish, is stable when properly treated, and resists tarnishing. A disadvantage in some applications is that it has a thermal coefficient of expansion less than that for steel or cast iron. Glass is another popular material for scales. It is easily polished, stable, and is able to work in both transmitted and reflected light. While ordinary glasses all have expansion coefficients 15 to 30 percent less than steel, some types recently developed have the same expansion coefficient as steel. Graduations are most often produced in glass by etching through a ruled wax or photographic resist activated by contact or projection printing. More recently, lines on glass scales are produced in the form of very thin deposits of metal capable of very high edge definition and highly resistant to wear. Photographic emulsion on glass is another popular medium for producing scales. Emulsions must be carefully protected from enviromental effects, especially high humidity. To a large extent, the accuracy attainable depends on the machine, known in the ruling business as an "engine," used to divide the intervals of the master, assuming control over environment necessary to obtain the accuracy desired. Most linear ruling engines utilize an accurate lead screw for successive indexing of the required interval. Natural limitations of screws are often overcome by incorporating correction cams for periodic or accumulating errors or both, which imposes the burden of finding the exact correction required in order to figure the cams. The ultimate in correction becomes possible through interferometer feedback control, which, in effect, measures positioning errors against the wavelength of a standard light source so that the engine behaves as if it always had perfectly figured correction cams.

A second type of ruling engine depends on duplicating a previously produced master scale, mounted in line with the scale to be ruled on the same carriage. The carriage is now successively positioned until master graduations are exactly in line with a reference in the form of a photoelectric microscope, whereupon the ruling mechanism produces a line. Accuracy attainable in this way can be very high, often limited only by the temperature environment and the ability to make and calibrate the master scale.

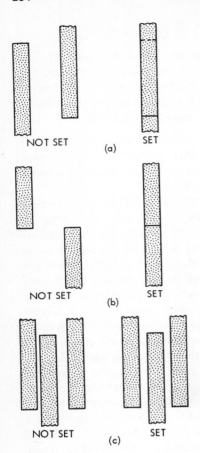

Fig. 9-12. Three basic types of visual scale line setting against an index: (A) Simple superposition; (B) Alignment (vernier) setting; (C) Symmetrical framing between two index lines corresponding setting precision, 3σ limit of an average observer using magnification of 1: a: $\pm$ 0.009 in. b: $\pm$ 0.0025 in. c: $\pm$ 0.00075 in.

Reading of Standard Scales. Visual scale reading systems depend on the naked eye which may be aided by microscopes of varying types, some with eyepieces but now more often with projection systems that reduce fatigue. It is worth noting that the type of index mark used plays a large role in the precision attainable under otherwise equal conditions. The three types illustrated in Fig. 9-12 are:

1. Simple superposition.
2. Vernier acuity.
3. Symmetrical framing.

The last is much preferred since, even with no magnification, one-sigma settings of 0.00025 in. are attainable under optimum conditions.

The line widths are not too critical, but sharply defined edges are. What distinguishes various visual readout systems most is the choice of method

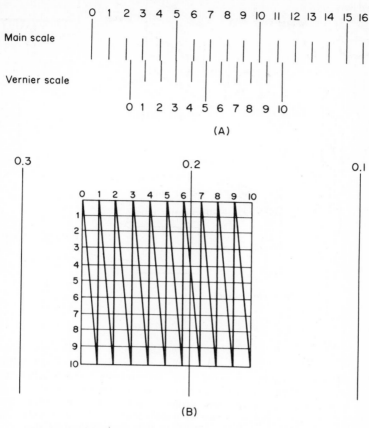

Fig. 9-13. Division of scale intervals: (A) simple vernier scale interpolating reading 0.23; (B) two-dimensional vernier makes possible scale subdivision into 100 parts. Reading: 0.264

by which the scale interval is divided into from 10 to 1000 subdivisions. The simplest is a vernier, as in Fig. 9-13A, since it requires no moving parts. In its one-dimensional form, it is limited to 25 subdivisions, but in the form of a two-dimensional array (Fig. 9-13B), 100 subdivisions are practical.

Other readout systems move an index point mechanically until it frames the scale line and reads optically on the same screen, or externally, the amount of movement required. Some typical examples are shown in Figs. 9-14 and 9-15. An alternate method is to leave the index mark fixed and move the image of the scale with a suitable optical device, such as a sliding lens or tilting glass plate. The required motions to achieve settings are displayed as before. A typical example is shown in Fig. 9-16.

FRONT VIEW OF SCREEN AFTER DOUBLE LINE HAS BEEN SET
Reading 1.21787

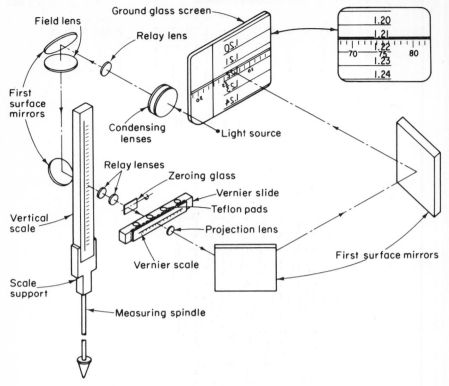

Fig. 9-14. Optical schematic of direct-reading optical gage. Scale is integral with measuring spindle and has 100 lines/inch. Graduations are imaged onto vernier scale and then both are projected superimposed on viewing screen. Position of vernier slide along incline acts as interpolating system when moved so that double index lines frame scale line. Reading: 1.21787 inches.

Fig. 9-15. Vernac readout system. (*Courtesy of Infrared Industries, Inc.*) One complete revolution of double spiral reticle around central vertical axis, controlled by knurled outside ring, corresponds to advance of 0.025-inch scale interval as magnified. Revolution is divided into 250 intervals around periphery, and read at bottom of viewer, so that each division corresponds to 0.0001 inch. Reading shown is 9.4593 inches.

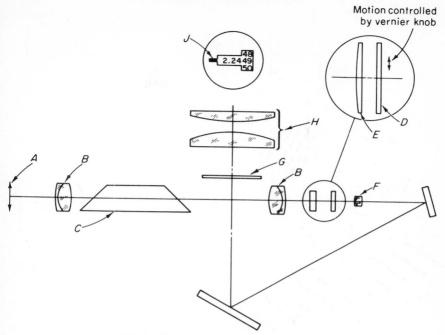

Fig. 9-16. Digital in-line scale readout Scale (A) (100 lines/inch, each numbered) is imaged by means of relay lenses (B) through Dove prism (C) onto plane of vernier number scale (D). Combined image is projected by lens (F) onto screen (G) and viewed through magnifier (H). In operation vernier slide with lens (E) is moved until scale line is symmetric with index (J). Readout is 2.449 inches (2.24″ line on scale (A), 49 out of 99 positions of vernier number scale (D)).

Photoelectric scale viewing systems to replace the eye have been designed to achieve either increased precision of settings, higher speed, remote viewing, or some combination of these advantages. An example is shown in Figs. 9-17, 9-18 and 9-19. The position of a scale line is continuously scanned by a rotating element in front of an objective which images the line onto a pair of photodetectors. At only one position is the light divided equally, which is sensed in suitable circuits. Simultaneously with the scan, and in phase synchronism, pulses are generated each with an effective linear scale equivalent of $\frac{1}{1000}$ scale interval, typically 0.00005 in.

Also required is a device for starting the interval-counting sequence once in each revolution. The result is a digital interpolation of the scale interval which is supplemented by information from a set of three-coded tracks, Fig. 9-18, which are scanned simultaneously and identify in digital form each scale interval. The scale pattern is shown more clearly in Fig. 9-19. Together with the viewing system, this provides a continuous digital display of position.

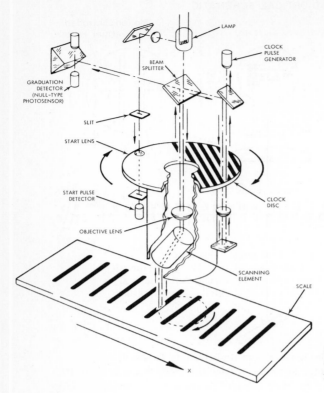

Fig. 9-17. DIG photoelectric digital scale-reading microscope, fine-line interpolating system.

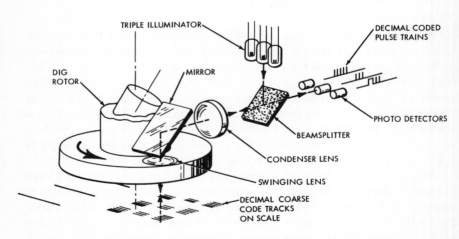

Fig. 9-18. DIG scale reading microscope. Coarse code track readout system. Three photodetectors receive light pulses reflected from scale line.

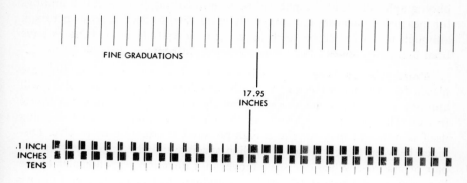

Fig. 9-19. DIG inch scale. Fine graduations spaced accurately at 0.05-inch intervals. Coarse tracks provide decimal identification of fine graduations for digital display. Alternate heavy lines in "inch" track add 0.05 to reading. Similar lines in 0.1-inch track start cycle.

Moiré Scales. Scales with a continuously repeating pattern of lines or grooves, often called gratings, occupy an important position in measuring systems, both linear and rotary. They are made with line spacings from 100 to 5000 per inch, in lengths up to 14 ft, some operating by reflection, others in transmitted light. Although visual sensing is possible, they are usually employed with photoelectric readouts. Since, in most cases, a single scale is used, the individual lines or grooves are not separately identified, so that all measuring must be incremental rather than absolute. Also, calibration is meaningful only in connection with a specific readout system. An important advantage is that position is sensed by the average of anywhere from 50 to 1000 lines, so that if a single line is out of place among n accurate ones, the effect is reduced by a factor n. Periodic errors whose period is less than n can be cancelled out completely, while the effect of random errors is reduced by $\sqrt{n}$. Position information is obtainable at rates that are limited only by the response speed of the photodetectors used or that of subsequent counting devices.

There are two types of continuously ruled scales. One, called amplitude gratings or Ronchi rulings, consists of strips approximately equal in width that are alternately opaque and transmitting (for transmitted light), or reflecting and nonreflecting (for reflected light systems). These are made with spacings up to 1000 per inch, occasionally up to 3000 per inch, and are replicated by one of several photographic procedures, in lengths as great as 14 ft. The second type of scale is one containing triangularly-shaped, contiguous grooves, as used in spectroscopic diffraction gratings, called prismatic or phase gratings. The required three-dimentional shape is not reproducible photographically, but is replicated by a resin casting process. Such gratings for measuring purposes are commonly ruled 2500 to 5000 grooves per inch, although up to 25,000 per inch have been successfully used. Lengths have been limited to ten in., but longer ones should become available soon.

Moiré Fringes. When two similar contiguous-type scales or gratings are placed face to face, or nearly so, with their lines nearly parallel, there will appear a series of parallel bands, alternately light and dark, known as Moiré fringes. They are readily visible to the naked eye even though the ruling itself is not, and may require a high-powered microscope to resolve. Distance between fringes depends on line spacing and the angle between the pair of gratings. When one scale moves in a direction perpendicular to the lines with respect to a stationary index grating, the fringes are seen to move at right angles to the motion and at a rate that corresponds to exactly one fringe for a motion of one scale interval. The coarseness of Moiré fringes allows them to be viewed with relatively simple optics, especially for scales 1000 lines per inch or coarser (Fig. 9-20). For the prismatic type of grating, it is necessary for maximum efficiency to consider diffraction properties of such a grating. The optimum arrangement, Fig. 9-21, shows the so-called minimum deviation arrangement. Light from the collimated source is split mainly into two approximately equal parts, one passing through undeviated (the zero order), the other diffracted by the angle θ, which is a function of the grating spacing and wavelength of the light. The index grating is mounted as shown, with the grooves in opposition. When viewed under the symmetrical configuration of Fig. 9-21, the zero-order ray is diffracted in the first-order direction, while the first-order ray now goes through undeviated as the zero order of the index grating. The result is to have two rays of equal intensity which interfere with each other to form Moiré fringes largely free of harmonics, i.e., with nearly pure sinusoidal intensity distribution.

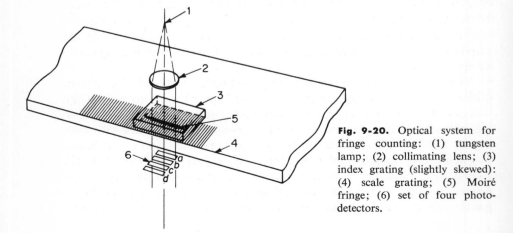

Fig. 9-20. Optical system for fringe counting: (1) tungsten lamp; (2) collimating lens; (3) index grating (slightly skewed): (4) scale grating; (5) Moiré fringe; (6) set of four photo-detectors.

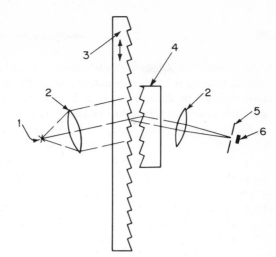

Fig. 9-21. Prismatic grating viewing system; (1) light source; (2) collimating lens; (3) scale grating; (4) index grating; (5) slit; (6) set of photodetectors.

In order to obtain Moiré fringe signals of high contrast, which is necessary for good electrical signals, attention must be paid to the distance between the scale and index gratings. For coarse rulings, the problem is not severe, but for the fine prismatic gratings, the spacing reduces to 0.005 in. and 0.0025 in. for the 2500 and 5000 lines per inch rulings respectively. One solution to the difficulties this gives rise to, at the expense of optical simplicity, is to eliminate the index grating entirely. This can be done by an optical system that images a scale back upon itself. Additional advantages of such an approach lie in the fact that now twice as many fringes are produced for a given scale motion and, in addition, the fringe pattern is not affected by slight rotation about an axis normal to the scale.

In principle, two photocells in the viewing optics spaced 90 fringe-phase degrees apart are capable of generating bi-directional fringe counting signals. In practice, better balance is obtainable with four detectors spaced at 0, 90, 180, and 270 fringe-phase degrees, and counting intervals of one-quarter of the scale interval are provided. Systems that can interpolate to 1/8, 1/10, or even 1/100 of a fringe are being used and depend on relatively sophisticated electronics.

Speed of counting is important since it may impose limitations on measuring speed or slide motions. Counters of 20,000 cps capacity are being replaced with 100,000. If the cost is justified, modern electronics can carry this up to 2,000,000 cps.

An obvious advantage of electronic counting systems is that they are adaptable not only to high-speed digital visual displays and printouts, but also to feedback control systems.

Scale Calibration. Scales can be calibrated by comparison against a nominally similar master scale, mounting both in line on a common slide underneath two measuring microscopes, visual or photoelectric. The master scale can be calibrated by a tedious method of successive subdivision, or by com-

271

parison against calibrated gage blocks used to locate the scale-carrying slide with respect to a fixed index. Contact points against the blocks should be coaxial with the scale axis and lie in the plane of the scale surface to avoid effects of errors in the motion of the slide.

More recently, measuring machines have been built that, in effect, substitute a measuring interferometer for the gage blocks so that direct comparison can be made between the scale graduations and the international standard of length, the wavelength of krypton 86 or mercury 198. In all high-accuracy calibrations, the most troublesome factor is control over temperature, although all other normal precautions must be observed as well. Settings on carefully ruled lines can be made to a precision better than $1\,\mu$in. with a good photoelectric microscope and, under ideal conditions, similar results have been obtained with Moiré fringes.

AUTOCOLLIMATORS

The popularity of autocollimators rests on their ability to sense remotely to high accuracy the angular rotation of a flat mirror around axes in the plane of the mirror. With sensitivities down to $\frac{1}{10}$ sec of arc, or even less under special conditions, it has become common practice not only to use autocollimators to monitor angular tilts as such, but to convert linear displacements into angular ones so that they can be monitored with this versatile instrument.

Optically, an autocollimator is merely a special form of telescope. It consists basically of an illuminated target pattern or reticle located in the focal plane of the telescope objective. A plane mirror perpendicular to the optical axis in front of this telescope will reflect an image of the pattern back upon itself in the same plane and in focus. A rotation of the mirror by an angle θ about its perpendicular position will cause the return image to be displaced by an amount d, given by the simple relation

$$d = 2f\theta$$

where f is the focal length of the autocollimator objective. A viewing system is required to observe the relative position of the image, which can be in the form of an illuminated slit or cross or, the inverse, a dark line or cross-hair in an illuminated field. A simple eyepiece may serve, or a compound microscope can be used, as in Fig. 9-22. The fiducial index should be designed for maximum precision in setting on the image, for example, a double line to frame a single line, and measurement is made by moving either the image or the index under micrometer control. While most autocollimators measure

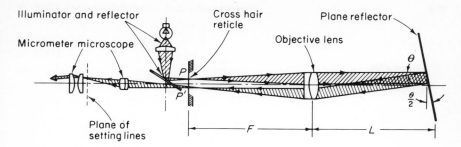

Fig. 9-22. Principle of autocollimation. (*Courtesy of Engis Equipment Co.*)

around one axis only, a suitable target pattern and a two-axial index micrometer system are all that is required to make readings about two axes. The sensitivity attainable can be readily judged from an example:

Focal length $f = 10$ in.
  Mirror tilt $\theta = 1$ sec of arc (5×10^{-6} radians)
  Image shift $d = 2f\theta = 2 \times 10 \times 5 \times 10^{-6} = 0.0001$ in.

Even a relatively low magnification eyepiece (10X) will enable a line framed in a double index to be judged well within 0.0001 in.

Mirror Characteristics

Since the reflecting mirror is part of the overall system, it is obvious that its properties, such as size, flatness, and distance from objective, all play a role in making measurements. A mirror much smaller than the objective will send rays back through different portions of the objective, depending upon where its center is located with respect to the optical axis. This will cause readings to vary, unless the objective is free of all aberrations, which is most unlikely. In fact, one test for quality of an autocollimator is to move a $\frac{1}{8}$-in. wide slit in front of the objective with the reflector mirror fixed, while observing whether the image shifts noticeably.

If the mirror is not flat, it will defocus the return image and present an undefined reference plane. Hence, high-quality autocollimator mirrors are held to flatness tolerances of $\frac{1}{4}$ fringe (2.5 μin.) or better. At first glance, it might seem that there should be no limit to the distance between an autocollimator and the reflecting mirror, since they are separated by light that is collimated, i.e., forms parallel rays. In practice, limitations arise from several sources. One is that light is never perfectly collimated, but a more direct limit is set by simple geometry. Assume a mirror is centered on axis a distance L away from the objective of diameter c, as in Fig. 9-23. When $L = c/\theta$, no light whatsoever is returned to the autocollimator. For a 2-in. diam objective, a mirror tilt of 10' of arc leads to $L_{\max}$ of 700 in. In practice, the mirror could not be further away than a fraction of this amount, say 200 in.

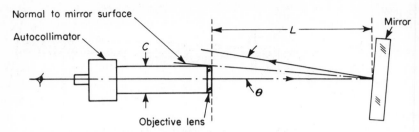

Fig. 9-23. No light is reflected back into the autocollimator when $L\theta \geq C$.

It must be borne in mind that the air path between the mirror and the autocollimator is a real part of the optical system. Measurements to 1 sec of arc over distances up to 5 ft in reasonably quiet environment seldom cause trouble. However, when higher resolution or longer distances or both are required, close attention must be paid to adequate shielding of the air path from drafts and, especially, gradients. Even a simple cardboard tube can be very helpful.

Photoelectric Autocollimators

Autocollimators which replace the judgment of the human eye with appropriate photoelectric systems have some important advantages that can outweigh their increased cost and complexity. Setting accuracy is increased and no longer differs between observers. Reading can be made remote and can be monitored continuously when required. Such autocollimators come in

Fig. 9-24. Schematic of photoelectric autocollimator. (*Courtesy of Engis Equipment Co.*)

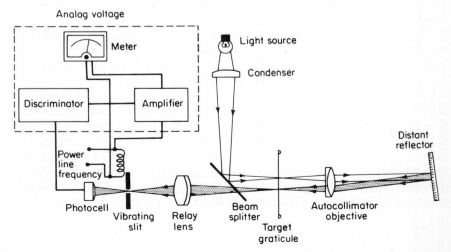

sizes from 1-in. cube (with null setting sensitivity better than 0.1 sec) to very large instruments with 10-in. objectives, for jobs such as guided missile alignment. Some provide merely a photoelectric null setting without measuring capability, while others have analog or digital readout with ranges from 10 sec to a full degree or more.

In the system shown in Fig. 9-24, the illuminated target reticle slit is imaged back in its own plane through the autocollimator objective and reflecting mirror, but displaced radially for convenience. It is then re-imaged onto a vibrating slit by means of a relay lens. Behind the slit is a photocell whose output is now modulated by the vibrating slit, which makes possible the phase discrimination required to make the amplified output sensitive to the direction as well as amount of mirror rotation from a central null position. Such a system can be used to read mirror tilt in analog fashion on the meter. If the vibrating slit assembly is moved with a precision micrometer, this serves to obtain a reading with the meter acting merely as a null indicator. In the latter case, the electronics need no longer behave linearly and can be simplified. Sensitivity of 0.1 sec of arc is readily obtainable.

A different type of system is shown in Fig. 9-25. Here, an entire grid pattern is imaged back on itself by the autocollimator optics. As a result,

Fig. 9-25. Continuous photoelectric autocollimator. Light from a monchromatic source (1) passes through a grid (2), a beam splitter (3), a collimating lens (4), and strikes a mirror (5) mounted on the rotating specimen to be tested (6). The image is reflected back into the specimen where it is directed by a beam splitter (7) to the stability reference photosensor (8). The image is also reflected by beam splitter (3) through a second grid (9) to the control photosensor (10) which generates a periodic signal as mirror (5) is rotated. (*Courtesy of Razelow Laboratories*)

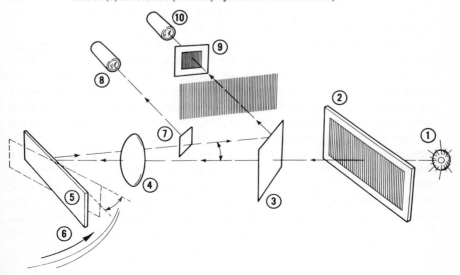

what a photodetector sees when the mirror tilts are periodic changes in intensity, the period being a function of grid spacing and the focal length of the objective and can vary from 10 sec to 10 min of arc. Corresponding ranges vary from 1° to 3°. Keeping track of these periods is equivalent to digitizing the angle of tilt and may be all that is required. For highest sensitivity, the analog position between periods can also be recorded. An important advantage of this approach is that a much larger part of the field is optically active, so that the systems can be made relatively compact even in applications where high sensitivity is combined with a long angular range. Illumination is much more effectively utilized, resulting in excellent signal-to-noise ratio.

Calibration

The only effective method for calibrating autocollimators is to monitor output or readings as the reference mirror is tilted through accurately controlled angles. The problem of how to generate small angles accurate to 1 sec of arc or better has been solved by designing special sine bar fixtures with a precisely-defined axis at one end, while at the other end a well-defined cylinder is raised or lowered with a special micrometer or with gage blocks.

Applications

In designing for applications of an autocollimator, the central thought must be that these instruments are sensitive to angular tilts only, not to translations. In this, they differ from alignment telescopes, for example. No series of measurements can be better than the angular stability of the surface on which the autocollimator rests. This tends to show up in such applications as the checking of a machine bed when the instrument is mounted on no more than a floor-supported tripod. A platform fastened directly to the casting involved is likely to be much more stable.

One such application, illustrated in Fig. 9-26, represents one of the autocollimator's most frequent uses—to check the straightness of a way or equivalent surface. The first objective is to convert deviation from straightness stepwise into successive tilts of a mirror carriage, as it is moved along a straight line in increments just equal to the distance between locating pads. At each point, readings are taken from a rigidly mounted autocollimator. These readings are then converted back to a profile curve, following the simple steps outlined in Fig. 9-26. Note that such a test says nothing about the geometry between the contact points of the mirror carriage. This requires some other type of assurance or traverses with a carriage of shorter base length. It may seem odd to go through such a double conversion to angles and back when all that is wanted is to measure straightness. Nobody would do so if there were readily available a direct-reading alignment device of equivalent sensitivity.

If the mirror carriage base length is 10.3 in., 1 sec. of arc (1″) corresponds to a tilt of 50 µinches.

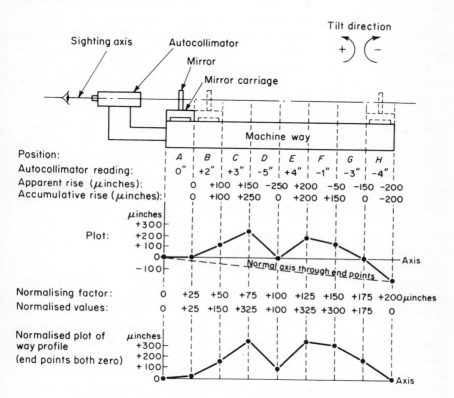

Fig. 9-26. Steps involved in converting machine way geometry into tilt of mirror carriage moved in steps equal to base length. Below it are successive steps of reconverting readings into way profile, in microinches deviation from a straight line arbitrarily established through the end points.

OPTICAL FLATS*

A previous section explained the phenomenon of interference and its application to metrology. The simplest method of application employs optical flats. It provides the most advantageous combination of precision and accuracy of any readily available measurement method. It has precision sufficient for the closest tolerances. Because it uses light waves for its standard, it has accuracy to match precision.

For practical application three things are needed in addition to the part to be measured. These are the optical flat, a monochromatic light source, and a suitable surface from which to work.

The wavelength of krypton 86 is the international standard for measurement of length. For practical use, however, certain factors must be considered. One of these is the definition of the fringe bands, i.e., how easily they are seen. Other considerations are cost and convenience. The light emitted by helium gas has proved most practical when all considerations are balanced. Its wavelength is 0.0000231 in. Several helium light sources are commercially available.

Optical flats are made in a range of sizes, shapes, and materials. Although they are available in sizes as large as 10-in. diam or more, most are from 1- to 3-inches. Materials range from inexpensive glass to very expensive sapphire. The majority are high-quality optical quartz. The measuring surface generally has one of three degrees of flatness. Working flats are 4 μin. (0.000004 in.). That is a unilateral tolerance, in that no point will deviate in height from any other point by more than that amount. *Master flats* are 2 μin. (0.000002 in.) and *reference flats* 1 μin. (0.000001 in.). Some manufacturers also furnish a commercial grade which is 8 μin. One or both surfaces may be finished for measurement. A finished surface is usually indicated by an arrow on the edge of the flat. The second finished surface adds very little additional cost. Generally, however, when one surface is worn out of tolerance, it is no longer clear. In order to use the other surface you must look through the worn surface; therefore expectancy of double life is unrealistic.

The flats are available with coated surfaces at extra charge. The coating is a thin film, usually titanium oxide, applied on the surface to reduce the light lost by reflection. The less light that is lost by unwanted reflection, the clearer are the fringe bands. The coating is so thin that it does not affect the position of the fringe bands, but a coated flat requires even greater care than an uncoated one. There are some relatively rare cases in which uncoated flats provide better contrast between fringe bands, such as carbon seals, whose reflectivity is very low.

*By Ted Busch, Vice President, Dundick Corporation.

The supporting surface on which optical flat measurements are made must provide a clean, rigid platform. If the measurements consist of the changes on one surface, little more is needed. If, however, the measurement involves comparison of two surfaces, the supporting surface becomes the factor limiting the precision of the measurements.

For the latter reason, optical flats are often used as support for the part. Steel flats, known as toolmaker's flats, are also available. These are simply steel optical flats to which parts and gage blocks may be wrung for measurement. Other precision-finished surfaces may also be used. The errors contributed by the supporting surface are of the independent type. They may combine with the measurement errors, thereby increasing the uncertainty of the overall system. Cleanliness is of tremendous importance in optical flat measurements. Even a stray particle of dust that might settle on the part before the flat is placed over it can completely destroy any chance for reliable measurement. It is advisable to have a non-shedding brush at hand to whisk off the parts at the last moment before placing the flat on them.

Temperature changes are more apparent when using optical flats than with most other kinds of measurement. Fortunately it usually involves relatively small parts that normalize quickly. Most optical flats have a lower coefficient of thermal conductivity than the metal parts with which they are used. They are heated rapidly by handling and, once heated or cooled, the flat requires a longer time to regain the ambient temperature.

When viewing, the more nearly perpendicular the line sight is to the surface, the more accurate the measurement will be. To achieve maximum clarity, the measurement surface should be as close to the light source as convenient. The reflex type of monochromatic light provides this automatically. In this type, a beam-splitter mirror is used to permit both the line of sight and the monochromatic illumination to be reasonably perpendicular to the measurement surface.

A gage block will begin to wring to an optical flat almost immediately unless one of three conditions prevent it. These are (1) insufficiently flat surface, (2) insufficiently fine surface finish, and (3) improperly cleaned surfaces.

There is difference of opinion about the degree of surface finish necessary. This results from the difficulty of measuring very fine surface finishes. Some say that a 4-μin. AA surface is required; other published figures are as low as 1.2 μin. As a basis for comparison, the best gage blocks have less than 1.0-μin. AA surface finish. A gage block, a part, or another flat should never be left wrung to an optical flat beyond the time required for measurement. If left overnight or longer, the flat might be broken in separating them. If they must be forced apart, use a wood block, never metal.

As soon as the part has begun to wring, fringe bands will appear. Continued wringing can cause the bands to run in any direction across the part.

Because of wear to the optical flat and danger of scratching, wringing should be as slight as possible to obtain the desired fringe pattern.

Actually, the fringe bands form in the air between the observer and the measurement surface. Therefore, to make fringe bands a practical measurement tool, a convention must be adopted, i.e., the parallel separation planes concept. While theoretically nonexistent, it is a great aid in actual measurement.

The convention consists of a set of imaginary planes all parallel to the working surface of the flat and one-half wavelength apart (Fig. 9-27). The intersections of these planes and the part are the dark fringe lines. The number of fringes thus represents separation between the surfaces in units of half-wavelengths. Because the two surfaces are so nearly parallel the cosine error is in billionths of an inch.

The air wedge configuration is easily demonstrated. After thorough cleaning, the part and the optical flat are wrung together until the fringe pattern crosses the part sidewise as shown in Fig. 9-28. The five dark bands or fringes show that there is an air wedge of five half-wavelengths height separating the flat from the part. At the moment, it is not known which way the wedge is facing. The open end is found by applying force to the ends. If there is no change, as in View B, the force is being exerted along the line of contact (wedge point). When the force causes the fringes to spread out, the open end of the wedge is being squeezed closed (View C). The situation, greatly exaggerated, is shown by comparing Figs. 9-27 and 9-29. Another method is to lower the line of sight. The bands then appear to move towards the open end of the air wedge.

The air wedge configuration would have applied equally well if the fringes were oriented lengthwise along the part (Fig. 9-30). After the contact has been found, the height can be determined by multiplying the number of fringes by one-half the wavelength of the light used. This will be 11.6 μin. (0.0000116 in.) for helium light. The general relationships are: *the fewer the bands, the narrower the angle; the more numerous the bands, the greater the angle.* More important is the understanding that *the number of bands is a measure of height difference, not of absolute height.*

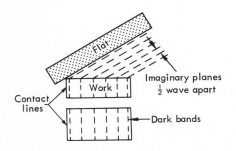

Fig. 9-27. The parallel separation planes concept envisions planes parallel to the working surface of the flat and one-half wave length apart. Dark fringes occur at their intersection with the part.

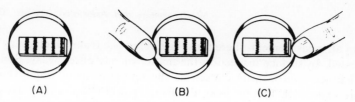

Fig. 9-28. The five fringes in (A) represent an air wedge with a height of five half-wave lengths. Pressure at the left in (B) does not change the pattern but pressure at the right in (C) does. The broadening of the fringes shows that the wedge is being closed. Thus the open portion of the wedge is at the right.

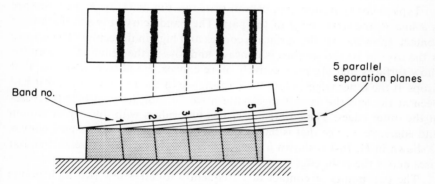

5 parallel separation planes

Band no.

Fig. 9-29. When the wedge is closed down tighter, the number of parallel separation planes, hence the number of fringe bands, decreases.

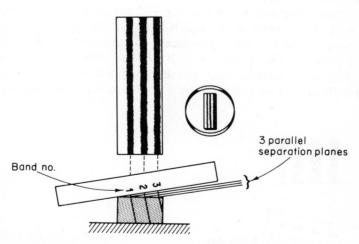

3 parallel separation planes

Band no.

Fig. 9-30. If the fringe bands had run lengthwise the contact still could be found by applied force.

As in all measurement, there must be a reference from which every length is expressed. In surface inspection the matter of reference is easy. Some part of the surface is arbitrarily chosen as the reference from which the other parts are expressed. In Fig. 9-30, the fringe pattern shows that the surface is flat, because the fringe bands are straight and uniformly spaced. A sharp drop-off would have shown as a change in the pattern. Thus, in Fig. 9-31, the closely spaced bands at the right show that the angle is larger along the right-hand edge of the test surface than along the other edge. The actual height change could be measured from this. Later examples will show that this is easier when the bands cross the area of height change.

Typical configurations are demonstrated in Fig. 9-32. In A the reference is a line *R*, the lower edge of the part. The bands curve toward the line of contact, showing that the surface is convex and high in the center. The reverse is the case in B; this surface is concave and low in the center. C, D, and E show surfaces that are progressively more convex. F indicates a surface that drops at the outer edges. Note the importance of the reference line; if it had been at the left, the same fringe pattern would indicate a surface that rises at the outer edges. The surface in G has two ridges with low center trough and edges. A surface that is flat at one end but becomes increasingly convex is shown in H. In I is shown a surface that is flat near the reference line but rises above the right edge.

The two points of contact in J frequently found, show two high points surrounded by lower areas. Note that in this case there is no air wedge. The points establish the reference. The fringe pattern is a true contour map of the surface.

Once surface configurations are recognized from fringe patterns, it is easy to measure the configurations. In A of Fig. 9-32 the surface is convex by one-third of a band. One-third of 11.6 equals 3.866 μin. or 3.9 μin. rounded off. The reverse is true in B, where the surface is concave or low in the center by the same amount. The surface in C is one-half wavelength high in the center; D is one wavelength high, and E is one and one-half wavelengths high. In millionths of an inch these are 5.8, 11.6, and 13.9 respectively. The

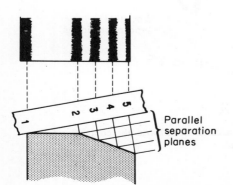

Parallel
separation
planes

Fig. 9-31. The sharp drop-off is clearly shown by the close bands on the right.

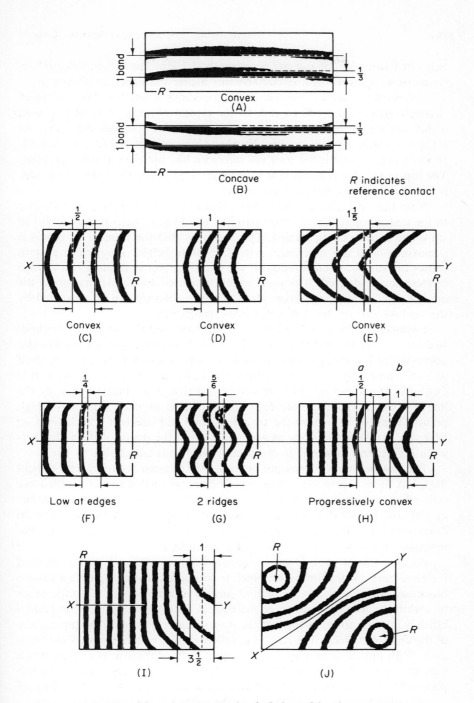

Fig. 9-32. Measurements are the deviation of bands compared to the distances between bands.

edges in F drop off one-quarter wavelength, 2.9 μin. The ridges in G are five-sixths of 11.6, or 9.7 μin. (0.0000097 in.) higher than the center trough.

Few surfaces are as uniform as in the above examples. Most of them change contour from end to end. In the typical example in H of Fig. 9-32 a flat surface becomes progressively more convex towards the right. At *a* the surface is 5.8 μin. convex. Further along at *b* it is 11.6 μin. convex. In I is a surface that is flat near the reference line but rises at the right edge. The top right edge is about one wavelength high while the lower right edge is about three and one-half wavelengths.

Note that in each case the fringe pattern could have been perpendicular to the ones chosen. These fringe patterns would have been just as useful to show the surface configuration. The reason is that the number of bands is a measure of height *difference*, not of absolute height. Any fringe pattern shows the surface conformation, if the contact point is known. If a change in elevation is desired, it is most easily measured by bands that cross the area in which the change takes place. Then the change can be measured by the amount that the band deviates from straightness.

Examples A through I of Fig. 9-32 demonstrated the air wedge method. In J the contact method is shown. This typical configuration has two contact points with a low trough between them. To measure with the contact method it is only necessary to remember that it is as far up hill to one point as it is down hill from another. The bottom of this trough is approximated by the line XY. Note that there are four convex bands on each side of the high points. That indicates that the trough is four and one-half wavelengths or 52.3 μin. (0.0000523 in.) low at a point. To find the depth of the valley between high points, add one to the number of bands and divide by two.

The parallelism of planes can be measured to great accuracy with optical flats, but there is a severe limitation. Fringes are visible to the unaided eye only when the separation distance is very short, seldom over ten fringe bands or 100 μin. (0.0001 in.). Because a standard set of gage blocks will make up dimensions to 0.0001-in. or 100 μin. increments, it is never necessary to have separations beyond the resolution of optical flats.

Assume that a gage block of questionable condition is to be checked for parallelism. If this unknown block is wrung to a flat along with a known block, we then know that the wrung surface of each is parallel to the other to within the limit of flatness of the optical flat. Assuming that the known block is in calibration, its top surface is very nearly parallel to the top surface of the unknown block. The lack of parallelism may be along two of the three axes. With optical flats, the rotation about both of these axes is determined simultaneously. Because the substitute reference plane is very near to the top plane of the unknown part, fringe patterns can be seen. The comparison of those on the known part to those on the unknown provides the measure of parallelism.

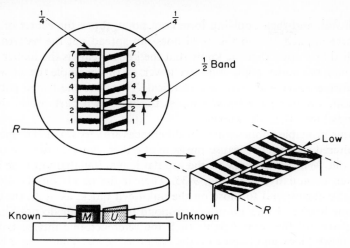

Fig. 9-33. In this example both surfaces have the same number of bands, but those on the unknown surface slant.

Figure 9-33 is an example. It reveals three facts. First, the unknown surface U is parallel longitudinally to the known surface M because it produces the same number of bands. Second, it is not parallel across the width because the bands on the unknown surface are at an angle to those on the known surface. Third, the amount that the unknown surface is out of parallel to the known surface is one-half band in one width. These differences may be measured in much the same way that the fringe patterns were read to evaluate flatness.

In this example an assumption was made that the unknown part had the same basic size as the known part. In most cases, there would be a small difference in height. The effect of this is shown in Fig. 9-34. Note the basic difference; the contacts are at different heights. After the known and the unknown parts have been wrung tightly to a flat and are positioned alongside each other, it is necessary to determine which one is the higher. This is done by placing the second optical flat over them, orienting the fringe pattern to

Fig. 9-34. Counting the bands on the unknown part provides the measurement of the height difference. x and y are points to apply force to find part.

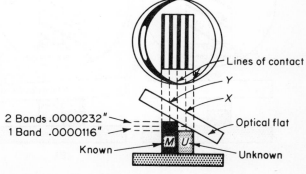

run lengthwise, and then applying force to a point above the center of each part. If force applied at x in Fig. 9-34 does not spread out the pattern, but force applied at y does, then we know that the known part is the higher. The reverse would, of course, apply if it were lower. In this example the air wedge triangles formed over each part are identical. Therefore the fringe patterns are identical. Counting the fringes across the unknown part shows that it is two bands lower than the known.

The same principle applies when the differences are very small. The method must be altered, however, because pressure at either x or y causes the bands to spread out. When this happens, the top flat is manipulated until the band patterns run diagonally, as in Fig. 9-35. Then if the bands on the known block exactly correspond to those on the unknown block, as at A, the parts are the same height. If they do not correspond in number or do not line up, the blocks are not the same height. In B the reference line intersects band 1 on the known block and band 2 on the unknown block. Therefore, 2 bands minus 1 band multiplied by 11.6 equals 11.6 μin. The unknown block is then 0.0000116 in. lower than the known block. The reference line could have been anywhere else along the fringe pattern. The difference would have been the same. In C the reference line intersects the first band on the known block and then crosses the unknown half between the second and third bands. The difference is $1\frac{1}{2}$ μin.

These same techniques and principles apply when the surfaces being compared are not nearly as flat as they have been in these examples, but it becomes vastly more complex. Only practice and patience will develop any degree of reliability. It is suggested that the beginner sketch the surface configuration of each block before making height comparisons. Reference to the sketches will often clarify confusing patterns formed by the two blocks together.

Fig. 9-35. When the differences are very small, diagonal patterns are used to measure height differences.

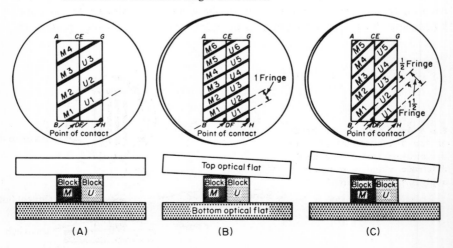

(A)   (B)   (C)

10

OTHER INSTRUMENTS FOR

COMPARATIVE MEASUREMENT

ULTRASONIC GAGING EQUIPMENT*

Ultrasonic gaging employs sound waves or mechanical vibrations whose frequency is above the audible range in the frequency spectrum. In testing and gaging, the sound is usually in the range from about 0.5 to 30.0 megacycles.

The sound is produced by a transducer which converts the electrical voltages generated in the instrument oscillator into mechanical vibrations or sound waves. The sound produced by the transducer is introduced into the part to be tested or gaged through a liquid couplant, and generally propagates in a fairly well-defined beam through the material. The propagation continues until some or all of the sound is reflected by a boundary.

*By John E. Bobbin, Sales Manager, Ultrasonic Testing Division, Branson Instruments, Inc.

The boundary may be a geometric boundary such as the far side of the part, a shoulder or a drilled hole, or it may be an internal discontinuity such as a crack or other flaw. Some sound is reflected from such minute boundaries as metallic grain interfaces. The amount of energy which is reflected at an interface is determined primarily by the area and the relative acoustic properties of the two materials making up the interface. Similar materials provide very little reflection, whereas interfaces of materials having different acoustic properties will provide maximum reflection.

Ultrasonic gaging is usually concerned with the time required for the sound to make a round trip through the part under test.

The basic relationship is: distance = velocity × time. Velocity in a material is a function of the properties of the material itself. Time for the round trip is measured by the ultrasonic test instrument, and the thickness or the distance the sound has traveled is determined from the other two factors.

The velocity V_L of the longitudinal sound waves (the ones most commonly used in testing and gaging applications) is expressed by the formula:

$$V_L = \sqrt{\frac{y}{\rho} \frac{(1 - \sigma)}{(1 + \sigma)(1 - 2\sigma)}}$$

where y = Young's modulus

ρ = density

σ = Poisson's ratio

The longitudinal velocity is generally assumed to be a constant for any given material. It may be slightly affected by heat treatment and other characteristics, but is independent of the test frequency. Table 10-1 lists the average sound wave velocities of a few of the more common materials.

TABLE 10-1. SOUND WAVE VELOCITIES IN COMMON MATERIALS

Material	Velocity	
Aluminum, titanium	6.3×10^5 cm/sec	248,000 in./sec
Brass	4.43×10^5 cm/sec	174,500 in./sec
Magnesium	5.79×10^5 cm/sec	228,000 in./sec
Steel (carbon)	5.85×10^5 cm/sec	230,000 in./sec
Stainless steel	5.66×10^5 cm/sec	223,000 in./sec

Instrumentation

Ultrasonic testing encompasses two basic methods or equipment types which are in common use. These are classified as *pulse-echo* and *resonance*. The propagation characteristics of the sound waves in each case are quite similar, although the electronic means of generating the acoustic signals, and the data readout vary considerably between the two classes of instruments.

Pulse-Echo.   The pulse-echo equipment operates much like its predecessor, Sonar, in utilizing a form of echo-ranging. A short pulse of sound is transmitted into the part, and echoes return from various boundaries. In thickness gaging, the instrument permits these echoes to be timed. Using either a known or assumed velocity, it is possible to determine the distance that the sound has traveled, and thus measure thickness. Several techniques have been employed with pulse-echo equipment to simplify gaging and to increase accuracy.

One of the earliest techniques utilizes a considerable number of multiple back reflections through the part to measure thickness. A simple proportion is established between the number of echoes and the thickness of a known specimen, and the number of multiple echoes and thickness of the unknown, both equalling some total distance. Figure 10-1 illustrates the CRT pattern and basic technique.

With this technique, an experienced operator can obtain accuracies in the order of one or two percent of nominal thickness. Greater accuracies

Fig. 10-1. Use of back reflections, or multiple echoes, to measure part thickness.

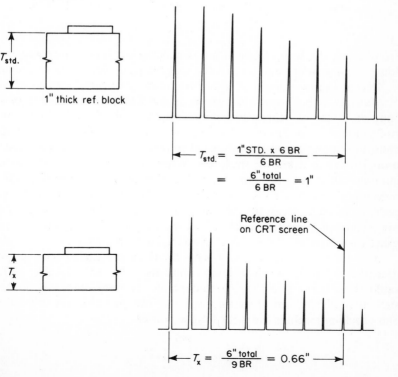

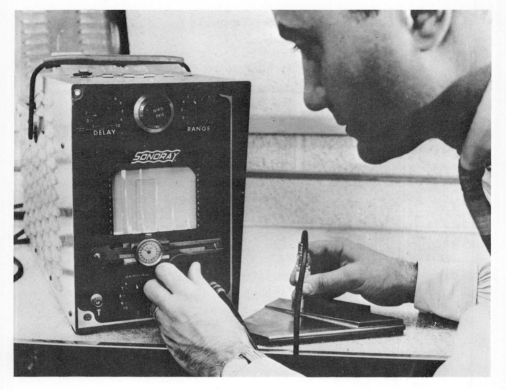

Fig. 10-2. Pulse-echo ultrasonic gage with modified dial caliper. (*Branson Instruments*, Inc.)

are obtained by using longer total distances, but this in turn requires the counting of greater numbers of back reflections, a rather tedious procedure.

Recent improvements in instrumentation, particularly with the advent of relatively linear horizontal sweeps on the CRT, permit the use of super-imposed scales or other calibrating devices. One of these, shown in Fig. 10-2, utilizes a modified dial caliper with index marks drawn on plastic indicators mounted on the caliper. The instrument sweep is adjusted to be proportional to a known thickness. When the transducer is placed on an unknown thickness, the movable index is made to coincide with the back reflection from that part. The thickness is read directly from the caliper scale, factored as necessary. Modifications of this technique, using expanded range settings or multiple back reflections, can produce very high accuracies, usually within a few thousandths of an inch in thicknesses up to six inches.

The use of pulse-echo instruments for thickness gaging has been widely accepted, inasmuch as these instruments also offer considerably more ver-satility than other types. They are adaptable for many other types of testing, such as the inspection of welds, inspecting raw materials for internal flaws, and checking machine parts for fatigue cracks.

Resonance Instruments.   The resonant type of ultrasonic equipment uses a frequency-modulated continuous-wave generator or oscillator to drive the ultrasonic transducer. A fundamental acoustic standing wave will be established in the specimen when the round-trip distance equals one wavelength. The basic relationships are:

$$T = \lambda/2$$

$$= \frac{V_L/2}{F}$$

$$= \frac{V_L/2}{F_0} \qquad \text{for fundamental}$$

$$= \frac{V_L/2}{F_N - F_{N-1}} \qquad \text{for harmonics}$$

Where $T =$ thickness

$V_L =$ longitudinal velocity

$F =$ frequency

$F_0 =$ fundamental frequency

$F_N =$ harmonic frequency

Harmonic resonances occur when twice the thickness of the part equals whole-number multiples of a wavelength. The difference between two adjacent harmonic frequencies equals the fundamental, which is used to determine thickness. The use of harmonics greatly extends the capabilities of the ultrasonic instrument by permitting a device having a relatively limited frequency range to be used to measure thicknesses over a much wider range.

The simplified operation of a resonance gage is shown in Fig. 10-3. The frequency of the oscillator circuit is changed by varying either the inductance or the capacitance, or both, in the circuit. The frequency-modulated oscillator drives the transducer at the oscillator frequency, which in turn intro-

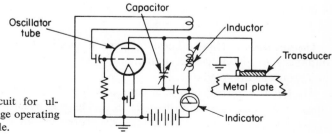

Fig.10 -3. Basic circuit for ultrasonic thickness gage operating on resonance principle.

duces the sound waves into the part. When acoustic standing waves are produced in the part, the frequency is detected and used. There are several basic readout systems to translate the frequency information into thickness.

The earliest practical resonance gage, called the Audigage, was a portable battery-operated unit in which an audible tone was produced in the operator's earphones when a resonance occurred. Frequency modulation was accomplished by means of a manual tuning dial calibrated in frequency. The operator was required to perform a simple calculation to determine the thickness. Quite a number of instruments of this type are still in use, providing accurate spot-check information of thickness of many diverse applications.

Another system uses a visual readout on a cathode ray tube. The sweep of the CRT is a frequency function, and the automatic frequency modulation is electronic. Resonance conditions appear as vertical pips on the screen of the instrument, and the frequency difference and thickness are determined directly by precalibrated scales which overlay the CRT. This type of instrument permits instantaneous and continuous readings as the transducer is moved over the part, or when the thickness varies rapidly. Expanded scale ranges increase the accuracy of the equipment. This type of instrument is used extensively in automatic installations, providing data for recording or initiating alarm and marking circuits.

Techniques

A number of specialized techniques have been developed to extend the usefulness of the ultrasonic equipment. These are primarily in the field of transducers and accessories.

Contact. The transducer contacts the part to be measured through a thin film of couplant. The couplant is used primarily to exclude air, but also acts as a lubricant. This technique was the earliest, and is still the most widely used.

Immersion. The transducer and the specimen are both immersed in a liquid bath. This usually requires extensive investment in equipment such as tanks, positioners, and other mechanical devices. Immersion testing permits fast scanning while maintaining uniform acoustic coupling. It has not been extensively used in gaging.

Liquid Delay Lines. These provide a modified immersion technique coupling the advantages of immersion without the need for tanks. Two configurations are available.

The *bubbler* consists of a semi-contained liquid column, with the specimen almost completely capping the open end. There is usually some slight flow of couplant, which can be minimized by proper design.

A *contained liquid column* is usually capped by a special rubber or plastic membrane. This technique still requires a slight liquid couplant film between the membrane and the specimen.

High Temperature Techniques.   Both the bubbler and the contained liquid column have been utilized for on-stream inspection. In this technique the liquid provides a thermal gradient to protect the transducer element. The contained column permits measurement at surface temperatures up to 700°F, and the bubbler up to 1300°F.

Solid Delay Lines.   These have been manufactured from special high-temperature-resistant rubber and plastic materials, as well as plastics having lower temperature characteristics. These provide more efficient transducer damping, thereby improving resolution.

Dual Transducers.   These utilize separate transmitting and receiving elements in a single housing, usually with a short built-in delay line. Dual transducers provide the maximum resolution for thin sections, down to less than 0.100 in. Dual transducers are feasible for thin measurements at low frequencies, since they eliminate the effect of extended transducer ringing. The dual transducers are used only for pulse-echo work, whereas the other types are equally applicable to resonance or pulse-echo.

Data Readout.   Most current thickness measurements utilize the basic cathode ray tube for the primary data readout. However, electronic monitors are available to convert the primary time or frequency information to a voltage. This voltage can be applied to a strip chart recorder or a digital voltmeter, or may be used to actuate tolerance indicators.

Accuracy and Dependability

The accuracy and reliability of the equipment depends on several factors. The thickness reading is related to velocity and frequency in resonance gaging, and to velocity and time in pulse-echo gaging.

Table 10-2 indicates the accuracy that can be expected under varying conditions of velocity and equipment setup.

TABLE 10-2.

Accuracy	Acoustic velocity	Equipment setup
2%–5%	Assume average velocity for material.	Precalibrated scales. Set up instrument "by the numbers."
$\frac{1}{2}$%–2%	Calibrate on part having similar metallurgy, heat treat, and geometry.	Precalibrated scales. Set up on part having similar geometry.
$\frac{1}{20}$%–$\frac{1}{2}$%	Calibrate on actual part in accessible area. Assure uniform metallurgy throughout.	Expanded range scales. Set up on actual part in accessible area. Maintain coupling uniformity.

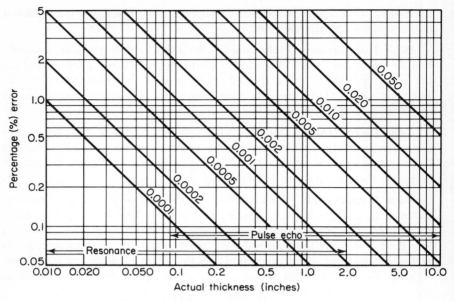

Fig. 10-4. Preferred thickness ranges for pulse-echo and resonance-type ultrasonic gages.

Under ideal conditions, with recording devices and uniform coupling between the transducer and the test specimen, accuracies as high as 0.02 percent of nominal thickness are obtainable if only thickness variations are desired.

System accuracies naturally vary considerably depending on individual parameters. Accuracy of the resonant systems is usually specified as a percentage of the nominal thickness being measured. Accuracy of the pulse-echo system is usually stated as a dimensional error covering some nominal thickness range. This is due to readout tolerances such as the width of the CRT trace or the line on the screen, or due to slight non-linearity in the system. Figure 10-4 shows the relationship between these differing terms, and also indicates the thickness ranges where each system is primarily used.

Applications

Ultrasonic gages, both pulse-echo and resonance, have been used on a tremendously wide variety of specific applications. In all cases, access to only one side of the specimen is required.

The following list is offered to indicate a small portion of the wide variety of possible materials and test situations. All are based on a thickness readout, although some might better be classified as flaw detection problems, rather than gaging.

Ultrasonic gaging offers a number of primary advantages: (1) it is nondestructive; (2) it is portable, goes to the job; (3) access to only one side is required; (4) its accuracy is usually $\frac{1}{10}$ of 1 percent to 1 percent of nominal thickness depending on technique and system.

These advantages enable it to be very broadly applied to such production tests as the following:

Tubing eccentricity and taper
Bored shaft eccentricity
Cable sheathing—lead and plastic
Pipe bends
Metal spinning
Compressed gas cylinders
Extrusions—following stretch forming
Aircraft propellers
Jet engine blades—hollow
Castings—core shifts
Rolled plate—following surface conditioning
Metal sheet—camber and crown
Sheet steel—sorting
Milled parts—in process
Chem milling and contouring
Cladding bond
Pipe braze quality
Plate glass
Ceramic radomes and nose cones
Plastic and fiber-reinforced plastics

NUCLEONICS THICKNESS AND DENSITY GAGES*

Nucleonics thickness and density gages measure many materials produced by America's basic industries. Their major use is for measuring either the thickness of sheet material or the density of fluids flowing through a pipe. Applications are found in the steel, rubber, paper, plastics, food, mining, chemical, petroleum, and cigarette industries.

Operating Principles

The operating principle of a nucleonics gage is simple. Penetrating radiation is obtained from a radioisotope source. This radiation is beamed

*By Henry R. Chope, Executive Vice-President, Industrial Nucleonics Corporation.

through the material under measurement. A radiation detector measures the amount of radiation that has passed through the material and yields a small current at its output. The detector current or signal thus provides a continuous, non-contacting measurement of the material's thickness or density.

As a beam of radiation passes through a material, its intensity is reduced according to an exponential law,

$$I = I_0 e^{-\mu \rho x} \qquad (10\text{-}1)$$

where I_0 and I are the intensity of the incident and the attenuated radiation, respectively. The term μ, called the mass absorption coefficient, is a function of the particular radiation selected. The greater the penetrating power of the radiation, the less the value of μ. It can be seen in Eq. (10-1) that the product of the material density ρ and the material thickness x appears as a power to the exponential base e. Thus, either ρ or x affects the signal I in an equal manner. The exponential equation shows that for materials of constant density ρ the gage measures thickness directly.

Figure 10-5 illustrates a thickness gage mounted on a sheet forming process, such as a rubber calender or a steel rolling mill. The source of penetrating radiation is mounted in the lower arm of a bracket below the sheet. The attenuated radiation is received by the detector mounted in the upper arm above the sheet. Small current signals obtained from the detector are amplified by the electronics which are shown here as mounted in the operator's station. In wide sheet applications, the source-detector unit often scans back and forth across the sheet so as to provide a reading on a recorder at

Fig. 10-5. AccuRay nucleonics gage measuring and controlling a sheet material. (*Industrial Nucleonics Corp.*)

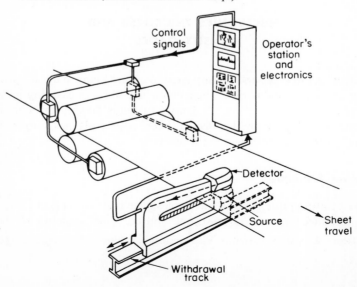

the operator's station. Large mechanical scanning mechanisms have been built to traverse sheets up to 500 in. wide. Control signals applied from the gage normally control the sheet forming process automatically. In Fig. 10-5, for example, the rolls would be adjusted so as to cause the sheet thickness to be maintained at some specified value.

If the sheet density is not constant, as in the case of many materials, such as sponge rubber, the nucleonics gage is calibrated to read the area density ρx in units of lbs/yd^2, or equivalent. The combination of source, detector, scanning mechanisms, and electronics shown in Fig. 10-6 provides a noncontacting and accurate measurement of moving sheet material thickness or area density.

High gaging accuracy must be maintained under all plant operating conditions and environments. A simple nucleonics gage cannot distinguish between the material being measured and build-up of foreign material in the gap between the source and the detector. Since these gages are often installed in severe operating environments, an automatic method must be provided to allow the gage to distinguish between the two kinds of materials, i.e., the measured material and foreign materials. To overcome the limitations of earlier gages employing either X-radiation or nucleonics radiation, an automatic recalibration or standardizing means was developed and is referred to as automatic withdrawal standardization (AWS).

With this standardizing system, the gage periodically withdraws from the measured sheet material and senses the environment in the measuring gap. While off the sheet, the gage senses any build-up of foreign material, such as dust, oil, or moisture. When the gage returns to its original on-sheet measuring position, it automatically takes these foreign materials into account through a computer scheme, to provide a highly accurate measurement of only the sheet material.

Equation (1) also explains the operation of a fluid density gage. Such a gage is shown in Fig. 10-6. In a density application, the dimension x is held fixed by the pipe or vessel containing the fluid. Since μ and x are constant for a given radiating source, the output signals from the detector and the gage depend only upon the density of the fluid or slurry being measured. Nucleonics density gages find wide use in the chemical, petroleum, and mining industries for applications such as blending, mixing, media separa-

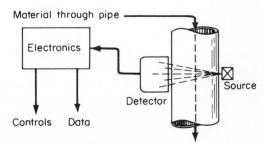

Fig. 10-6. Nucleonics gage measuring the density of a material within a pipe.

tion, and extraction. They have also been extensively employed to control the density and flow of raw materials in cigarette manufacturing and food processing.

The key component providing the high inherent accuracy in these gages is the self-powered radiating source. These sources emit radiation whose penetrating power depends upon the radioisotope selected. The radioisotope for a particular application is securely held in a multiply encapsulated source container within the gage. Actual sources have withstood total plant destruction due to industrial fires and explosions.

For measurement of thinner materials, a beta emitter, such as krypton 85 or strontium 90, is used. These emitters provide the radiation for measuring metallic films and strips ranging in thickness from $1\,\mu$ in. (1×10^{-6} in.) to about 30 mils (30×10^{-3} in.). Beta rays are high-speed electrons given off by the disintegrating nuclei of certain radioisotopes. The sources for gages measuring heavier and thicker materials may be of two kinds: (1) gamma emitters, or (2) beta-excited X-rays. Gamma radiation is a highly penetrating electromagnetic radiation arising from the nuclear decay of certain radioisotopes. Typical gamma emitters are cesium 137 and cobalt 60. Gamma rays can be used to penetrate and, hence, measure steel materials ranging in thickness from 10 mils to 2 in.

A unique source now finding increasing favor in both industrial thickness and density gages is the beta-excited X-radiation source. In this source, beta rays (or high-speed electrons) are caused to strike a suitable target similar to those used in electrical X-ray tubes. The target, when bombarded by the high-speed electrons, yields a penetrating X-ray due to the conversion of the beta-ray energy. By proper selection of exciting beta-ray energies and target material, X-ray sources of widely varying characteristics are obtained. Further, the shielding of the primary beta emitter is relatively simple when compared to shielding requirements for gamma emitters.

Applications

Quality control of manufactured products through the use of nucleonics gaging and control systems is a routine and widespread industrial practice. For example, more than 95 percent of the fabric calendered for all automobile tires manufactured in this country is automatically controlled by nucleonics gage-control systems. Eighty percent of the tin plate used in tin can manufacture is similarly controlled during its production.

In many applications, signals from the nucleonics gage cause the automatic control or adjustment of process machinery. Figure 10-5 illustrates a rolling or calendering process automatically controlled by signals from the nucleonics gage. On a tandem steel rolling mill, for example, the nucleonics gage automatically adjusts either the rolling pressure or else the tension applied to the rolled strip. The tiny signal from the gage thus commands the exertion of thousands of tons of force applied by the rolling mill. In the manufacture of paper products on a Fourdrinier machine, the final measurement of paper basis weight is fed back to contol automatically either the flow or the density of the raw stock onto the paper machine.

Many basic materials could not be controlled to the precision required for subsequent manufacturing operations by other than nucleonics gaging methods. For example, tin plating is now controlled to a fraction of a micro-inch by such methods. Cold-rolled steel is being rolled to 0.0065 in. with a tolerance of ±0.0002 in. Nucleonics gaging, when teamed up with electronic controllers and computers, now provides the manufacturing engineer with entirely new technologies for improving processes and materials. Future applications of these technologies can be as broad and dramatic as the imagination and vision of the engineers applying them.

Economic Impact

The basic manufacturing processes to which nucleonics gaging and control systems are applied usually have high annual dollar throughput of materials. For example, a tandem cold-rolling mill will process $30 million of raw materials per year. A high-speed, wide Fourdrinier paper machine may process from $3 to $9 million worth of product per year. Thus, any savings in raw materials or increased machine utilization will have a major impact on the costs and economics of the manufacturing operation.

Some typical annual savings in various industrial applications are as follows: steel rolling, $200,000 to $600,000; rubber calendering, $65,000 to $150,000; paper making, $65,000 to $200,000; laminated plastics, $140,-000; coated abrasives, $96,000. Dr. Willard Libby, former Atomic Energy Commissioner, estimates that nucleonics systems save the American economy $5 billion each year.

It is expected that further extensions of the nucleonics measurement and control techniques will provide still greater savings in terms of new and improved processes and materials.

Operator Safety

Although nucleonics gages use a penetrating source of radiation, each is designed so as to provide complete safety for operating personnel. The source material for each gage is processed so as to be chemically inert and insoluble in common solvents. The inert source material is then encapsulated in a source container which will withstand high temperatures and mechanical impact. The overall source-detector geometries are designed so as to minimize the external radiation field. Even operators in the immediate vicinity of the gage do not receive any appreciable radiation. There has never been a case of damage to property or personnel arising out of the use of these nucleonics systems in over 10,000 installations.

RADIOLOGICAL MEASURING DEVICES*

In industry, perhaps the most frequently employed nondestructive testing (NDT) probes are of the optical, electromagnetic, radiation, magnetic, and sonic types. The first three of these are different manifestations of the same phenomenon, electromagnetic energy. They are simply different in frequency or energy. The highest energy (shortest wavelength) of these in normal use is the gamma photon. However, industrial metrology is also accomplished with neutral particles such as neutrons, and charged particles, such as alpha (helium nuclei) and beta particles, all of which are available from radioactive isotope source units. Industrial radiological measuring devices are usually so named because they utilize these higher-energy electromagnetic photons or charged particles emanating from isotope source units. These sources

TABLE 10-3.　RADIOACTIVE ISOTOPE SOURCES

Radioactive source	Type of emission and energy (mev)	Half-life (yrs.)*
Cobalt 60	gamma 1.33 & 1.17	5.25
Cesium 137	gamma 0.66	33
Radium 226	gamma 0.188	1620
Promethium 147	beta　0.30	2.25
Strontium 90	beta　0.54	25
Krypton 85	beta　0.72	9.4
Americium 241	alpha　5.4	475
Polonium 210	alpha　5.3	0.3

*The half-life is expressed as the time required for emission to decay to one-half its original value. This characteristic is indicative of the high degree of stability of these radiation source materials.

are extremely stable, rugged, and simply designed. They are unaffected by changes in environmental temperature or pressure. A few examples of commercially available sources are listed in Table 10-3.

The "no-power" requirement and, consequently, the associated source power supply regulation problems are nonexistent. This stability of radioac-

*By Charles O. Badgett, Technical Program Manager, Industrial Nucleonics Corporation.

tive isotope sources, coupled with the fact that they do not require separate power source, makes them the choice for many industrial applications. Their high energy and portability characteristics have created a completely new industry, that of gamma radiological flaw inspection. Suitable equipment for this use is commercially available. Many types of castings to several inches in thickness are regularly examined with cobalt 60 for voids and internal cracks, using gamma radiography.

Cobalt 60 sources in use range from 0.1 to 25 curies per source with 75 percent of them having strengths ranging from 0.5 to 2.5 curies. Most of the cobalt 60 sources are cylindrical, with dimensions of $\frac{1}{8}$ in. by $\frac{1}{8}$ in. to $\frac{1}{8}$ in. by $\frac{1}{4}$ in. The high-strength sources have dimensions close to $\frac{1}{4}$ in. by $\frac{1}{4}$ in. and are affixed to a long cable which permits them to be removed from their shielding cart and inserted into the part to be radiographed.

Iridium 192 sources range from 3 to 50 curies per source with cylindrical dimensions close to $\frac{1}{4}$ in. by $\frac{1}{4}$ in. Cesium 137 sources are usually 0.5 to 5 curies per source with dimensions similar to those for cobalt 60.

More recently, neutron radiography and low-energy beta-excited (promethium 147) gamma radiation sources are being used in conventional X-ray application, but without the associated source power supplies. A major chemical company,[1]* using radioactive iridium 192 and also cobalt 60 in a new portable device, recently examined piping to detect signs of deterioration without shutting down the operation. Continuous inspection saves many dollars in "turnaround" maintenance. Rocket solid-propellant grain is also inspected by radiographic technology for imperfections.

The above applications are the more familiar. In the past few years, many newer uses have been made of isotopes.[2] Among these are: porosity determinations, concentricity measurements, lubrication and wear studies, surface-roughness measurements, particle-size distribution, timing, and weighing.

Other applications have already been described under "Nucleonic Thickness and Density Gages," and many more are in regular use in composition analysis.

Beta radiation from a strontium 90 source is being used to determine the hardness of sheet steel as it exits from the annealing furnace. This high-temperature, non-contacting method of measurement is accomplished to the same degree of accuracy obtained statically with the more conventional Rockwell hardness gage.[3] Measurement curves are shown in Fig. 10-7. This measurement is included in a control circuit arrangement permitting control loop closure for fully automatic control of the annealing line. They are similar to those systems previously shown in Fig. 10-5.

*Superior numbers indicate specific references listed at the end of this chapter.

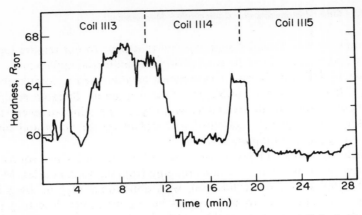

Fig. 10-7. Hardness charts of coils as inspected by a radiological instrument.

Concentricity is gaged in a manner similar to that for thickness measurements. Figure 10-8 illustrates two radiation paths through the article to be measured. These beams are compared on a differential basis to show concentricity.

A British firm offers a portable instrument utilizing beta radiation to measure coating thicknesses on materials. Its range, expressed in weight per unit area, is 0 to 4 oz. per square foot. In theory, the device can be used to measure the thickness of many different coatings and base material combinations but requires calibration for each of these various combinations.

Also available is an accurate pipe wall thickness gage (Fig. 10-9) for use in pipe inspection. This small, lightweight unit (less than 8 lb), is powered

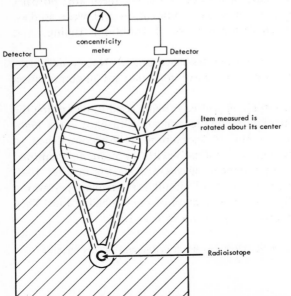

Fig. 10-8. Concentricity meter.

by flashlight battery. Pipes up to 8-in. diameter with $\frac{1}{4}$-in. walls can be measured for changes in wall thickness as small as 2 to 5 percent.

Neutrons generated from a plutonium-beryllium source are used to determine moisture content in foundry sand.[4] If the sand is too wet, scab and blow holes form, creating rework and scrap losses. This gage measures 3.4 percent moisture content to an accuracy of ±0.05 percent in a batch sand-feed system.

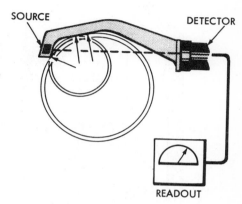

Fig. 10-9. Portable pipe wall thickness gage.

Wear and lubrication studies are carried out by irradiating the metallic component or adding tracers to the lubricants. For instance, much is learned concerning lubricating properties of oils by measuring the amount of radioactive material which has worn off the metal part and distributed itself into the lubricant. The usual laboratory-type counters and detectors are employed in these measurements. These techniques permit wear measurements in parts per million.

The level of molten brass and aluminum in continuous casting machines can be measured with radioisotopes, as shown in Fig. 10-10. The measurement is accurate to $\pm\frac{1}{16}$ in., which could not be made prior to radioactive isotope application. The same measurement is made to ±0.01 in. accuracy in molten glass furnace forehearths.

These applications demonstrate that radioisotopes are ideally suited to continuous, non-contacting, non-destructive measurement and testing. The examples described are not, in even the least sense, exhaustive.

A variety of source shields and handling devices are available from commercial suppliers. These may be permanent or portable types. To extend a source several feet or more into "hard-to-get-at" positions, remote control is available. Most shields are made of steel-cladded lead, but other alloys are used in many cases.

Devices for the manual transfer of source capsules are available in a variety of designs. In general, they all have the forms of long-armed forceps or fish poles with or without magnetic tips.

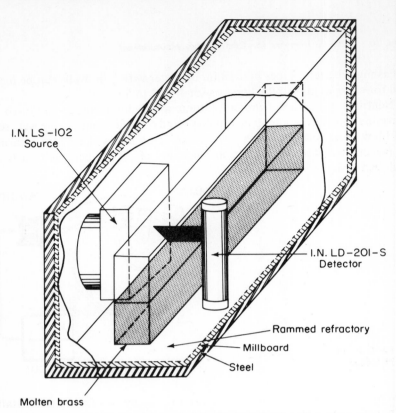

I.N. LS –102
Source

I.N. LD–201–S
Detector

Rammed refractory

Millboard

Steel

Molten brass

Fig. 10-10. Continuous casting level control of molten brass. (*Industrial Neucleonics Corp.*)

Before using radioactive isotopes, consult the manufacturer of the equipment to be used. He can guide the uninitiated in the use of his equipment without the user having full knowledge of its operation. A number of publications are available through the Office of Technical Services, Department of Commerce, Washington 25, D.C.

REFERENCES

1. "Radioisotopes Make Routine Inspection Possible on Valves and Piping," *Chemical Engineering*, October 29, 1962.

2. "From the Nuclear Field—Isotopes for Design Jobs," *Product Engineering*, November 13, 1961.

3. "Hardness Gaged 'On the Fly'," *The Iron Age*, September 19, 1963.

4. "Neutron-Moderation Gages Water in Foundry Sand," *Nucleonics*, August, 1961.

11

GEOMETRIC CONSIDERATIONS IN

LINEAR MEASUREMENTS*

Whereas other chapters have discussed in detail the "tools of measurement," this chapter is concerned with the choice and precautions that must be considered for the effective use of instrumentation to solve problems requiring the accurate assessment of geometric configurations.

The logical approach to this discussion will be to first recognize the basic geometric elements into which all product specifications can and must be resolved. After identifying the characteristics of these elements, the approaches to measurement will be discussed.

*By Stuart L. Nisbett, Assistant Professor, Process Engineering Department, General Motors Institute.

STRAIGHT LINEAR MEASUREMENT

Straight linear measurement is not only the most frequent type of measurement but also the simplest. Specifications for straight-line measurement can be reduced to the following geometrical conditions:

Conditions of Size or Magnitude (Fig. 11-1, A items)†

Straight linear measurements or those calculated from straight-line measurements comprise the great majority of dimensions. Examples of such

†Superior numbers indicate specific references listed at the end of this chapter.

Fig. 11-1. A part specification, showing examples of : (A) conditions of size; (B) nominal dimensions; (C) limiting dimensions; (D) conditions of form; (E) conditions of positional relationships.

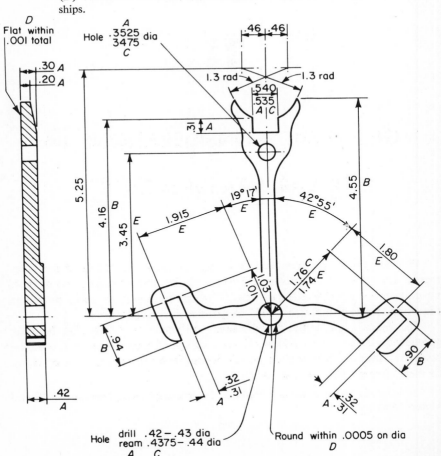

measurements include distances such as width, breadth, depth, length, radii, diameters, etc.

Although the measurement of straight linear size is relatively simple, the choice of instrumentation and precision of technique may well depend upon the character of the dimension.

A nominal dimension (Fig. 11-1, B items) may require only a casual assessment while basic and design dimensions demand the best accuracy attainable. Limiting dimensions (Fig. 11-1, C items) may be satisfied in one instance by determining whether the dimension is within or outside the specified tolerance limits or, in a statistical approach, will require an exact determination of magnitude. Interpretation of specifications for measurement also requires an understanding of the difference between a tolerance and an allowance, and a sensitivity as to the relative significance of each.

Need for such an appreciation is frequently observed in a situation that is so common that even responsible individuals often fail to notice it. This is the familiar case of machining shafts and holes to attain a desired fit. A specific example was observed (Fig. 11-2) in which the design engineer had specified a 0.7500-in. diameter hole with a 0.0002-in. plus tolerance. The allowance at maximum material condition was 0.0002-in. clearance to gain the desired quality of fit. This gave the shaft a diameter with a design size of 0.7498 in. and this carried a 0.0002-in. minus tolerance. The designer plainly indicated that the maximum material condition was the best condition for "perfect" assembly and function. This means that the 0.0002-in. clearance is very important and that the sizes of both hole and shaft should depart as little as possible from this condition. In other words, maintenance of the unilateral tolerance concept is paramount to correct assembly and function.

Fig. 11-2. Design specifications for a mating bearing and shaft.

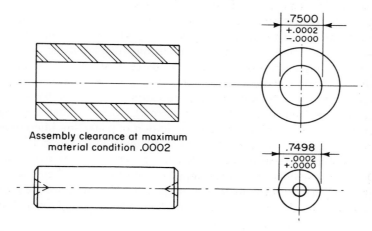

.7500
+.0002
−.0000

Assembly clearance at maximum
material condition .0002

.7498
−.0002
+.0000

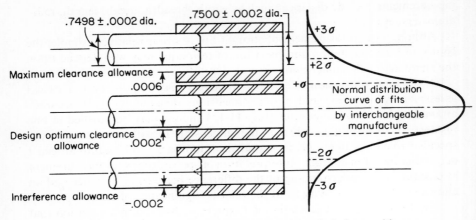

Fig. 11-3. Range and distribution of bearing-shaft fits resulting from modification of design specifications for easier processing.

To reduce the manufacturing cost by specifying a larger manufacturing tolerance, and to permit the use of statistical quality control techniques, the process engineer chose to disregard the definitions of *allowance* and *tolerance* (if he knew them) and combined the specified quantities. Then, by changing from the unilateral tolerance system to the bilateral, he had provided both the shaft and the bearing with twice the manufacturing tolerance provided in the original design. Also, at minimum material conditions the total size difference would not exceed 0.0006 in. in accordance with the original design. The in-process inspection gaging was designed to agree with the processing, which is logical and correct.

As logical as such processing appears on the surface, assembly of the parts on an interchangeable basis would, as shown in Fig. 11-3, produce problems. As long as bilateral tolerances of this magnitude are employed in the manufacturing of the mating components, either the maximum material condition or the minimum material condition will be outside of the specifications. In this case, although over 90 percent of the production on a normal distribution could be assembled with relatively close to 0.0002-in. clearance, actually only half of the production would assemble within the fit specification. The other half would assemble with less than the required clearance allowance, with an extreme condition of 0.0002-in. interference.

The only possible solution to such a dilemma is to resort to the slow process of part segregation into tolerance groups, and selective assembly to regain some semblance of the original intent of the design engineer. Even though there are excellent matching gages available, the selective assembly process always results in storing inevitable banks of odd size parts that seldom find a mating part of the right size.

Conditions of Form or Shape

Straight linear measurement may, to a limited extent, be applied to conditions of form or shape. The two applications in this category are measurement of straightness and planarity. . . . The assessment of the straightness of the axis of a hole, a shaft, or the edge at which two planes are joined, would satisfy the first condition as illustrated in Figs. 11-4 A and 11-1D. The deviation of a surface from the texture of a true plane, which would include out-of-flatness, waviness, and roughness would be included in this second condition as shown in Fig. 11-4 B.

Fig. 11-4. Linear measurements and conditions of form.

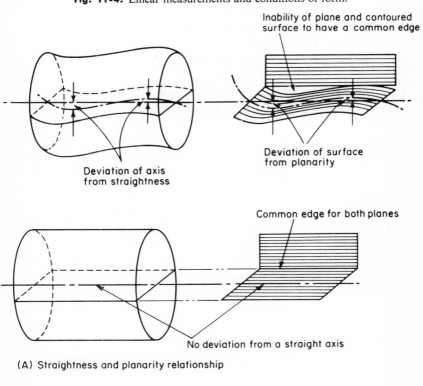

Inability of plane and contoured surface to have a common edge

Deviation of surface from planarity

Deviation of axis from straightness

Common edge for both planes

No deviation from a straight axis

(A) Straightness and planarity relationship

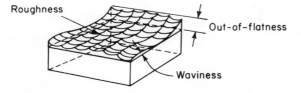

Roughness

Out-of-flatness

Waviness

(B) Surface texture characteristics versus planarity

Conditions of Positional Relationship

The third condition to which straight linear measurement applies is to the majority of positional relationships. As illustrated in Figs. 11-5 and 11-1 E, this condition includes the following familiar typical examples.

1. Alignment and coplanarity have common position characteristics. As shown in Fig. 11-5 A, alignment may involve two or more holes or shafts longitudinally displaced but having a common axis. An axis is nothing more than a line which may, in another geometrical setting, be a section of a plane. An infinite number of radially connected parallel lines laid side by side generate a plane. Thus when two or more comparable sections of two or more planes are in alignment, the planes of which they are a part are coplanar.

Fig. 11-5. Linear measurement and positional relationships.

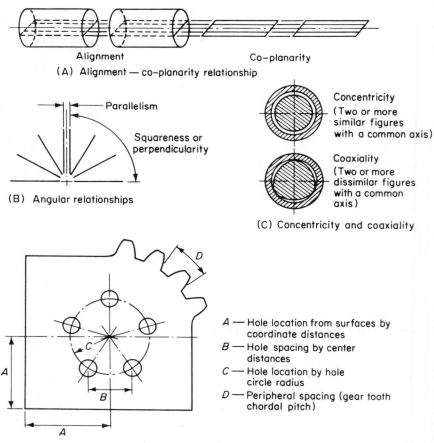

Alignment   Co-planarity

(A) Alignment — co-planarity relationship

Parallelism

Squareness or perpendicularity

(B) Angular relationships

Concentricity
(Two or more similar figures with a common axis)

Coaxiality
(Two or more dissimilar figures with a common axis)

(C) Concentricity and coaxiality

A — Hole location from surfaces by coordinate distances

B — Hole spacing by center distances

C — Hole location by hole circle radius

D — Peripheral spacing (gear tooth chordal pitch)

(D) Location and spacing relationships

2. Angular relationships are relative positions of surface features, of which parallelism and perpendicularity or squareness are merely special cases. This feature is illustrated in Fig. 11-5 B.

3. Concentricity and coaxiality are both conditions in which two or more geometrical figures have a common axis. Two figures of the same form and orientation having a common axis, such as cylinders, are concentric. However, it is difficult to visualize geometrical forms of varying shapes such as a cylinder and a lobed out-of-round as being concentric even though they have a common axis as shown in Fig. 11-5 C. Coaxiality, however, amply describes all such relationships, of which concentricity is a special condition.

4. Spacing relationships, of which there are three common types, are illustrated in Fig. 11-5D:

   (a) Hole relationships when specified either by coordinates or by chordal and radial positioning.
   (b) Hole-to-surface relationship by coordinates.
   (c) Surface-to-surface relationships such as hole spline or gear tooth spacing.

Perhaps the most important concept to be realized and understood is that specifications for conditions of size, form, and positional relationships must not only be separated analytically, but also must be measured independently of each other when form or position is more critical than size. This frequently requires the selection of totally different instrumentation to measure the different conditions. It also may require visualizing the influence one condition may have on the accuracy of measuring another condition. For example, if a measurement is to be made accurately to within 0.0001 in., the surface roughness must not exceed 6 μin. if the surface texture is not to defeat the intended accuracy of the measurement. Of course this is also assuming a negligible waviness feature.

How does out-of-round lobing affect the diameter of a cylinder? This can be a real source of frustration since the diameter may check within specifications and the part nevertheless cannot assemble with its mating hole or shaft (Fig. 11-6A).

Again, what influences do environmental conditions such as temperature have on size measurement? It all depends upon the conditions. If the part is made of the same material as the instruments and they are both at the same temperature, there is no adverse influence (Fig. 11-6 B). However, if the workpieces come out of a parts washer and are delivered to the inspector almost too hot to handle, as is frequently the case, there can be an appreciable error. Steel, for example, has a coefficient of thermal expansion of approximately six millionths of an inch per degree per inch. A steel part with a 4-in. dimension that is at 140°F, and being measured with an instrument at 75°F, would produce an error of 0.00156 in. from this source alone.

$$0.000006 \times (140 - 75) \times 4 = 0.00156 \text{ in. error}$$

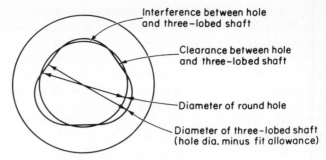

Out-of-round lobing versus cylindricity

(A)

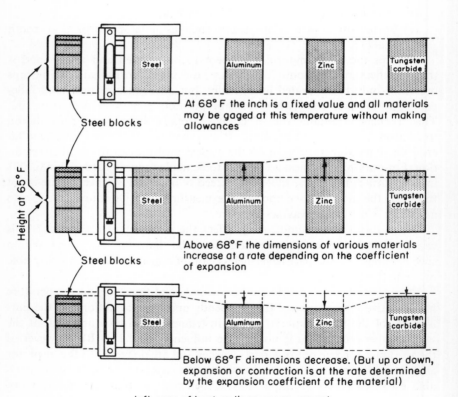

Influence of heat on linear measurement

(B)

Fig. 11-6. Influence of conditions of form and temperature on linear measurement. (*View B courtesy of Wilkie Brothers Foundation.*)[2]

The measurement of parts made of material other than that of which the instruments are made, at temperatures other than standard, will produce a similar error of appreciable magnitude. Take the example used above and substitute aluminum parts for steel. Aluminum alloys have a coefficient of thermal expansion of about 12 millionths of an inch per degree per inch (twice the value for steel). Since all materials are considered the same size at 68°F (20°C) standard temperature, the problem becomes slightly more complicated. Thus,

$$0.000012 \times (140 - 68) \times 4 - 0.000006 \times (75 - 68) \times 4 = 0.003288 \text{ in.}$$

error due to the combination of temperature and material coefficient of expansion difference. In many cases such errors would be greater than the total manufacturing tolerance.

GEOMETRY OF CONDITIONS OF FORM
OR SHAPE

It was previously indicated that straight linear measurement of form was basically limited to straightness and planarity. These are probably the best applications for direct linear measurement of the form concept. However, there are several other form conditions, other than straightness and planarity, in which linear measurement is an indirect means of assessment of this quality.

Roundness would seem to offer a simple linear measurement. By mathematical definition a circle must have a radius of constant length at all points, yet many able men have struggled to develop a practical engineering concept of this geometrical configuration. Not only is it necessary to understand the various types of out-of-roundness but also to realize that the measurement of the condition normally depends upon the nature of assembly and/or function intended for the surface and cannot be restricted to the mathematical definition alone. The discussion of this condition should also include cylindricity, conicity, and sphericity for, in some respects, they have common features as far as roundness is concerned.

It is first necessary to identify the various types of roundness. Basically, out-of-round surfaces are classed as surfaces having either an even or odd number of lobes that create the out-of-roundness as shown in Fig. 11-7. It is observed in the case of the even lobes that the variation in the diameter is proportional to the variation in the radius. Thus, the out-of-roundness can be determined by measuring the variation in diameter length, which is a linear measurement. Out-of-roundness due to an odd number of lobes is not so obvious as with the lobes of even number. In this case, there is present a constant-length diameter at all points but a varying-length radius. Thus,

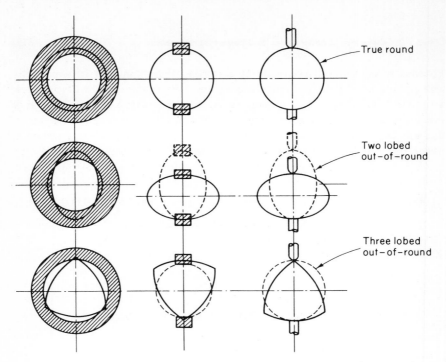

Fig. 11-7. Comparison of odd- and even-lobed out-of-roundness conditions with that of true roundness.[4]

any two-point diameter measurement indicates a round surface even when the lobes are so pronounced they can be readily detected with the eye. A different approach must be made to detect and measure this type of out-of-round condition and it will be discussed later in the chapter.

The lobing condition is usually thought of in terms of a few lobes, probably not over ten or twelve. There is another class of out-of-round condition that, for want of a better descriptive expression, might be called multiplicity lobing. This condition may have as many as thirty or forty lobes on a cylindrical surface and greatly affects the functional life of a bearing journal. The problems of detecting and measuring this type of out-of-round are quite different from the previous two groups discussed.

Tables 11-1[3] and 11-2[3] provide a quite complete analysis of the various types of out-of-roundness with some indication of their causes and measurement approach.

In addition to roundness, cylindricity involves the measurement of the straightness of the cylinder and the uniformity of the size of the cylinder throughout its length. The cone not only must be measured for straightness but also for the uniformity of the taper or change in size of cone throughout its length. The sphere, having no axial length, must be of uniform size as well as roundness at, theoretically, an infinite number of random cross sections.

314

TABLE 11-1. CHARACTERISTIC IRREGULARITIES OF BASICALLY ROUND FORMS

Cross-sectional diagram (exaggerated)	Designation and description	Potential origin and meaningful characteristics
	Oval with unequal axes approximately perpendicular to each other and of essentially symmetrical position.	Misalignment in the machine tool centers and/or the center holes in the part. Significant dimension is the difference between the major and the minor axes.
	Egg-shaped, essentially oval yet the major and minor axes are not symmetrically located.	Inaccurate centers and/or worn out center holes. The effect on the radial separation of envelope circles is usually indicative for the extent of functional consequences.
	Angularity characterized by odd number undulations, of essentially similar spacing. Typical numbers of undulations along the circumference are 3, 5, 7, and 9.	Centerless grinding, when not adequately controlled, tends to generate forms displaying characteristic departures from the ideal round. These irregularities have usually little effect on the consistency of the diameter, but can be detected in V-block with appropriate included angle. Radial separation of enveloping circles and number of undulations are functionally meaningful.
	Contour undulations (medium frequency lobing). Departures of the contour from the basic round are essentially consistent in spacing and amplitude.	Vibrations in the machine tool or the setup and/or insufficient rigidity of the workpiece. Measurable either by the amplitude of undulations ascertained as the separation of the envelope circles, or by vibration analyzing instruments. The frequency of the undulations can also be of functional significance.

TABLE 11-1.   **CHARACTERISTIC IRREGULARITIES OF BASICALLY ROUND FORMS (cont.)**

Cross-sectional diagram (exaggerated)	Designation and description	Potential origin and meaningful characteristics
	High frequency undulations (frequently associated with surface roughness). Very closely spaced, low amplitude undulations of the contour, detectable only with sensitive tracer instruments or by optical means.	Usually correlated with the characteristics of the manufacturing process, like grinding wheel grain size, feed rates, etc. Frequently intentionally disregarded or suppressed by electrical or mechanical filtering when preparing roundness tracings, because considered inconsequential in many applications.
	Roughness superimposed on angularity. The basically angular contour is not a smooth line, but displays closely spaced undulations (secondary form irregularities).	This combination of two different types of form irregularities originates from the simultaneous occurrence of conditions responsible for each of them separately. A rather frequent variety of roundness irregularities, whose precise analysis requires chart tracings made without the suppression of details.
	Random irregularities characterized by nonperiodic occurrence of significant departures from the basic round form.	Could originate from various conditions not properly controlled in the grinding process, frequently associated with inadequate stability in the work positioning and holding. Complete analysis is predicated on true roundness charts prepared by an instrument having sensitive response.

TABLE 11-1.   CHARACTERISTIC IRREGULARITIES OF BASICALLY ROUND FORMS (cont.)

Cross-sectional diagram (exaggerated)	Designation and description	Potential origin and meaningful characteristics
	Form irregularities of basically round surface sections whose designed cross-sectional contours are regular circular arcs.	Departures from the basic form can be the combined effect of roundness irregularities and displaced arc centers. This latter contributory factor with error-causing potential requires the roundness measurement to be made with the rigorous observance of the arc center and of the inspection plane locations.
	Roundness deficiencies superimposed on coaxiality errors with conjugate effect on the functional adequacy of the part.	Digressions from a common datum during the manufacturing process will cause errors of form which are superimposed on the form deficiencies of the individual surfaces. The adequacy of the part will be affected by the resultant irregularity. Measurements must be referenced from the functionally correct axis.

TABLE 11-2.   APPLICATION EXAMPLES OF ENGINEERING PARTS WITH FUNCTIONAL NEED FOR ROUNDNESS

Diagrammatic sketch	Application category and example of harmful form irregularities	Typical functional effect of deficient roundness
	Running fits with clearance locally bridged by isolated lobes.	Protuberances which extend beyond the predominant surface can interfere with the intended clearance of the fit, and by breaking up the hydrodynamic lubricant film, cause harmful metallic contacts.

TABLE 11-2   APPLICATION EXAMPLES OF ENGINEERING PARTS WITH FUNCTIONAL
NEED FOR ROUNDNESS (cont.)

Diagrammatic sketch	Application category and example of harmful form irregularities	Typical functional effect of deficient roundness
	Press fits with contact concentrated on the narrow crests of the mating surfaces.	The limited area crests can collapse under high specific loads caused by stress concentrations much in excess of the designed values. The loosening of the press fit will result.
	Sealing fits with depressions and crevices penetrating beneath the predominant contact surface.	Gaps in the contact area between mating surfaces (e.g. a plunger in a cylinder) due to interruptions in the continuous contour can cause leakage of fluids which ought to be restrained by tightly fitting members.
	Measurement over the diameter for mating and segregation when the measured part diameter differs from the minimum diameter of the hole capable to contain the part.	In current shop practices mostly, and in automatic gaging almost exclusively, the diameter of the basically round part is considered the representative dimension of its size. Differences between the measured diameter and the diameter of the hole into which the shaft will actually fit can be the cause of functional or assembly inadequacy.
	Axle supported in plain bearing when the journal of the axle has out-of-round form.	Out-of-roundness with widely spaced lobes, such as oval, egg-shaped, triangular, etc. is detrimental to the locational stability of the rotating shaft, although the wraparound design of the plain bearing tends to damp the harmful effect of roundness irregularities.

TABLE 11-2   APPLICATION EXAMPLES OF ENGINEERING PARTS WITH FUNCTIONAL
NEED FOR ROUNDNESS (cont.)

Diagrammatic sketch	Application category and example of harmful form irregularities	Typical functional effect of deficient roundness
	Antifriction bearing roller with non-uniform diameter (diametrical out-of-roundness).	An important function of the rolling elements in the antifriction bearing is to consistently maintain a uniform distance between the outer and inner ring of the bearing. Varying diameters of the individual rolling elements will interfere with this function.
	Ball bearing with surface defects affecting the ideal sphericity.	The ball bearing's smooth operation is contingent on the precise sphericity of each of its balls. Interruptions in the basic form, whether depressions or protuberances, will unfailingly reflect on the bearing performance and can cause audible noise.
	Antifriction bearing ring pathway with undulations of critical frequency and amplitude.	Undulations of the basically round surface have an amplitude measurable as radius variations, and a frequency associated with the number of lobes on the circumference. Vibrations in the operating bearing which are caused by these form irregularities become particularly detrimental when related to the natural frequency of the supporting members.

Planarity is the comparatively simple assessment of a surface for its flatness, waviness, microroughness, and irregular flaws.

MEASURING THE GEOMETRY OF FORM OR SHAPE*

The conditions of roundness, external and internal, demand the most attention of any form or shape measurement, since this type of geometry comprises the great majority of mechanical form conditions in manufacturing operations. Roundness measurement falls into two basic systems which depend upon the choice of the datum surface from which the measurement is taken.

The conventional method which uses points on the surface of the part for reference is called the "intrinsic datum" system and is illustrated in Fig. 11-8. The "extrinsic datum" system illustrated in Fig. 11-9 depends upon an external reference of known precision from which the measurements are taken.

*Credit for many of the ideas expressed at this point is given to Dr. Francis Farago. (See reference 3.)

Fig. 11-8. Systems of roundness measurement with intrinsic datum.[3]

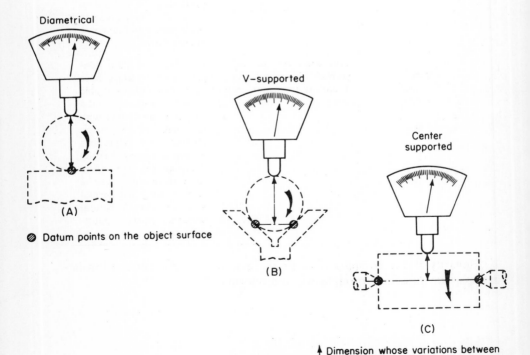

Diametrical

V-supported

Center
supported

(A)

⊘ Datum points on the object surface

(B)

(C)

↕ Dimension whose variations between
different rotational points of the
object are measured

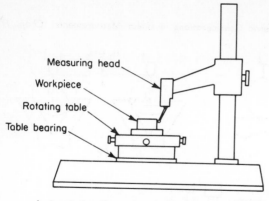

Instrument with rotating workpiece table:
sensing head stationary

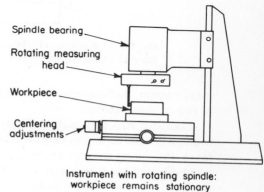

Instrument with rotating spindle:
workpiece remains stationary

Fig. 11-9. System of roundness measurement with extrinsic datum.[1]

Roundness Measurement With Intrinsic Datum

The necessary equipment for this measurement method is fairly inexpensive, is adequate for many applications, and is considered standard instrumentation in most manufacturing plants. It is rugged, simple to use, and provides relatively quick measurement. Measurement, however, is slow when compared to most size determinations. Much work needs to be done to develop instrumentation that can quickly and even automatically measure and classify parts for form quality comparable to size measurement capabilities.

Figure 11-10 is an amplified sketch of the three types of the intrinsic datum system introduced in Fig. 11-8. View A reveals the two-point or diameter measuring operation. Variations in the measurement may be the indication of an out-of-round condition due to an even number of lobes. However, there are two major possibilities for a false analysis: (1) the surface area may not conform to what is apparent from the specific measurement taken, and (2) there can be present out-of-roundness not revealed by a diameter

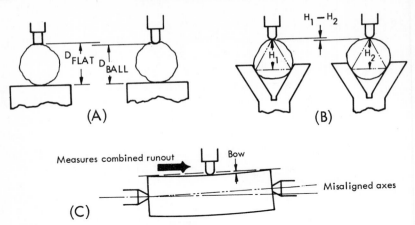

Fig. 11-10. Analysis of dimensions actually measured using intrinsic datum system.[3]

measurement. Surface areas are commonly judged by specific measurements in two or three selected spots.

Localized flats may make a highly cylindrical part appear greatly out-of-round when the condition may be in an area so small as to be of minor importance. Presenting the part to the gage must be done in a manner to produce a smooth reading. A rough or jerky technique may result in damage to either the instrument or the part, or the vibration set up by the dynamic action may reveal a false indication of the true geometry of the area.

A comparator with a large flat contact point would tend to bridge any such odd irregularities and give a truer reading. On the other hand, a part that has a multiplicity of undulations may need the pointed or convex contact to reveal the true geometry of the surface of rotation. The assessment of the conditions of form or shape connot be identified as one of the "instant" processes. The second observation is probably more dangerous than that just cited for it will not reveal equidiametral out-of-roundness.

View B, Fig. 11-10, shows the same setup as in View A except that the anvil of the comparator has been replaced by a V-block. Rotating the part in the V-block will reveal an out-of-round condition with an odd number of lobes. Measurement, however, is not that simple. Counting the number of times the comparator rises and falls while rotating the part in the V-block through 360° is the first step and can be accomplished with almost any convenient V-block so far as the included angle is concerned. The act of rotating the part can introduce inaccuracy, because the human touch frequently is not sensitive and smooth enough to reveal the exact condition. Also, perfect contact with the V-block is most difficult to maintain.

In order to *measure* the existing out-of-roundness, it is necessary to have the correct-angle V-block for the number of lobes present. Essentially, the altitude of an isosceles triangle is being measured and the maximum-minimum variation in altitude is needed to calculate the out-of-roundness. Thus, a three-lobed out-of-round condition requires a V-block with a 60° included angle; a five-lobed condition requires a 108° V-block, etc., as calculated by the formula shown in Fig. 11-11. Since the only standard V-block available is one with a 90° included angle, it is necessary to have blocks made up to these special angles ahead of time or be willing to wait for them to be made up when they are needed.

Figure 11-11 also describes the nature of the geometry of the three-lobed out-of-round condition as being typical of this kind of out-of-roundness.

Fig. 11-11. Geometry and V-block measurement of three-lobed out-of-round figure.[1]

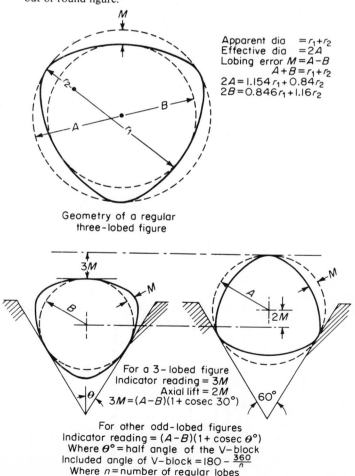

Apparent dia $= r_1 + r_2$
Effective dia $= 2A$
Lobing error $M = A - B$
$A + B = r_1 + r_2$
$2A = 1.154\, r_1 + 0.84\, r_2$
$2B = 0.846\, r_1 + 1.16\, r_2$

Geometry of a regular
three-lobed figure

For a 3-lobed figure
Indicator reading $= 3M$
Axial lift $= 2M$
$3M = (A-B)(1 + \operatorname{cosec} 30°)$

For other odd-lobed figures
Indicator reading $= (A-B)(1 + \operatorname{cosec} \theta°)$
Where $\theta° =$ half angle of the V-block
Included angle of V-block $= 180 - \dfrac{360}{n}$
Where $n =$ number of regular lobes

The relationship between the comparator variation (3M), axial displacement (2M) and a true inscribed or circumscribed circle (M) is shown. The deviation of the figure from an average circle would be $\frac{1}{2}$M.

In addition to the problems attending manipulation techniques, there are other sources of non-fiducial measurements. As indicated previously, the setup presupposes the equidistant displacement of the lobes that make up the figure being measured. A lack of symmetry in the geometry of the figure will adversely affect the accuracy of the measurement. If there is any variation in the size of the part, it may be misinterpreted as out-of-roundness if special precautions are not taken. It is well to have the part rotated against an end stop to prevent longitudinal shift during rotation.

A conical part becomes exceptionally difficult to handle in this setup, since the technique is based on the assumption that cylindrical surfaces are straight and parallel to the central axis.

View C of Fig. 11-10, showing the center-supported setup for out-of-roundness measurement, is very popular and is preferred by many technicians and engineers. It is generally more stable and will reveal all conditions of roundness variation. However, it too presents hazards to reliable measurement. Any misalignment of the centers holding the part will reveal itself as an error in cylindricity. The condition of the centers is vital to the accuracy of the measurement. Center points are frequently burred over at the point, providing an inaccurate location which is equivalent to a misalignment. A part that is bowed throughout its length will "whip" and indicate an out-of-roundness which may actually be only a lack of cylindricity. Where centers must be supplied to a part with a center hole, there is the quality of the arbor itself, plus the nature of the contact with the hole to constitute additional sources of error. If it is a tapered arbor, there is the severe contact with deflection on one end of the hole coupled with a very light or, maybe, no contact with the arbor at the other end of the hole. There is always the question as to how well this system picks up the true center axis of the part. Most expanding arbors are of good quality and offer a superior type of contact and location with the part.

The discussion so far on the intrinsic datum system has dealt exclusively with external cylinders and spheres. The problems of measuring internal roundness is equally important and somewhat more difficult. The same logic applies to the measurement of both internal and external surfaces; it is the instrumentation that must differ (Fig. 11-12). Two-point hole bore gages will

Fig. 11-12. Hole measurement using the intrinsic datum system.[5]

 Two point gage contact for measuring true round and even-lobed out-of-round holes

 Three point gage contact for measuring true round and odd-lobed out-of-round holes

reveal variations in diameter which may or may not reveal variations in radius. Three-point contact bore gages may be used to reveal the out-of-round holes with odd-numbered lobes. Since the three-point bore gages are generally supplied with the fixed contact points rather arbitrarily spaced, it is doubtful if the total indicator reading will be readily converted to a true measure of out-of-roundness. Furthermore, the exploring of a hole with most bore gages requires superior ability in manipulation and false readings are very easily obtained.

Roundness Measurement With Extrinsic Datum

The other system for measuring the roundness of surfaces of rotation obviates using any part of the workpiece as a datum and, therefore, it is called the extrinsic system. The referencing is accomplished from some external qualified member such as an ultra-precise spindle with almost perfect roundness of rotation. Several instruments of this type are available (Fig. 11-9). Some support the part on a stationary fixture and rotate the spindle an exploring point around the part. Other instruments support the part on a rotating spindle and explore the surface with a stationary electronic height gage contact point. Some instruments have ultra-precise mechanical bearings for the spindles, while the newer instruments are using the hydrostatic or air bearings. All of the instruments include a polar chart recorder and some provide an additional strip chart.

These instruments provide a choice of amplifications of the surface geometry. As a result, the microwaviness and roughness may be suppressed to permit revealing the more meaningful aspects of the roundness at the selected radius. On the other hand, the complete surface texture may be traced to the finest detail. Although a true image of the roundness of the part at the point selected can be obtained for evaluation by a variety of methods, it is also true that over-amplification of the out-of-roundness, and workpiece location errors, can produce an exaggerated image so distorted that a false analysis may easily be made (Fig. 11-13).

Continuous tracing around the entire surface in the selected plane obviates the possibility of disregarding errors which can easily be missed by point-to-point or by less precise methods of measurement.

Extrinsic measurement is relatively very slow and is typically confined to the standard-temperature metrology laboratory. The perfection with which the spindle or table traverses a circle is the key to the value of the instruments. All of the available instruments are of good quality but some are better than others. The advent of the air bearing is being watched with a great deal of interest for signs of superior performance. Staging the part is critical and requires extra technical skill and ability. The quality of the graph obtained

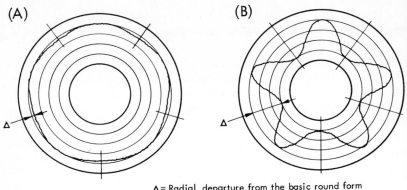

(A)

(B)

Δ = Radial departure from the basic round form

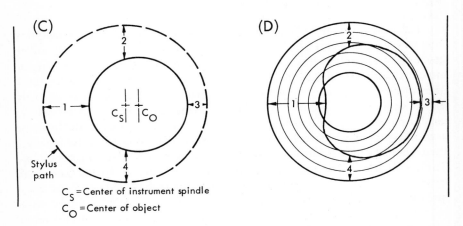

(C)

Stylus path

C_S = Center of instrument spindle
C_O = Center of object

(D)

Fig. 11-13. Four common causes of distorted polar graphs from extrinsic cylindrical measurement.[3]

depends considerably upon the human factors in the setup and measurement process.

The extrinsic system of measuring roundness is definitely superior to the intrinsic methods for obtaining a quality analysis. Unfortunately, the instrumentation is extremely expensive and distribution of the units is rather sparse. The most complete analysis can be obtained from an instrument that produces both a polar and a strip chart of the surface.

A second procedure for extrinsic determination of the truth of a cylindrical, conical, spherical, or plane surface employs the age-old bluing process. At best, this process is an estimation and not a measurement. A highly skilled technician can produce a pattern approximating the contact of the master but not exact, because movement of the surfaces in contact is required to produce the pattern. The pattern reveals approximate areas that do and do not conform to the area contour of the master, but it does not measure the depth of the areas of nonconformity. The method has useful applications, but the true nature of its limitations cannot be disregarded.

In addition to the bluing process, which serves as only a visual examination, measurement of out-of-planarity is best treated from the intrinsic and extrinsic points of view. Surface microroughness is popularly measured by the intrinsic system. However, microroughness together with waviness and flatness are readily measured by the extrinsic system.

Tracer heads for microroughness analysis of surfaces by the intrinsic system are normally constructed in such a manner that a stylus moves with reference to one or two skids that glide over the surface high points (Fig. 11-14). Thus, the contoured surface located by the peaks of the surface roughness essentially becomes the datum from which the microroughness is measured. The word "essentially" is advisedly used because the radii of the skids will provide a slight deviation from the surface described. As a result, the datum is not an established surface, but only a point or short line that constantly changes as the tracer head moves over the surface. In this way all characteristics of out-of-flatness and all but the shorter waves are excluded from the analysis. The extent to which the shorter waves are included in the assessment depends upon the roughness-width-cutoff at which the measurement is taken. When using an instrument which has a selection of roughness-width-cutoff values, a more complete analysis of the microroughness can be made by comparing the difference in the cutoff values with the change in microroughness readings. Thus, if a shift in the cutoff value is made from 0.030 in. to 0.100 in., and there is very little increase in the microroughness reading, it can be reasonably well assumed that the 0.030-in. setting included all or most of the waviness within that wave frequency setting. For machined surfaces this normally includes the lay waviness. The observer must be certain the microroughness is taken at the roughness-width-cutoff value specified. Further, the micro-

Fig. 11-14. Skid-stylus relationship of surface roughness analyzer on surfaces of varying degrees of roughness. (*Courtesy of Product Engineering.*)

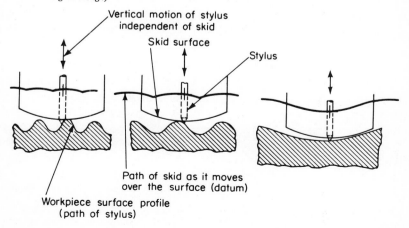

Vertical motion of stylus
independent of skid

Skid surface

Stylus

Path of skid as it moves
over the surface (datum)

Workpiece surface profile
(path of stylus)

roughness value is not a full analysis of the surface texture but only of the microroughness. Out-of-flatness and/or waviness may, in many cases, be the cause of many more functional problems than those which the microroughness presents.

Probably the greatest source of error with this type of instrument is the damage the diamond stylus does to the surface being investigated. The sharp diamond point will make some mark on any material because it is harder than any of them. The damage increases with decrease in work material hardness, until it is practically useless on pressed carbon seals, zinc and aluminum die castings, soft brass, etc. The mark or scratch made may either destroy the functional service of the surface or provide questionable information. How closely does the roughness at the bottom of a scratch represent the surface condition?

Assessment of the flatness and waviness of a surface texture can be accomplished in a variety of ways with comparable degrees of fidelity. One of the oldest ways of testing a surface for flatness is to sweep it in several places with a knife edge and observe where and how much light leaks through between the part surface and the reference knife edge (Fig. 11-15). Many surfaces may be adequately checked in this fashion, but there are sources of possible error to be considered. First, since a beam of light shining through a slit has the quality of spreading, it thus appears much larger than it actually is. Observing an appreciable ray of light under the knife edge should be followed by some means of positive measurement to determine the extent of out-of-flatness. A second source of error can result if the knife edge is not rotated on the surface. Sweeping the surface in one direction could indicate a plane, while sweeping it at right angles could reveal significant departure from planarity.

Intrinsic measurement of flatness and long waviness may be accomplished by the familiar parallel bridge. Although the contour of the surface is compared to the undersurface of a parallel, the parallel itself is located from the surface being assessed (Fig. 11-16 A). It is not difficult to determine the surface variations between two points; however, it takes some careful planning

Fig. 11-15. Importance of correctly orienting knife edge to workpiece surface for revealing out-of-flat surface condition.

Curved surface of workpiece

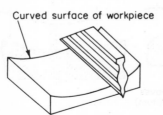

Knife edge

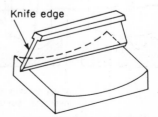

Relative position of curved surface to knife edge reveals apparent plane as no light passes under knife edge

Relative position of curved surface to knife edge reveals surface contour as maximum light passes between knife edge and workpiece surface

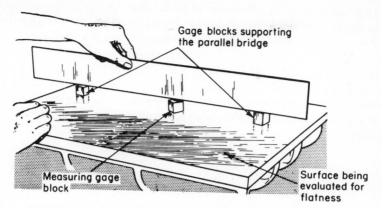

(A) Parallel bridge setup for measuring surface flatness

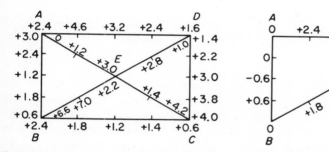

Typical observed readings from a bridge for a selected area

Points *A*, *B* and *D* adjusted to zero to establish a datum plane

(Measurement unit = 0.0001 inch)

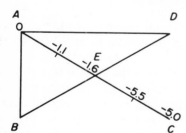

Diagonal *AC* adjusted to points *A* and *E*

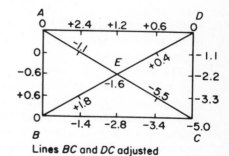

Lines *BC* and *DC* adjusted

(B) Method of adjusting readings to a selected datum

Fig. 11-16. Measuring flatness by use of a parallel bridge. (View *A*)[6]; (View *B*)[4]

to relate the various datum points to each other, and to apply accurately the necessary corrections to the observed values (Fig. 11-16B). The adjusted data as shown in the lower right-hand diagram of View B is not meaningful, in that it produces a clear mental image, until it is resolved into an isometric surface contour such as that shown in Fig. 11-17. The errors of the surface are sufficiently amplified to scale to make a visual appraisal of the surface contour possible. These steps in data development are necessary to the complete analysis, no matter which bridge technique is used for taking the measurement.

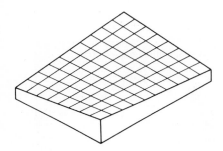

Fig. 11-17. Typical resolution of adjusted data to a true view of the surface planarity.

A second source of inaccurate measurement is the natural sag of the parallel between the supporting blocks (Fig. 11-16A). The extent of sag depends upon the design of the parallel and the position of the supporting blocks. The sag should first be checked against a qualified reference plane to determine the extent and nature of this characteristic. This error can be rendered negligible by bringing the support blocks toward the center, usually about one-fifth the length of the parallel. The weight of the overhanging ends will provide a leverage that will prevent the center from sagging appreciably. Many parallels designed for this specific function are marked at the Airy points at which they should be supported for minimum sag deflection.* Some of the cast-iron parallels have special support bosses prepared for locating the support blocks.

The device for measuring the relationship of the surface to the parallel may take a variety of forms. Stacks of gage blocks are frequently used, although this usually entails rough abrasive treatment for quality gage blocks. Also, the gage blocks cover an area of the surface locating from the high points. Any waviness within the area covered would be excluded from the measurement. For this reason, the rectangular block would provide a more accurate reading than the square block. Another fixed gage device is a tapered

*The Airy formula states that, for a simple beam of uniform cross section to be supported for minimum sag deflection, the supports should be spaced equidistant from the beam ends and 0.577 of the beam length apart.—*Ed.*

plug gage on which annular rings have been inscribed at specified increases in diameter. Slipping the gage between the unknown surface and the parallel until it contacts both surfaces, and reading the ring that is nearest to the contact point, is a quick method. By making plugs with small taper angles, rings in steps of 0.0001 in. can be made. However, it is usually necessary to have several progressive plugs for such fine readings because, although there is only a line contact, the length of the line must be kept as short as possible to exclude unnecessary errors. Various types of dial indicators and micrometers can also be adapted to the task. A two-point dial bore gage is applicable to this type of measurement.

Fig. 11-18. Fluid level gage for measuring surface flatness.

An interesting variation of the bridge is the fluid level gage as shown in Fig. 11-18. This inexpensive fluid holder can be welded up in varying lengths to suit the sizes of the surfaces being inspected. The end supports should provide three-point location, i.e., two points at one and one point at the other to provide the necessary stability. Once the fluid has come to rest (15 to 30 minutes), it forms a horizontal reference surface quite independent of the general level of the surface being measured, and it has no sag. The measuring device is a pointed screw-thread measuring micrometer spindle mounted in a C-shaped frame that extends around the trough to a three-point location on the surface being measured. The point of the micrometer spindle should be above the median of the triangle formed by the three locating points. As the micrometer is screwed down towards the oil level, a mirror reflection of the approaching conical point can be seen in the oil.

There is at least one instrument available that can make an extrinsic assessment of a flat surface (Fig. 11-19). Like the microroughness analyzer

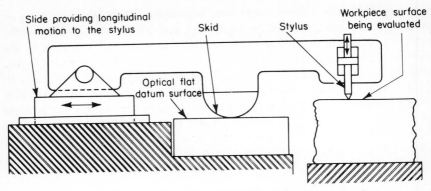

Fig. 11-19. Schematic component diagram of instrumentation for extrinsic evaluation of surface texture.

described previously, this instrument explores the surface with a diamond stylus. However, instead of the vibrations of the stylus being referenced to a skid, it is guided from an optical flat that acts as an external datum. This instrument reveals the total texture profile of the surface traversed by the stylus in relation to the optical flat. The findings are recorded on a strip chart and, by applying electronic filters, it is possible to record either the total profile, the microroughness only, the waviness or the flatness separately. (For more details, see Chapter 13.)

Optical tooling for measuring surface contours, alignments, etc., may be either intrinsic or extrinsic, depending upon how they are mounted. When an autocollimator or alignment level is mounted on the surface being checked, it would be intrinsic because it would be using that portion of the part surface as the datum from which the rest of the surface is to be compared. When the instrument is located on a tripod, stand, or some support outside the surface being analyzed, then it is an application of the extrinsic system. In this particular application there is no great advantage to either system, except that when the instrument is mounted on the surface, there is a large area that is excluded from critical examination, i.e., the area occupied by the instrument.

The optical instruments have the advantage of establishing an optical horizontal reference plane from a single point, and all points within sight can be measured to it. Most of the instruments available are reliable. However, stability and rigidity are required, since the slightest deflections can produce gross errors at the far end of an optical beam. The second point of consideration is the ease and handiness with which the instruments can be set up and used. Some optical equipment, although exceedingly accurate, seems to be awkward to use. Other equipment of comparable quality seems to be designed and made for efficient usage. (See Chapter 12.)

INSTRUMENTATION FOR POSITIONAL RELATIONSHIPS

Many of the instruments used for measuring conditions of size and form may also be applied to measuring conditions of positional relationships. For example, the optical contour comparator can measure angles and surface spacings, etc., as readily as it measures size. The optical theodolite and alignment scopes can measure surface relations with high accuracy. The area to be considered under this heading will be the measurement operations generally described as "surface plate setups," "surface plate inspection," "toolroom inspection," and the like.

Measurement from a reference plane is probably the nearest the metrologist can get in duplicating pure mathematical geometry in physical materials. He applies the basic theorems he learned in high school geometry, measuring the physical dimensions and calculating those that must be determined indirectly. Measurement by this means can be either remarkably precise or very crude, depending upon the analytical ability of the inspector, his skill as a measurement technician, and the instrumentation available to him.

ENVIRONMENTAL CAUSES OF INACCURACY

There is almost always a best way of making any measurement. More often than not, when the technician must start improvising for lack of the proper instrumentation, in spite of superior ingenuity, the fidelity of the end result will suffer. Next to not having an adequate variety of instrumentation is the absence of an effective instrument maintenance system. Measuring instruments are special types of machine tools and suffer from wear, dirt, deflection, and mutilation the same as other tools. Measurements taken by instruments that are worn beyond reasonable limits (one tenth the value of their least count) present a greater hazard then does the lack of an instrument. An instruments that provides false data as though it were truthful can only lead to expensive trouble. Dial indicators seem to suffer most from this neglect; gage blocks run a close second. It is hard to find a better measuring instrument for the money invested than a dial indicator, yet experienced toolmakers and inspectors will use them year in and year out without ever considering a need for checking them for accuracy as long as the hand will move without sticking. For this reason, it is highly recommended that each inspection job be repeated with as nearly as possible a different set of instruments and altered procedure. This will aid in revealing both instrumentation error as well as human error in reading and calculating.

Surface plate work is subject to many errors that are not readily apparent. A particle of dust, a speck of grit or burr far smaller than the human eye can see and frequently finer than can be felt, may well be the tolerance difference in the measurement between a good and a rejected dimension. Surface plates, parallels, angle irons, gage blocks, etc., must be continuously inspected and serviced to keep them in condition. All instruments need at least an annual inspection and most of them much oftener.

The influence of temperature on measurement has been previously discussed. The factors affecting measurement fidelity due to a lack of temperature control are just as important with surface plate work as they are for any other measurement method. There are so many sources of errors that not one can be ignored, because they can easily combine to make a measurement error equal to or greater than the dimension tolerance, when as a matter of fact they should never combine to exceed one tenth the tolerance.

LEVELS OF ACCURACY

In the pattern of the calibration structure from the national standard for length to the part tolerance in the shop, five basic levels or echelons of accuracy in precision measurement can be identified, as indicated in Table 11-3.

TABLE 11-3.   THE FIVE ECHELONS OF ACCURACY FOR DIMENSIONAL CONTROL*

Level of Measurement	Measurement means	Required accuracy, in.
Production	If the PRODUCTION PART to be inspected has a tolerance of only one thousandth of an inch,	0.001
Inspection	the GAGE that inspects the part may vary in size only plus or minus one-half of one ten-thousandth of an inch,	0.0001
Gage laboratory	the PRECISION INSTRUMENT that checks the gage must be accurate to one hundred-thousandth of an inch,	0.00001
Gage laboratory standards	the WORKING GAGE BLOCKS that are used to set the instrument must be accurate to four millionths of an inch,	0.000004
Metrology laboratory	the MASTER BLOCKS that measure the working blocks must be calibrated to light wave accuracy—to the millionth part of an inch.	0.000001

*Data adapted from Sheffield Gage Laboratory data.

REFERENCES

1. Wilbraham, F. R., "The Accuracy of Industrial Measurement of Length and Diameter," Proceedings of Conference at National Physical Laboratory, Teddington, England, April 1962, Her Majesty's Stationery Office, London, 1963. Crown copyright reserved.

2. Busch, Ted, *Fundamentals of Dimensional Metrology*, Wilkie Brothers Foundation, Delmar Publishers, Inc., Albany, N.Y., 1964.

3. Farago, F., "Roundness Deficiencies—Their Functional Effect and Methods of Measurement," Tech. Paper SP 64–31, American Society of Tool and Manufacturing Engineers.

4. Berndt, G., "Engineering Dimensional Metrology," Proceedings of Conference at National Physical Laboratory, Teddington, England, October 1953, Her Majesty's Stationery Office, London, 1955. Crown copyright reserved.

5. Kennedy, C. W., *Inspection and Gaging*, The Industrial Press, New York, 1951.

6. *Precision Measurement in the Metal Working Industry*, Dept. of Education of IBM Corp., Syracuse University Press, Syracuse, N.Y.

12

OPTICAL ALIGNMENT EQUIPMENT

AND METHODS*

Optical alignment, more often called optical tooling or optical metrology, is a recently developed system for alignment and measurement. It is based on surveying principles, but utilizes far more accurate methods and instrumentation. With it, alignment control can be established by a single measurement to within plus or minus one second of arc, which corresponds to plus or minus one part in 200,000. Linear measurements can be determined with slightly greater accuracy.

The system is used chiefly for controlling the size, shape, and position of large jigs, products, or assemblies when high accuracies are required, but it is often used for smaller odjects like gear teeth or surface plates, and larger objects like rocket tracks as long as a mile and a half. It is used in manufacture, installation, adjustment, checking, and maintenance.

*By Philip Kissam, C. E., Professor of Civil Engineering, Princeton University.

Optical tooling is too broad a subject to be covered completely in a limited space. The material presented is designed to provide a clear understanding of what optical tooling is and does and what can be expected of it so that the possibilities inherent in the system can be visualized and a decision reached whether or not optical tooling should be applied in a given situation.

REQUIREMENTS FOR OPERATION

In operation, the system is rapid, simple, and easily understood. In addition, it requires less skill and experience to attain high accuracies than other methods of measurement. However, in order to plan the most efficient procedure, the engineer must have a considerable knowledge of the principles on which the instruments are based and the possibilities inherent in the system. Usually the most efficient procedure is the simplest that can be devised—one that requires the minimum number of measurements and thus results in higher accuracy and less expenditure of time.

Furthermore, while the system is so flexible that it can be applied to almost any jig or product, it can be used more effectively when the measurement procedure is designed along with the product itself and thus made part of the plans and specifications.

By coordinating the design of the measurement procedure and that of the product, difficult and weak measurement procedures are avoided and the product is thus made to closer tolerances. For example, if clear lines for sights or measurements are not provided, the positions of the parts must depend on a series of measurements, each of which introduces errors in the final positions of the parts.

A few applications are described at the end of this section but as each application is usually unique, the best approach to the subject is through a study of the instruments.

FUNDAMENTAL PRINCIPLES OF THE INSTRUMENTS

The high accuracy of optical tooling depends on three fundamental requirements which must be inherent in every instrument or operation. These are: (1) telescopic sights; (2) reversibility; (3) the use of gravity as a reference direction.

Telescopic Sights

Figure 12-1 schematically shows a typical telescopic sight. The objective lens forms an inverted image on the plane of the crosshairs. This image, together with the crosshairs, are observed through the eyepiece which erects and magnifies them so that the observer sees the crosshairs apparently engraved on the object which is magnified 25 to 30 times.

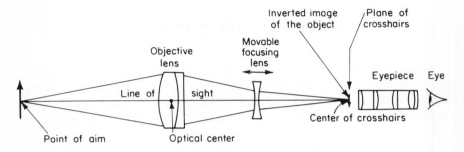

Fig. 12-1. The principle of a telescopic sight.

The point on the object where the center of the crosshairs appears is on a line, called the *line of sight* or the *line of collimation*. This line, which extends from the center of the crosshairs through the optical center of the objective lens, is absolutely straight in undisturbed air. It can be aimed at a target, a target can be placed on it, or, with special scales, measurements to an accuracy of 1:200,000 can be made from it. The reference line itself is accurate to 0.003 in. at 100 ft (approximately 0.001 in. at 30 ft).

Reversibility

Alignment within each instrument or operation must be capable of being checked by reversing the instrument or operation, so that any error is doubled and thus evaluated and then eliminated by adjustment or averaging. The methods of reversing are explained in the descriptions of the individual instruments.

Gravity as a Reference Direction

The direction of gravity can be determined with a spirit level to almost any desired accuracy if the temperature of the spirit in the vial is uniform. With a few exceptions, a spirit level is used in all alignment instruments and operations to establish one step in alignment. Gravity thus provides a level surface at any desired elevation.

In optical tooling the word *vertical* means in the direction of gravity and *horizontal* or *level* means perpendicular to gravity.

INSTRUMENTS

The Optical Tooling Level

Figure 12-2 shows an optical tooling level. It consists of a *tubular spirit level* attached to a telescopic sight and so adjusted that, when the line of sight is perpendicular to gravity, the bubble is centered. This assembly is mounted on a *tilt axis*. By turning a micrometer screw, the assembly can be tilted slightly up or down on this axis until the bubble is centered. The whole assembly is mounted on an *azimuth* spindle and bearing so that it can be aimed in any desired horizontal direction (azimuth is another name for horizontal direction). The *azimuth axis* (created by the spindle and bearing) is set vertically with the aid of a circular level and a *leveling head*. The leveling head is manipulated by three or four leveling screws. (As will be seen later, the telescopic sight may be equipped for auto-collimation.)

Even though the circular level is not very sensitive, it should be kept in good adjustment and carefully centered in use, since it indirectly affects the accuracy of the results. The adjustment of the circular level is based on the principle of *reversal*. To test the adjustment, the bubble is centered in one position, and then the upper assembly is turned in azimuth through an angle of 180°. If the bubble remains centered, the azimuth axis is vertical. Otherwise the instrument must be taken out of use and adjusted.

Fig. 12-2. An optical tooling level. (© *Keuffel & Esser Co.*)

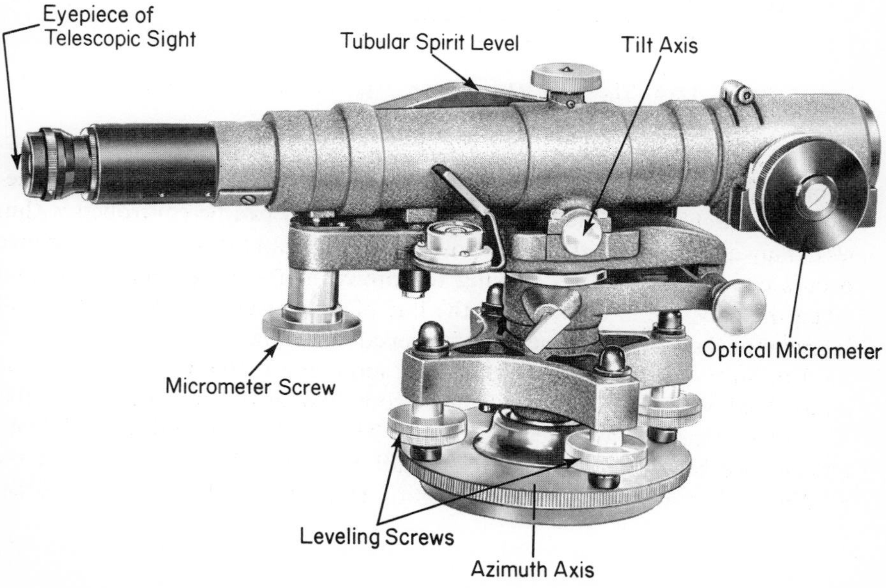

Eyepiece of
Telescopic Sight

Tubular Spirit Level

Tilt Axis

Optical Micrometer

Micrometer Screw

Leveling Screws

Azimuth Axis

After the instrument has been leveled with the circular level, it is turned toward the scale to be read and focused on it. The tubular level is then precisely centered with the micrometer screw.

The tubular level is a long glass vial internally ground to a barrelshaped enclosure and partially filled with a very low-viscosity liquid such as ether or pentane. The larger the radius of curvature of the enclosure, the more sensitive is the spirit level. Usually the sensitivity is such that the bubble moves about 2 mm when the tilt of the vial is changed 15 sec of arc. The bubble is observed through an optical device which brings the two ends of the bubble together as shown in Fig. 12-3. It is then called a coincidence

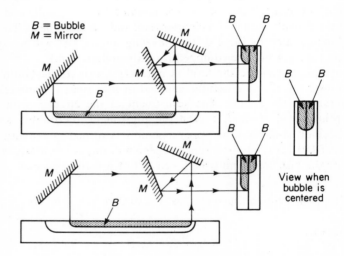

Fig. 12-3. The principle of one type of coincidence-reading device.

bubble. With this optical device, the two ends of the bubble can be so accurately matched that the slope of the line of sight can be controlled within less than a second of arc. The position of the bubble where coincidence occurs can be adjusted by moving the optical parts. It is adjusted so that when the ends are in coincidence the line of sight is horizontal. Adjustment is accomplished by the principle of reversal as follows:

Two firm objects are selected 50 ft or more apart. Readings are taken on scales held vertically on each object from two instrument positions, one near one object and one near the other. The bubble ends are brought into coincidence before each of the four readings. If the difference between the readings taken at one instrument position is not the same as from the other

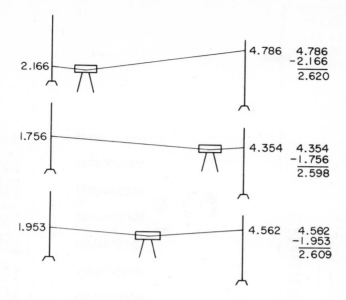

Fig. 12-4. If the line of sight slopes when the bubble ends coincide, the differences in the readings, 2.6200 and 2.598, will be unequal, as shown. By equalizing the lengths of the sights, after adjustment, the true difference, 2.609, will be obtained.

position, the instrument is out of adjustment. Figure 12-4 shows this condition.

In use, the horizontal lengths of the sights are made as nearly equal as possible to eliminate any residual error.

Scales

Optical tooling scales are marked every 0.1 in., and read with *optical micrometers* (described later). Since a crosshair is $2\frac{1}{2}$ to 3 sec wide, it cannot be aimed accurately enough at a thin line, and paired lines must be used. The crosshair is so placed that it bisects the white space between the lines. The white space should be about 3 or 4 times as wide as the crosshair for the greatest accuracy. Accordingly, each 0.1 in. is marked with a set of paired lines with different separations so that the pair that gives the best sight can be chosen for various lengths of sight. Figure 12-5 shows how the scales are marked. The scales are made of steel. The zero point is at the end which is hardened to prevent wear. Small levels or right-angle magnets are used to align the scales.

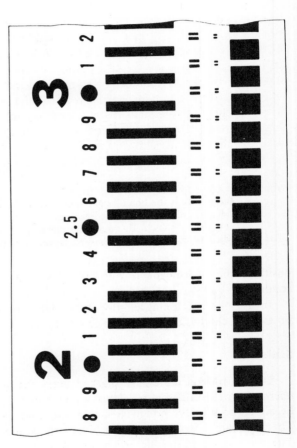

LOCKHEED
OPTI-VERNIER SCALE
L705*22-1

75 TO 110 FT.

7 TO 25 FT
2 TO 7 FT

25 TO 75 FT

10.000
9.920
9.840
9.760
9.680
9.600
9.520
9.440
9.360
9.280
9.200
9.120
9.040
8.960
8.880
8.800
8.720
8.640
8.560
8.480
8.400
8.320
8.240
8.160
8.080
8.000
7.920
7.840
7.760
7.680
7.600
7.520
7.440
7.360
7.280
7.200
7.120
7.040
6.960
6.880
6.800
6.720
6.640
6.560
6.480
6.400
6.320
6.240
6.160
6.080
6.000

© Keuffel & Esser Co.

Fig. 12-5. Typical optical tooling scales.

The Optical Micrometer

An optical micrometer is a device which moves the line of sight of a telescopic sight *parallel to itself* over a range of usually at least ±0.100 in. There are several methods of accomplishing this; the simplest is illustrated in Fig. 12-6. The device is either mounted on the telescope in front of the objective lens (see Fig. 12-2) or incorporated in the instrument. It consists of a flat disk of optical glass with parallel sides which can be rotated by a graduated knob, shown on the right in Fig. 12-6. When the flat disk is perpendicular to the line of sight, the line of sight passes through without change of direction. When the disk is rotated, the line of sight emerges parallel to its original direction but offset by some distance which increases as the tilt increases. The knob is calibrated to read the movement of the line of sight in 0.001-in. increments. To take a reading, the line of sight is moved until it bisects the paired-line pattern at a certain tenth of an inch (2.6 in. in Fig. 12-6). To this, the reading on the knob (0.072 in. in Fig. 12-6) is added, which in the present example gives 2.672 in.

Optical micrometers and optical tooling scales can be used with all telescopic sights to measure the perpendicular distance between a physical object and the line of sight. Measurements can be taken horizontally, vertically, or at any desired slope.

Fig. 12-6. The operation of an optical micrometer. (© *Keuffel & Esser Co.*)

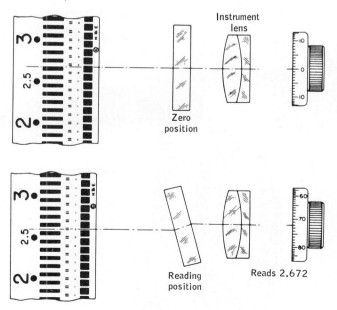

Devices for other Linear Measurements

For long measurements the lines of sight are positioned with the aid of gage bars (described under "Optical Tooling Bars") or optical tooling tapes. To permit precise positioning, optical micrometers or verniers are used in conjunction with them. Measurements between physical objects are made with standard inside micrometers and extension rods.

In general, no angle-measuring devices are used in optical tooling as it is almost impossible to build an instrument by which an angle can be established to an accuracy of one second in one setting. Theodolites are used in optical tooling to establish angles but, although they read to one second, a complicated procedure of measuring the angle repeatedly is required to eliminate the systematic instrumental errors in order to attain an accuracy of ± 1 sec. Accordingly, as a rule only right angles are used and other angles are established by linear rectangular measurements.

The Jig Transit

A jig transit basically is like a surveyor's transit without any circles for reading angles. However, it has a telescope level, an optical micrometer, and especially accurate plate levels. In addition, the following equipment, explained later, are added: an arrangement for *autocollimation* and *projection*, and *telescope-axle mirrors* (see Fig. 12-7).

Fig. 12-7. A jig transit. (© *Keuffel & Esser Co.*)

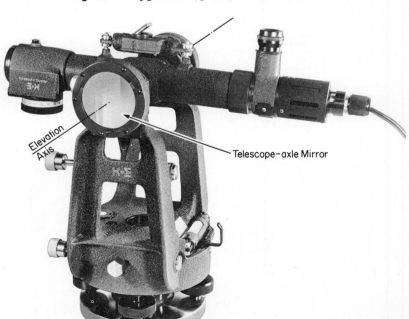

Elevation Axis

Telescope–axle Mirror

Figure 12-8[1]* shows the fundamental requirements of a jig transit. The elevation axis must be perpendicular to both the azimuth axis and the line of sight, and the three lines must intersect at a point (the instrument center). The plate levels shown must indicate level when the azimuth axis is vertical. All of these requirements can be tested by reversal and attained by adjustment.

For example, to test for the right angle between the elevation axis and the line of sight, aim at a target with the telescope reversed (upside down), reverse the telescope (turn it right side up) and read a scale in the opposite

[1]*The illustrations thus indicated are taken from *Optical Tooling for Precise Manufacture and Alignment* by Philip Kissam, McGraw-Hill Book Co., New York, 1962, with the permission of the publisher.

Fig. 12-8. The fundamental requirements of a jig transit. (© *Philip Kissam.*)

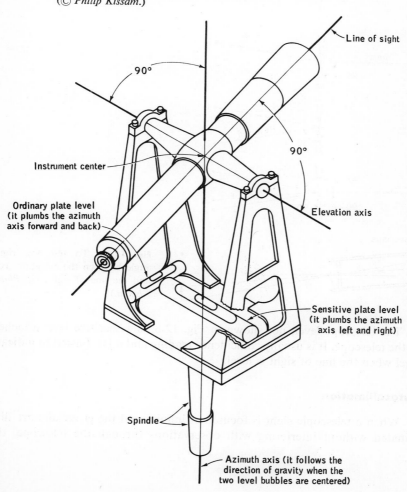

Line of sight

90°

90°

Instrument center

Ordinary plate level (it plumbs the azimuth axis forward and back)

Elevation axis

Sensitive plate level (it plumbs the azimuth axis left and right)

Spindle

Azimuth axis (it follows the direction of gravity when the two level bubbles are centered)

direction from the target. Keeping the telescope right side up, turn in azimuth to the target. Reverse the telescope. The scale reading should be the same in both directions.

Figure 12-9[1] shows that the angular error e appears doubled in both directions on the scale. Consequently, an adjustment equal to one quarter of the observed error will be necessary.

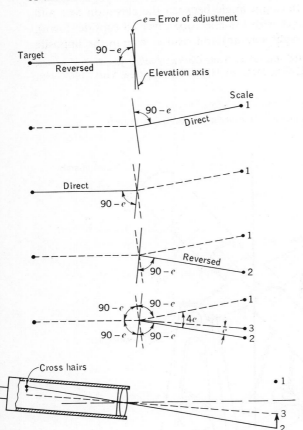

Fig. 12-9. To test the right angle between the elevation axis and the line of sight. (© *Philip Kissam.*)

The telescope level, not shown in Fig. 12-8, is a sensitive level attached to the telescope. It is usually coincidence reading and it is adjusted to indicate level when the line of sight is level.

Autocollimation

When a telescopic sight is focused at infinity and the crosshairs are illuminated without interfering with observations through the telescope, the

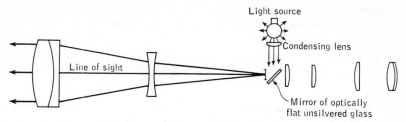

Fig. 12-10. The method of illuminating the crosshairs. (© *Philip Kissam.*)

instrument becomes an autocollimator (see Fig. 12-10[1]). The glass mirror reflects enough light to illuminate the crosshairs and the observer can see the crosshairs through it.

When a telescopic sight is focused at infinity, any set of parallel light rays that pass through the telescope are brought together (focused) on the plane of the crosshairs. Conversely, when the telescope is focused at infinity, if the crosshairs are illuminated the rays that radiate from the crosshair intersection emerge from the telescope parallel to each other and to the line of sight.

If a mirror is placed in front of the telescope at any distance from it, and nearly perpendicular to it, these parallel rays will be reflected back into the telescope. They will still be parallel to each other but not necessarily parallel to their original direction. When they pass through the telescope lens, they will be focused on the plane of the crosshairs and form an image of the reflected crosshairs beside the actual crosshairs. Looking through the eyepiece, the observer will see both the actual crosshairs and the reflected image.

If, then, the mirror is turned until the image of the crosshairs coincides with the actual crosshairs, the mirror surface will be perpendicular to the line of sight (see Fig. 12-11). To attain infinity focus, the observer merely changes the focus until the image appears and is clearly defined.

This process is called *autocollimation*.

Fig. 12-11. Autocollimation.

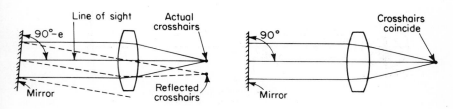

Projection. The light shown in Fig. 12-10 can be made dim for autocollimation and bright for *projection*. When it is bright, the image· of the crosshairs is projected and can be picked up on any light-colored surface just as any projector will project slides on a screen. The telescope must be focused just as any projector is focused. This process has certain uses in optical tooling.

The Telescope-Axle Mirror. As shown in Fig. 12-7 this is a mirror attached to the end of the elevation axis. It can be adjusted so that it is exactly perpendicular to the elevation axis as follows: The telescopic sight is aimed at the reflection of any well-defined point as seen in the mirror. Rotate the mirror through 180° by turning the telescope on its elevation axis. The image of the point should remain on the crosshairs of the telescopic sight. The mirror is adjusted until this occurs.

When the line of sight of a jig transit is swung around the elevation axis, it follows or *generates* a plane perpendicular to the elevation axis. With a telescope-axle mirror, this plane can be made perpendicular to another line of sight by autocollimation.

Autoreflection. Autoreflection accomplishes the same result as autocollimation but with less accuracy. This method can be employed with a telescopic sight not equipped for autocollimation. As shown in Fig. 12-12,[1] the target is placed around the objective lens or behind it. When the reflection of the target is placed on the crosshairs, the mirror is perpendicular to the line of sight.

Fig. 12-12. Autoreflection. (© *Philip Kissam*.)

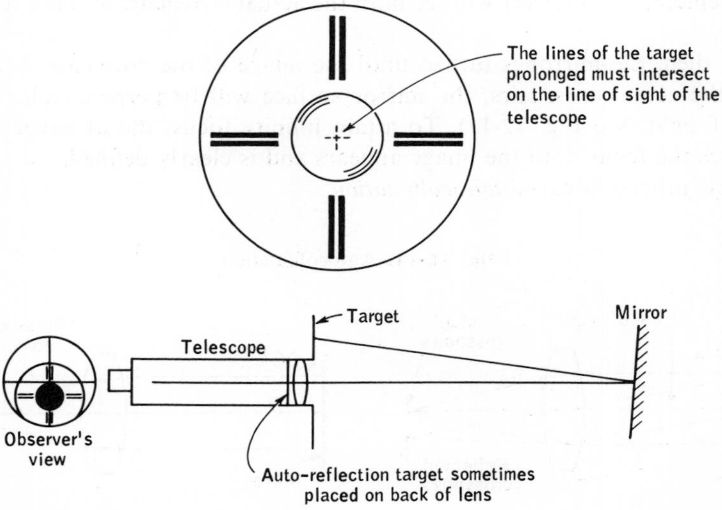

The lines of the target prolonged must intersect on the line of sight of the telescope

Mirror

Target

Telescope

Observer's view

Auto-reflection target sometimes placed on back of lens

The Alignment Telescope

Figure 12-13 shows an alignment telescope mounted in its *cup mount* and *bracket*. Essentially it consists of a telescopic sight built in a heavy, steel, cylindrical barrel whose outside surface is held to extremely close tolerances. The line of sight is placed so that it exactly coincides with the axis of the cylinder. The cylinder is either permanently attached to, or can be positioned and locked in the concentric bore of a section of a sphere (called a spherical mount). The sphere is held by a spring in a *cup mount* which can be precisely positioned and rotated or locked in the desired position. To the base of the cup mount, a *bracket* is attached. This bracket holds the other end of the cylinder, and provides thumb screws by which the telescope can be aimed a few degrees up or down and left or right. The base of the cup mount can be placed so that the telescope aims vertically up or down, or horizontal but upside down.

To establish a reference point in optical alignment work, targets with similar cup mounts are used.

Fig. 12-13. A typical alignment telescope mounted on its cup mount and bracket. (© *Keuffel & Esser Co.*)

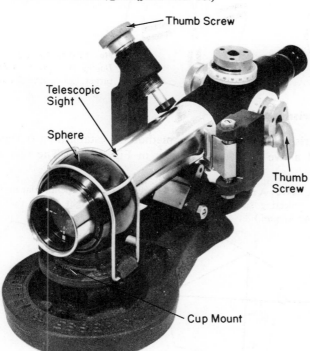

For close tolerance work, such as establishing a permanent reference line on a jig that must be frequently checked for alignment, the alignment telescope and a target are carefully positioned and the cup mounts locked. When the telescope is aimed at the target the line of sight is established. The telescope and the target in their spherical mounts can then be removed and replaced or even interchanged without losing the position of the line of sight.

The alignment telescope is usually equipped with an internal, optical micrometer system that will measure left and right and up and down.

Targets

Targets are used for many purposes in optical tooling to give a point of aim for a line of sight. Several types of patterns have been adopted. Figure 12-14 shows two of them. They are usually made of glass and illuminated from behind. Some are engraved on a mirror surface.

Fig. 12-14. Typical targets. (© *Boeing Aircraft Co.*) Paired line target. (© *Keuffel & Esser Co.*)

The Pentaprism

A pentaprism provides another method of establishing a right angle. It consists of a five-sided prism shown in Fig. 12-15.[1] The two reflecting

Fig. 12-15. A pentaprism can be turned in a plane perpendicular to the reflecting surfaces without disturbing the right angle. (© *Philip Kissam.*)

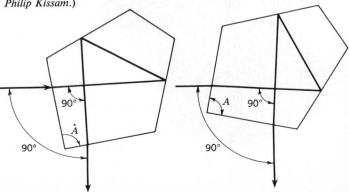

surfaces have a 45° included angle, therefore the device turns the entering line of sight by exactly 90° in a plane mutually perpendicular to the reflecting surfaces. To avoid secondary errors, this plane must be closely aligned with the line of sight. The pentaprism is usually mounted on a tube with crosshairs or on an alignment telescope.

The Leveling Mirror

Figure 12-16 shows a leveling mirror. A glass disk with parallel sides, both of which are mirrors, is suspended by two very thin ribbons. A balance screw is regulated to make the mirrors hang vertically. The device is approximately leveled with the circular level shown. When a telescopic sight is aimed at a mirror and set so that it autocollimates, the line of sight is level.

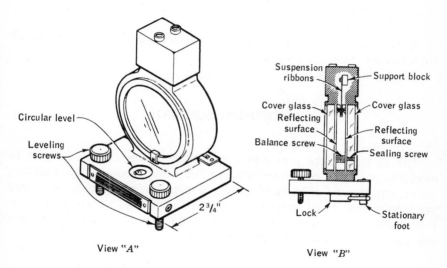

View "*A*"   View "*B*"

Fig. 12-16. A Farrand leveling mirror. (*Lockheed Aircraft Co.*)

The leveling mirror can then be turned in azimuth and thus the reflected line of sight can be aimed in almost any desired direction. Since it will remain level automatically, it can be used for leveling.

The Plumbing Mirror

Figure 12-17 shows a plumbing mirror. The mercury pool provides a mirror surface that is automatically horizontal. The oil and the glass reduce waves caused by vibration. An accurate vertical line is obtained by placing a telescopic sight so that it autocollimates on this surface.

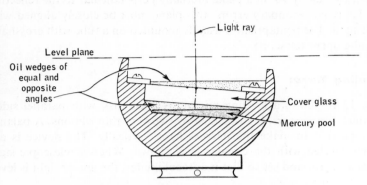

Fig. 12-17. A plumbing mirror. (*Lockheed Aircraft Co.*)

Several other mirror instruments or devices are used, some of which are described under *applications*.

INSTRUMENT SUPPORTS

The jig transit, the pentaprism, and other devices frequently must be placed so that two conditions are satisfied simultaneously. For example, the jig transit must often be placed so that its line of sight coincides with two targets while its azimuth axis is vertical. This process is called *bucking-in*. Instrument supports are designed to facilitate this process as well as to provide convenient supports for the instruments.

Instrument Stands

Figure 12-18 shows one type of instrument stand. It can be rolled into position and then supported on three sharp steel points. The height can be easily adjusted. To allow a left or right adjustment without throwing the instrument much out of level, jig transits are mounted on a *mechanical lateral adjuster*. When very nearly in position, the transit is precisely leveled, and the optical micrometer is used to buck-in the line of sight.

Optical Tooling Bars

An optical tooling bar consists of a light, stiff metal beam, with one flat outside surface, mounted horizontally or vertically on adjustable supports

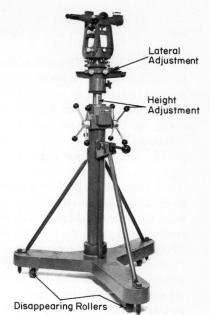

Lateral Adjustment

Height Adjustment

Disappearing Rollers

Fig. 12-18. A typical instrument stand with a mechanical lateral adjuster. (© *Keuffel & Esser Co.*)

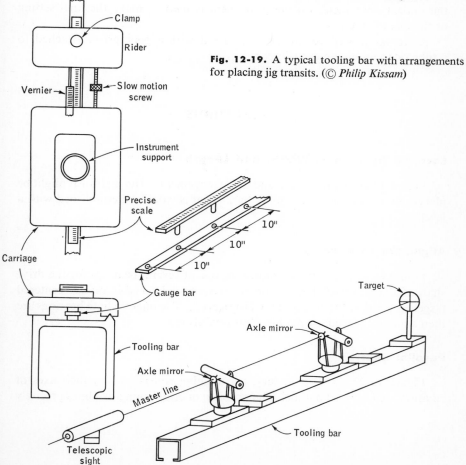

Clamp

Rider

Vernier

Slow motion screw

Instrument support

Precise scale

Carriage

Gauge bar

Tooling bar

Telescopic sight

Axle mirror

Axle mirror

Master line

Target

Tooling bar

10"

10"

10"

Fig. 12-19. A typical tooling bar with arrangements for placing jig transits. (© *Philip Kissam*)

(see Fig. 12-19.[1]) The flat surface carries a V and a flat to provide ways for an instrument support or carriage and a rider. These bars are placed parallel to the major axes of the work so that measurements can be made along them. When an instrument is placed on the carriage it can be slid along the bar without moving much out of its working alignment and orientation. The master line shown is established by optical tooling methods parallel to the major axis of the work and used to regulate the aim of the jig transit.

A gage bar is held in guides along the surface of the tooling bar. The gage bar has jig-bored holes spaced 10 in. apart, and is clamped to the tooling bar at one end, where its reference to the work is established. An optical tooling scale, with studs on its reverse side, is set in the holes where desired. The carriage and rider are moved into an approximate position, the rider is clamped, and the carriage is positioned exactly with a micrometer screw which connects it with the carriage. The scale is read with a vernier (with reference to the center of the instrument) or directly, by aiming the telescope, through a hole in the spindle. If the scale is graduated in 0.1-in. increments, the optical micrometer on the instrument is used to make the final setting of the line of sight.

A similar procedure can be carried out with a pentaprism attached to a tube or to an alignment telescope.

APPLICATIONS

Location by Height, Width, and Length

Figure 12-20[1] shows two standard arrangements. The jig transit might be placed on a stand or on a tooling bar. Heights would be established with a level.

Alignment of Bearings

Figure 12-21 shows the alignment of one of several bearings for the drive shaft of a large vessel. The alignment telescope is bucked-in on two centered targets, placed at the first and the last bearing. The intermediate bearings are then similarly placed on the line thus established.

Parallel Shafts

Figure 12-22 shows a method for aligning rollers so that their axes of rotation are level and parallel. The problem of establishing two lines precisely

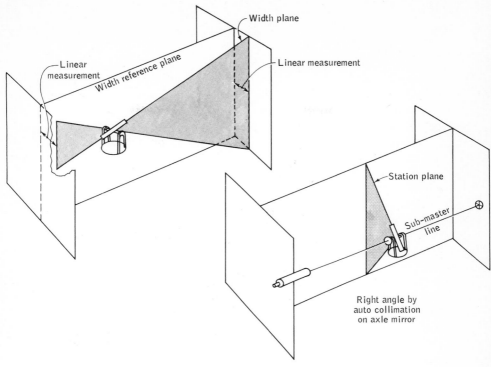

Fig. 12-20. The principle of location by three linear dimensions. Height is established by leveling. (© *Philip Kissam*)

Fig. 12-21. The target and target holder used for aligning a bearing. (© *Keuffel & Esser Co.*)

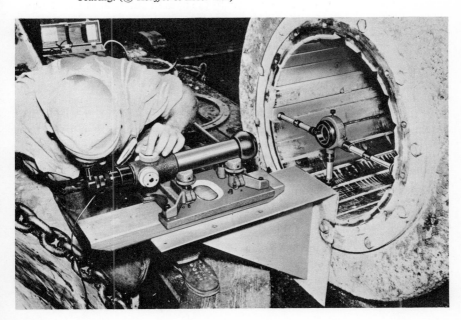

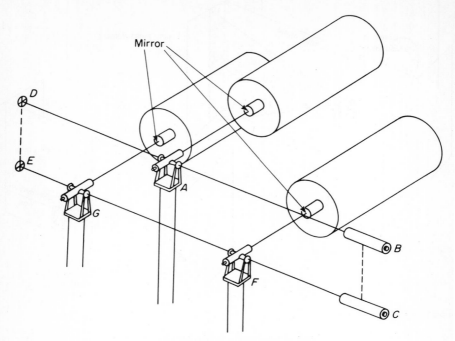

Fig. 12-22. Alignment of axes of rollers.

parallel to each other is always extremely difficult and a detailed description is too long to include here. However, the principles are easily described.

It is best to establish permanent fixtures that hold cup mounts which establish lines like *BD* and *CE*. These lines should be level and parallel in a vertical plane as well as perpendicular to the axes of rotation of the rollers.

In addition, a mirror with a center target should be permanently attached to the end of each roller. Each mirror must be adjusted so that it is perpendicular to the axis and its center mark is at the center of rotation. In other words, each must be adjusted so that, when observed with a telescopic sight as the roller is rotated, both the center mark and the reflection of a stationary target will remain stationary.

With this arrangement, the alignment of the rollers can be checked with an alignment telescope and a jig transit as shown. The transit is placed so that its axle mirror autocollimates the alignment telescope and the line of sight of the transit is leveled with the telescope level.

When accuracy of position is important, the rollers can be leveled with an optical level and the transit can be mounted on a tooling bar.

Bed of a Milling Machine

Figure 12-23 shows the alignment of a milling machine bed perpendicular to the axis of rotation of the cutting tool. A pentaprism is mounted on the

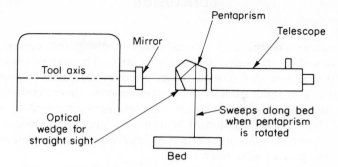

Fig. 12-23. Checking the alignment of a milling machine.

telescope. It is arranged with shutters so that the observer can look straight ahead or at 90° as desired. The telescope is rotated so that the 90° line sweeps the bed.

Lathe Alignment

Figure 12-24 shows the alignment of a lathe. The drawing is self-explanatory.

Fig. 12-24. The alignment of a lathe. (© *Keuffel & Esser Co.*)

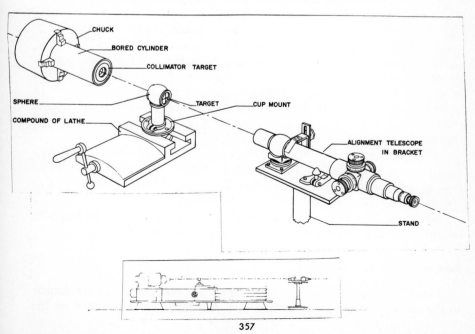

CONCLUSION

It is evident that whenever high accuracies are required, optical tooling methods should be studied as a possible solution. The system always saves time in the long run, and in many cases provides accuracies impossible by other means. The application of the system depends almost entirely on the ingenuity and ability of the engineer who designs the method to be used, his knowledge of what equipment is available, and his understanding of how the geometric relationships in the instruments are maintained and utilized to the greatest advantage.

13

SURFACE TEXTURE MEASUREMENT*

Surface metrology may be broadly defined as the measurement of the difference between what the surface actually is and what it is intended to be. It is treated separately from length measurement because length measurement is concerned with the relationship of two surfaces on a workpiece, whereas surface measurement is involved with the relationship of a surface on the workpiece to a reference which is not actually on the workpiece.

By far the most common aspect of surface metrology is the measurement of surface roughness as an average deviation from a mean center line. At the present time some 99 percent of the surface measurements made in the United States today are measurements of this average roughness height. This does not mean that the other types of measurements are not equally important, but usually the cost involved in the other types of measurement has not been justified.

Many of the concepts of surface metrology are defined in ASA Standard B46.1-1962, "Surface Texture," as follows:

*By Charles H. Good, Sales Manager, Micrometrical Manufacturing Company.

Roughness. Roughness consists of the finer irregularities in the surface texture, usually including those irregularities which result from the inherent action of the production process. These are considered to include traverse feed marks and other irregularities within the limits of the roughness-width cutoff.

Roughness Height. Rated as the arithmetical average deviation expressed in microinches measured normal to the center line.

Roughness Width. The distance parallel to the nominal surface between successive peaks or ridges which constitute the predominant pattern of the roughness. Roughness width is rated in inches.

Roughness-Width Cutoff. The greatest spacing of repetitive surface irregularities to be included in the measurement of average roughness height. Roughness-width cutoff is rated in inches. Roughness-width cutoff must always be greater than the roughness width in order to obtain the total roughness height rating. Standard tables list roughness-width cutoff values of 0.003, 0.010, 0.030, 0.100, 0.300, and 1.000 in. When no value is specified, the value 0.030 is assumed.

Waviness. The usually widely-spaced component of surface texture and generally of wider spacing than the roughness-width cutoff. Waviness may result from such factors as machine or work deflections, vibration, chatter, heat treatment, or warping stains. Roughness may be considered as superposed on a "wavy" surface.

Waviness Height. Rated in inches as the peak-to-valley distance.

Waviness Width. Rated in inches as the spacing of successive wave peaks or successive wave valleys. When specified, the values shall be the maximum permissible.

Lay. The direction of the predominant surface pattern, ordinarily determined by the production method used. Symbols shall be specified as shown in Figs. 13-3 and 13-4.

Flaws. Irregularities which occur at one place or at relatively infrequent or widely varying intervals in a surface. Flaws include such defects as cracks, blow holes, checks, ridges, scratches, etc. Unless otherwise specified, the effect of flaws shall not be included in the roughness height measurement.

The following definitions have not been standarized but are concepts which help to clarify the subject:

Waviness-Width Cutoff. The greatest spacing of repetitive surface irregularities to be included in the measurement of waviness height. Wider spaced irregularities shall be considered error of form. Waviness-width cutoff is rated in inches.

Error of Form. Very widely-spaced repetitive irregularities occurring over the full length of the work surface. Common types of error of form are bow, snaking, and lobing.

Roundness. The radial uniformity of a work surface measured from the center line of the workpiece. Out-of-Roundness is expressed in inches.

Straightness. The linear uniformity of a work surface measured from an external reference. Out-of-straightness is expressed in inches.

From the above definitions it can be seen that the various characteristics which can be measured in surface metrology are defined by their height and their spacing, that they constitute a whole spectrum of irregularities, as measured from an ideal reference, and that they can be classified into categories so that only the necessary characteristics need to be controlled. For example, on a seal surface it may be desirable to have the part extremely straight, but the surface finish may not be critical since the irregularities will tend to mate with the opposite surface. In this example, a single flaw could be the cause for leakage. In another case, such as the side of an O-ring groove, the surface roughness may need to be very small, but the error of form may not be critical at all.

In considering the various types of surface characteristics, there are some *functional* characteristics which are sometimes of concern.

Bearing Area. Bearing area is a term applied to a surface to indicate what portion of the surface will be available to support a load after some percentage of the total roughness height has been removed through wear or through a finishing process such as lapping. Figure 13-1 shows a typical

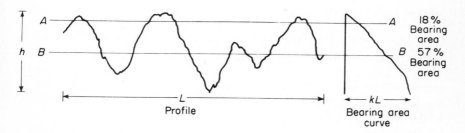

Fig. 13-1. Relation of bearing area to material removed in a finishing process.

profile of a surface with line *A* representing 10 percent of the roughness height removed, and line *B* representing 50 percent of the roughness height removed. The curve at the right is called the bearing area curve and shows the percent bearing area for various levels below the extreme peak.

Reflectivity. Reflectivity is a function of the uniformity of the surface texture, and not a function of the deviation of the surface from a norm. Where reflectivity is the functional requirement of the part, it is usually measured in terms of a percentage of light from a collimated source which is reflected from the surface in relation to the amount of light cast on the surface. If the percentage is less than 100 it implies that some of the light

Fig. 13-2. Surfaces of differing reflectivity, but same average roughness value.

is scattered from the collimated beam. Figure 13-2 shows two surfaces having different reflectivity but the same average roughness value.

SPECIFYING THE CHARACTERISTICS
OF SURFACE TEXTURE

In specifying the parameters for measuring surface finish, the designer should follow practice set forth in ASA Standard B46.1-1962, "Surface Texture."

Under this standard, the symbol used to designate surface irregularities is the check mark with horizontal extension as shown in Figs. 13-3 and 13-4. The point of the symbol shall be on the line indicating the surface, on the extension line, or on a leader pointing to the surface. The long leg and extension shall be to the right of the drawing as read. Typical applications of the symbol on a drawing are shown in Fig. 13-4.

Only those ratings required to adequately specify the desired surface shall be shown in the symbol. Those characteristics which are not standardized must be stated in notes.

TOLERANCES OF FORM

These tolerances state how far actual surfaces are permitted to vary from the perfect geometry implied by drawings. Expression of these tolerances (errors of form) refer to straightness, flatness, parallelism, squareness, angular displacement, symmetry, concentricity, roundness, etc.

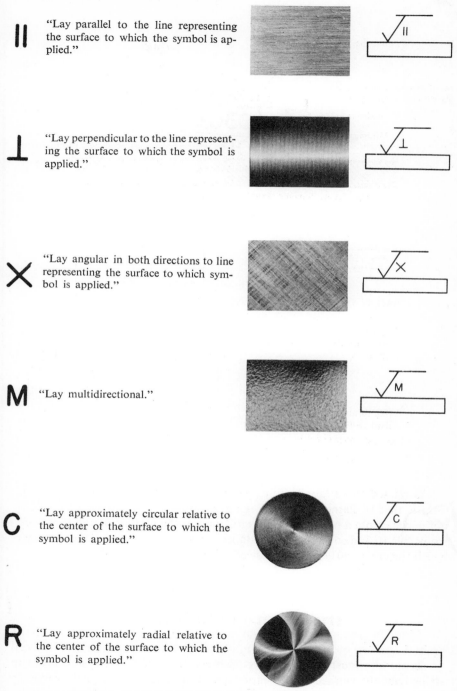

"Lay parallel to the line representing the surface to which the symbol is applied."

"Lay perpendicular to the line representing the surface to which the symbol is applied."

"Lay angular in both directions to line representing the surface to which symbol is applied."

"Lay multidirectional."

"Lay approximately circular relative to the center of the surface to which the symbol is applied."

"Lay approximately radial relative to the center of the surface to which the symbol is applied."

Fig. 13-3. Symbols indicating lay of the surface pattern.

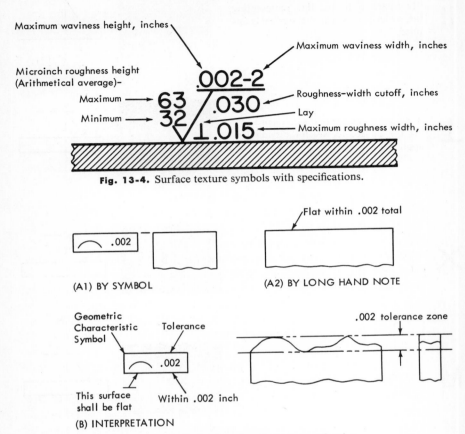

Fig. 13-4. Surface texture symbols with specifications.

(A1) BY SYMBOL

(A2) BY LONG HAND NOTE

(B) INTERPRETATION

Fig. 13-5. Methods of surface flatness specification.

As related to surface texture measurement, the most relevant error of form is that of flatness. Flatness is the condition of a surface which does not deviate from a plane. A flatness tolerance is the total deviation permitted from a plane, and consists of the distance between two parallel planes between which the entire surface so toleranced must lie (see Fig. 13-5).

STYLUS SYSTEM OF MEASUREMENT

By far the most common way to measure surface finish is to move a stylus over the surface, and measure an average electrical signal produced by a transducer attached to the stylus. Other means used less frequently include stylus profiling where a chart record is produced instead of an average number, reflectivity meters, pneumatics, and optical interference. The stylus averaging unit is most common because it is fast, repeatable, quite easy to interpret, and relatively inexpensive.

Stylus systems embrace the following essential elements: the surface, the stylus, the drive to move the stylus with respect to the surface, the reference, the amplifier, and the data presentation.

The Surface

The surface has certain characteristics which define the type of measurement which can be made. The nominal contour, the size, the hardness, and the texture pattern are the essential elements.

The *nominal contour* is critical because there must be a means to move the stylus along a path which is the same as the nominal contour. It is easy to provide a straight-line motion to check a flat part, and quite simple to provide a circular motion to check a round part. But, to check cam surfaces and gear teeth the problem is more difficult.

The nominal contour becomes more of a problem as the *size* gets smaller. While it is possible to check 20 in. deep in a $\frac{1}{4}$-in. diam hole, it is much more difficult to reach 1 in. deep in a 0.090-in. diam hole. The size of the part will have an influence on the type of reference used, as well as on the roughness-width cutoff used.

The *texture pattern* or *lay* of the part will have an influence on the direction of trace and also on the interpretation of the reading. For example, if a part is shaped so that it has a series of parallel furrows, the variation from true will be much larger if measured at right angles to the furrows than it would be if the trace were made parallel to the furrows in the bottom of one of them. For this reason the ASA standard states that the stylus should be moved in a direction that will give a maximum reading, which is across the lay or across the furrows, unless otherwise specified.

The *hardness* of a part will determine the amount of stylus pressure that can be applied and this, in turn, combined with the amplitude of the irregularities determines the speeds of trace that can be used and still allow for a faithful following of the surface. Thus, we see that the workpiece itself plays an important role in the selection of proper measuring techniques.

The Stylus

In current metrology, much emphasis is being placed on the tips that are being used on standard height gages, as well as on the gaging loads. This is done because different-shaped tips with different loads will produce different measurements on a part, due to the different conformity of the different-size tips to the fine irregularities on the surface and to the differences in deformation of the workpiece. The same thing applies to surface texture styluses as well. In surface texture the stylus must be of sufficient sharpness to penetrate the roughness irregularities. Figure 13-6 shows the effect of stylus radius on the reading of a surface.

The stylus used to follow the surface irregularity can be a light beam, a jet of air, or a condenser plate, but most typically a diamond having a 90° cone and a spherical tip of 0.0005 in. or 0.0001 in. is used. This is because the diamond can be formed into the above configuration and stay that way uniformly, while it is difficult to confine the light beam, air jet, or condenser plate to a small enough size to be able to follow the surface irregularities.

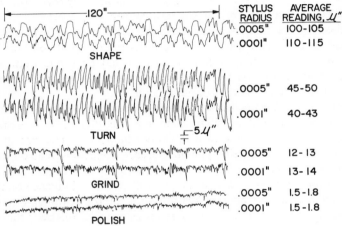

Fig. 13-6. Surface profiles (about $\frac{1}{7}$ size) and roughness reading of representative surfaces using tracer points of 0.0005- and 0.0001-in. radius.

The standardized stylus shape for averaging measuring instruments has the 0.0005-in. tip radius because it is the best compromise between ability to follow detail, the ability to resist wear, and the ability not to mar the surface. The stylus load is 1 to 2 grams for averaging-type instruments, since these loads are necessary to follow the surface irregularities and still not mar the surface. Where necessary, other stylus shapes and pressures can be used to offer better life, more detail, or reduced marring, but some other characteristic must be minimized to do this. For example, if it is desired to measure on dead soft copper, then marring is of concern. The stylus load can be reduced to a half gram or less, but then the system cannot measure rougher surfaces because the stylus may not always stay in contact with the surface. Marring could be further reduced by using a blunter stylus, but this would reduce the detail that the stylus could measure.

The Reference

The reference from which surfaces are measured is the item that makes surface metrology unique. This reference is not some other surface on the part, but either the surface being measured or some exterior reference not on the part at all. In average measuring, the most common reference is the workpiece surface being measured. The surface is actually traversed by two styluses, one of the type described above, and the other one of much greater radius. Typically, this larger radius is in the range of $\frac{1}{4}$ in. This larger-radius stylus is called a "skid" reference. The measurement is a measure of the motion of the sharp stylus, which follows up and down the fine irregularities on the surface, and of the skid, which because of its large radius cannot ride up and down the surface irregularities, but rather rides over the tops of them.

In some cases, the surface is not large enough to allow both the stylus and the skid to be on the surface at the same time. In these cases an external reference is required. The measurement thus obtained is the motion of the stylus relative to the path of the tracer body as determined by the accuracy of the external reference used. Since the spacings of the irregularities being measured are quite small, 0.010 in., for example, the accuracy of the external reference needs only to be considered over a short section of the reference. Thus long, slight errors can be eliminated by means of electronic circuitry.

If, now, it is desired to measure wider-spaced irregularities, then the accuracy of the reference must be greater. Thus, in surface profiling, if roughness, waviness, and error of form are to be measured, the reference must be more accurate than the part being checked. Usually the accuracy of the reference for profiling has a deviation from nominal in the range of 0.000001 in. to 0.000050 in. For straight-line profiling the reference is usually a precision ball slide or an optical flat. For circular profiling, ultra-precise spindles of all types have been produced. At the present time no standard means exists for checking the accuracy of the reference, other than using the reference with the remainder of the measuring system and checking an optical flat or precision sphere.

The Drive

There must be some means to move the stylus across the workpiece, whether it be an operator's hand, a synchronous motor coupled with a drive screw, a friction drive, a magnetic plate drive, or a hydraulic drive. The requirements for this drive are that vibration be held to a minimum, that the speed be both known and constant, that the speed be such that the stylus can stay in contact with the surface, and that the readout device is capable of properly indicating the measurement. For averaging types of measurement the vibration problem is not too severe if a skid reference is used. This is because the vibration is most apt to move the workpiece, and both the skid and the stylus would be driven together, there thus being no relative motion between the skid and stylus due to the vibration.

When an external reference is used, any vibration due to the drive system will have a different effect on the stylus and the reference. The reading will be the relative motion of the stylus and the reference caused by the vibration as well as the surface irregularities. The effect of vibration can usually be measured by checking on a surface which has a very low roughness value, or by holding the tracer on a surface but detached from the drive system, and letting the drive system run. The reason for having a constant speed is that the roughness-width cutoff of a measuring system is affected by the tracing speed as follows:

$$\text{roughness-width cutoff (inches)} = \frac{\text{speed of trace (inches/second)}}{\text{amplifier low-frequency cutoff (cps)}}$$

Thus, it is apparent that any change in speed will change the roughness-width cutoff.

Amplifier

The amplifier of a surface measuring system must have a very high gain or magnification, very specific response characteristics, and be very stable. If the full-scale reading on an averaging type of instrument is 3 μin., and if the full scale width is 3 in., then the gain of the amplifier is 1,000,000 times. This gain at the low frequencies required for the roughness-width cutoffs obtainable with this type of equipment is not available even in top-quality high-fidelity amplifiers. For surface profiling, gains of up to 100,000 times are used. This would mean that 0.0000025 in. of variation on the workpiece would show up as $\frac{1}{4}$ in. on a chart.

The stability of the amplifier is necessary to assure that all of the variations which are shown are due to the workpiece rather than the electronics. This is best shown by substituting some known signal from a stable source for the transducer and noting whether or not the readout system indicates any variations. If this method is not feasible, then any variations can be shown by having the system operating but not moving the stylus with respect to the workpiece. Under these circumstances, if a variation is observed, it is due either to unstable electronics or to vibration.

Probably the most critical aspect of the amplifier is the response characteristics. As indicated in the section on drives, roughness-width cutoff is inversely proportional to the amplifier low-frequency cutoff. This is the lowest frequency to which the amplifier can respond.

Terms such as "response" and "low-frequency cutoff" are easy to visualize and understand by analogy to a high-fidelity amplifier, or any radio that has bass and treble controls. If the bass control on a radio or hi-fi set is changed, the clarity of low notes is altered. Low notes are produced by a slow reverberation in the range of 25 to 500 times per second. If a reverberation is 100 times per second, as may be produced by a bass fiddle, adjusting the bass control on the radio may or may not permit the bass fiddle to be heard. It does this by changing the lowest frequency which it will amplify. With the bass control off, the lowest frequency which a radio can pass may be 500 cps. Since the bass is producing a signal of 100 cps, the amplifier in the radio excludes the signal from that which it is amplifying and it is not heard. If the bass control is then turned all the way on, then perhaps the amplifier can pass as low as 25 cps, and the bass fiddle can be heard because its 100 cps signal will be passed by the amplifier.

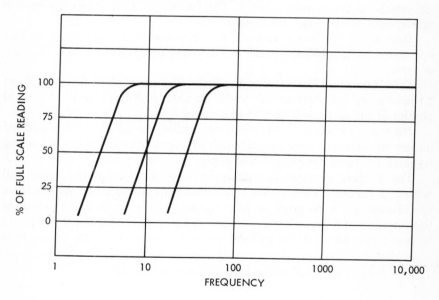

Fig. 13-7. Amplifier response to frequency.

This situation is identical to that which exists in a surface measuring amplifier, except that the low frequency limit of the amplifier is in the range of from 2 to 10 cps instead of the 25 to 500 cps found in the hi-fi set. Also, instead of a continuously variable low-frequency cutoff as is found in the hi-fi set, one, two, or three fixed frequency cutoffs are used.

At the high-frequency end of the scale a typical amplifier used for measuring surface texture has a high frequency of 5000 to 10,000 cps, which is normally much more than is needed to show the finely spaced irregularities on the surface. A typical system response curve is shown in Fig. 13-7.

THE DATA PRESENTATION

The three common means for presenting the surface measurement are: a panel meter, a chart record, or a digital readout. Here again, the characteristics of these devices have an effect on the measurement obtained. In the typical averaging instrument a panel meter is used to show the reading obtained.

ASA Standard B46.1-1962 states the required characteristics of meters as follows:

Response Time. The time to attain 95 percent of final deflection when driven by a suddenly applied signal shall be no shorter than 0.5 sec or $10/f$ sec, whichever is the longer period. The frequency (f) in cycles per second corresponds to the long wavelength cutoff point.

Damping. To reduce overshoot to a minimum and still provide as fast a response as possible, the coefficient of damping shall be not less than 0.6 of critical.

Scale Linearity. The scale of the indicating meter shall be linear from 20 percent of full scale to full scale. Departures from linearity below 20 percent of full scale shall be held to a minimum.

Integrated Roughness Meters. For instruments having meters that indicate integrated roughness over a fixed length of trace, the specifications regarding response time and damping do not apply.

The purpose of these characteristics is to assure that the meter will achieve a readable level within a reasonable length of time. Within these specifications, a wide range of meter responses can be used. The effect of the variation in response time is shown in Fig. 13-8. From this figure it will be noted that for perfectly uniform surfaces this response time makes little

Fig. 13-8. Meter response to uniformity of surface.

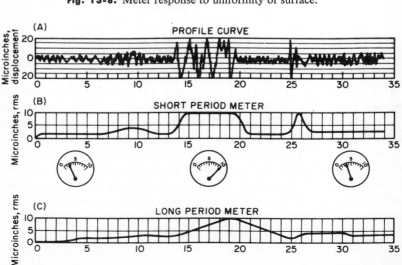

difference in the reading. However, for non-uniform surfaces (and most surfaces are non-uniform), the different response times will give different values. The continuously averaging measuring system keeps instantaneously showing the average over the last roughness-width cutoff length. If the surface varies, the instantaneous average should vary and thus the meter needle will swing. The rate at which the meter swings depends on the meter damping characteristics, and the amount the meter swings depends on the amount of non-uniformity of the surface. The ASA standard defines how this swinging meter should be read. It states "the roughness value is that value around which the needle tends to dwell."

Some meter systems come up to a fixed value. These systems are based on a fixed length of stroke, proportionate to the roughness-width cutoff. As the trace is made, the energy is stored, and at the end of the trace the needle comes to rest at the roughness value. In this system it is very easy to read the roughness height value. The problem with this system is that the roughness value so obtained may not be the best indication of the surface.

When one considers that the roughness height is used to define a whole area, and that it is derived over a single line trace, one must recognize that a very large portion of the surface was not considered. The taking of traces at right angles to the predominant lay pattern helps to assure that the highest readings are obtained, but it still cannot be flatly assumed. When the continuously averaging instrument traces over a surface, it will give some indication of the non-uniformity of the surface, but when a fixed-stroke direct readout system is used, there is no way of telling anything about the uniformity of the surface.

A great deal more information about the surface is given by a profile chart. The extra information is very useful, but the chart presents the problem of how to apply a single number to it. It is necessary first to know the means of obtaining the profile chart, what it really shows, and then how to attach some significant single numbers to it.

The recording meter presents the same problem as the panel meter, namely, that it must move fast enough to show the proper values, but in this case "fast enough" is much faster than required for the panel meter. In this case the meter must be able to record variations that occur as often as 100 times per second. Some recorders can move that fast, others cannot. The high-frequency response is very critical if it is intended to show roughness profiles. For example, if a part were machined with a 0.010-in. feed, this would mean that there would be 100 feed marks per inch of surface. If the surface were traced over at 0.3 in. per second, this would mean that in 3.3 sec the tracing means would have gone one inch and over 100 feed marks or, stated another way, over approximately 33 bumps in one second. If the recorder can only reproduce those irregularities occurring at 2 bumps or cycles and slower, the recorder could not pass a signal having such a high frequency. If, however, the recorder could faithfully reproduce events happening at 100 cps, then the true profile would result.

A third readout system, the digital counter, is coming into more and more common use. At the present time its application is limited to representing the average roughness value instead of using a panel meter. Also it is best suited to the fixed stroke type of measurement, and indicates other characteristics of the surface in digital form, such as the number of peaks that occur in a fixed length of stroke. This peak count has proved useful in determining both the uniformity and density of the surface irregularities. A new and growing application of the digital readout will be in measuring the surface texture of irregular shapes. If the digital information can be obtained at close enough intervals, then it will be possible to obtain a digital profile of a surface which, because of its irregular shape, cannot be magnified enough on a chart to have the roughness irregularities assume any measurable magnitude.

TWO SURFACE MEASUREMENT SYSTEMS

There are two prevalent surface measuring systems: (1) an averaging type of system which can be adapted to show a surface profile as well, and (2) a profiling system that can be adapted to do averaging as well. The following paragraphs discuss the relationship of the individual elements and their effect on the system.

The Averaging System (Figs. 13-9, 13-10)

The workpiece to be assumed for this example will be a part which is supposed to measure 64 μin. arithmetical average and which has been turned with a feed of 0.015 ipr. With a 0.015-in. feed, a roughness-width cutoff of 0.030 in. should be selected because it is a value in the table of preferred values wider than the roughness spacing value. Once the roughness-width cutoff value is selected, then the minimum length of stroke is determined. The standard length of stroke must be 20 times the roughness-width cutoff, according to the ASA standard. This would be a value of 0.6 in. minimum. If a fixed stroke system is used, the whole travel must be in the one direction. If a continuously averaging system is used, the stroke must still be 20 times the roughness-width cutoff, but the stroke need not be all in one direction. It may be as short as five times the roughness-width cutoff and allowed to oscillate back and forth across the surface twice, thus permitting a stroke length of only 0.150 in. Next, if a tracing speed

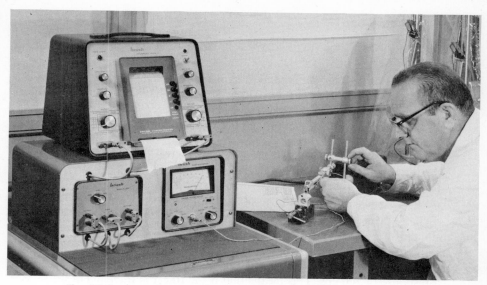

Fig. 13-9. Averaging-type Brush Analyzer (*Brush Instruments, Division of Clevite Corporation*).

Fig. 13-10. Portable averaging-type Profilometer without recorder (*Micrometrical Division, The Bendix Corporation*).

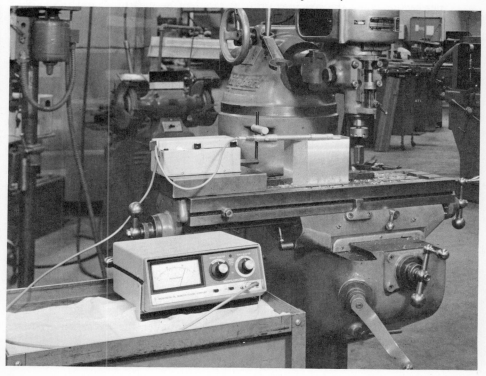

is selected of 0.10 in. per second, then the amplifier low-frequency cutoff can be decided upon. This is $0.1/0.030 = 3.3$ cps. This value now determines the minimum response time of the averaging meter, which is $10/3.3$ sec.

The roughness-width cutoff value also determines the minimum skid radius which is eight times the roughness-width cutoff in the direction of trace. This value is selected because the chordal height of an arc, the radius of which is eight times the chord, prevents most penetration of the irregularities by the skid for most measurements. In our example, the skid radius must be at least 0.240 in. in the direction of the trace. The other elements such as stylus, shape, and pressure are not critical and will be adequate if standard.

To such a simple averaging system there could be added a recording device to show the surface profile as well. Assume that the recorder has a response of 100 cps. This means that if the tracer is traveling at 0.1 in. per second, irregularities having widths of $0.1/100 = 0.001$ in. and wider can be recorded. At the other end of the scale, the amplifier can pass only 3.3 cps and thus we cannot see any irregularity wider than $0.1/3.3 = 0.030$ in. This means that the widely-spaced irregularities cannot be shown. If the amplifier is not changed, then to show the wider spacings the speed of trace must be changed. If the speed of trace is reduced to 0.01 in. per second, then spacings up to $0.01/3.3 = 0.003$ in. can be measured. If the speed is increased to 1 in. per second, then the spacings up to 0.3 in. can be measured, but the narrowest spacings are 0.010 in. Therefore, it is apparent that the amplifier must be changed too. To take meaningful profiles, a d-c amplifier must be used, in which the low-frequency cutoff is 0 cps. Thus the roughness-width cutoff becomes 0.1/0 or infinity. The surest test for d-c amplifier is to trace over two gage blocks of slightly different heights. If the trace shows the difference in height, then it is a d-c amplifier. If it does not show such a difference, true profiles cannot be obtained.

If a d-c amplifier is used, there is a mechanical cutoff which is determined by the reference. If a skid reference is used, we indicated that the skid must have a radius eight times the roughness-width cutoff. This would mean that the reference would have to be of infinite radius or a straight line. If this is not so, then the skid will ride up and down the wider-spaced irregularities with the diamond, and the wider-spaced irregularities will not show. From the above example it is possible to see the problems involved in trying to obtain true surface profiles, including the wider-spaced irregularities, when using equipment designed primarily for surface roughness.

The Profiling System (Figs. 13-11, 13-12)

In a system designed primarily for profiling, a d-c amplifier is used. Assuming the same workpiece, as discussed under the averaging system,

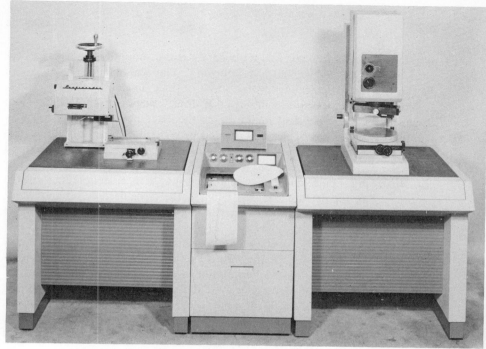

Fig. 13-11. Profiling-type Proficorder for showing roundness and straightness, in addition to roughness and waviness (*Micrometrical Division, The Bendix Corporation*).

Fig. 13-12. Profiling-type Talysurf for showing both profile and average finish (*Engis Equipment Company*).

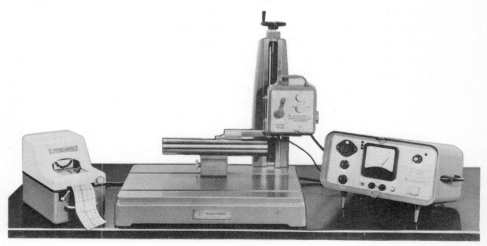

a tracing speed of 0.005 in. per second, a d-c amplifier, and a recorder response of 30 cps we find the following: The widest spacings that can be shown are still determined by the speed of trace divided by the roughness-width cutoff, i.e., 0.005/0 or infinity. Obviously there is a limitation which, in this case, is the physical limitation of the reference. If the reference is a skid, it is the radius of the skid divided by eight; if it is a straight line, it is the length of stroke. The narrowest spacing that can be shown is the speed of trace divided by the recorder response, i.e., 0.005/30 or 0.000166 in. For less than full chart deflection, higher response is available out of the recorder than the rated response. Thus, if the irregularities are not "full scale," then they may be even narrower than 0.000166 in., and can be recorded properly.

To obtain an average reading from a profiling system, the length of stroke computations must again be the same. The amplifier low frequency is now 0.005/.030 or 0.0167 cps. The minimum meter response is now 10/0.0167 or 60 sec. In using an averaging system for obtaining profiles, there are shortcomings, such as not being able to show the wider-spaced waviness; so there are shortcomings in using profiling instruments to obtain averages. These include the time it takes to obtain the reading and the problem of obtaining a sharp cutoff at such a low frequency.

TESTS FOR INSTRUMENT ACCURACY

Accuracy is a broad term for denoting quality. A user must have some way of determining the quality of his instrument and the following are characteristics which are readily checked: vibration level, repeatability, sensitivity, stylus shape, and system accuracy.

Vibration can be checked by having the stylus in contact with the work-piece, but without moving the stylus. The indications on the readout device are indications of ambient room vibrations. A method for checking for vibration due to the drive mechanism was discussed in the section on drives. A means for checking system vibration is to run the system on an optically smooth surface and note the level of signal. If the system check is of the averaging type, it is difficult to attribute the signal to vibration or to the workpiece, unless it is compared to another averaging rating on the same surface. If the system is of the profiling type, a repeatability check can be run as described below.

Repeatability can be checked by taking repeat traces over the same surface and recording the result. This can be done for either averaging or profiling. On polar recording, it is sufficient to let the recorder run several revolutions without stopping. With a strip recorder, several repeat traces can be run and the charts sectioned and laid over one another. Repeatability is no assurance of absolute accuracy, but is an indication of how reliable comparative measurements will be. Absolute accuracy requires repeatability and proper sensitivity.

Sensitivity is ultimately based on a length standard. Usually, this standard is a step of a few microinches which can be calibrated by interferometric means. The step itself is the sensitivity check for profiling instruments, but for averaging instruments a repeating surface pattern must be obtained. A mechanical sensitivity check, such as the Cali-block or a glass specimen, is usually calibrated by using a profiling instrument. This type of check is convenient because it can be done in the workplace. However, this type of check is influenced by the stylus shape. A more reliable calibration is to drive the stylus though an oscillating amplitude, using an electrical driving means. This system is not dependent on the stylus shape. The amplitude can be determined by interferometric or other means. The sensitivity thus obtained is the true sensitivity, and the effect of stylus shape can be determined by other means.

If the mechanical means of determining sensitivity has been used, then, in the case of the Cali-block, it is possible to get an indication of the shape of the stylus by using a finer ruling which is more susceptible to the stylus shape. This system is again useful in the workplace, but a more reliable measurement of the stylus shape is to observe the stylus shape directly under a microscope having at least 100X and preferably 250X magnification. This allows the stylus shape to be measured without dependence on the sensitivity.

Finally, overall system accuracy can be checked by using a workpiece of known characteristics. For profiling, this is usually a near perfect flat or sphere and some sort of step specimen. For averaging, this is usually a Cali-block or a glass specimen. It is important, if the system is shown not to be accurate, that each element of the system be checked to see which one is inaccurate, rather than to make all corrections in one element of the system regardless of which element is wrong. This can lead to a more erroneous reading than existed before the "correction."

14

GAGING AND MEASUREMENT

OF SCREW THREADS*

The first attempts to obtain interchangeability by the standardization of screw threads were made in 1841, when the Whitworth thread system was proposed in Great Britain. In 1868, the United States Standard (Sellers) system of screw threads was adopted by the United States Navy. This system included a recommendation for a standard gage for bolts, nuts, and screws.

Both systems underwent a long period of development and refinement, emerging eventually as the Unified Screw Thread System, which has received universal acceptance.

Gaging and measurement of gages are integral parts of the Unified Screw Thread System. They designate the degree of dimensional conformance to

*By Russell F. Holmes, Technical Assistant to the Director, Engineering Standards, General Motors Corporation and Jay E. Watson, Chief Engineer, Cutting Tool and Gage Section, Pratt and Whitney Machine Tool Division, Colt Industries, Inc.

size limits to assure interchangeability in the assembly of mating threaded components.

Geometric aspects of screw threads are relatively complex with respect to the interrelationship of pitch diameter, variation in lead, helix, and flank angle. Such elements have presented many obstacles which have retarded the development of screw thread measurement and gaging, as contrasted with other geometric features such as diameter and length.

Under favorable environmental conditions a 1-in. unit of length can be measured to within ± 0.000002 in. with reasonable reliability, whereas the elements of a 1-in. nominal size thread plug gage, such as pitch diameter and lead, can be measured to within ± 0.00005 in. only under the most precisely controlled conditions. Due to the problems in measuring internal threads, the sizes of thread ring gages are determined by the fit on the thread setting plug as measured.

Complete sets of standards are available which include product thread limits of size, gaging, and measurement for Unified screw threads, Taper pipe threads, Acme and Buttress threads, and other miscellaneous threads. Such standards are available from various sources, including American Standards Association (ASA), Society of Automotive Engineers (SAE) Industry Standards, and the National Bureau of Standards of the United States Department of Commerce (Handbook H-28[1]*.)

SCREW THREAD GAGING FOR MANUFACTURING

Screw Thread Gaging Methods

The gaging of screw threads is the process of investigating or determining the extent to which screw threads conform dimensionally to prescribed limits of size. Dimensional gages are the means for determining conformance.

Gages and gaging practice are supplemental to screw thread standards. They are intended to facilitate adherence to specified size limits without restricting the requirements more severely than the screw thread standards specified. Adherence to the gaging principles set forth in the standards assures interchangeability in assembly, the acceptance of satisfactory threads, and the segregation or rejection of threads that are significantly outside of prescribed limitations.

Two general methods are used for the dimensional inspection of threads: (1) inspection by attributes, and (2) inspection by variables.

*Superior numbers indicate specific references listed at the end of this chapter.

1. *Inspection by attributes* involves the application of limit gages to assure that the product is within the prescribed limits of size. This method generally forms the basis for the acceptance or rejection of threads with respect to specified limits of size.

2. *Inspection by variables* involves the application of indicating gages or measuring instruments to measure the extent of deviation of the individual elements of screw threads. This method is primarily useful in the control of tools and manufacturing processes. It may be applied, when necessary, to enforce the limits on deviations of individual thread elements, or to collect data for the analysis of screw thread defects.

In the manufacture of product threads it is necessary to control the limits of size and the various individual thread elements so that the threads produced will be acceptable with final conformance gages. In the United States, the adoption and use of specific gages is the prerogative of individual organizations. If the producer uses gages other than those described in Tentative American Standard B1.2,[2] he should evaluate the results obtained to assure correlation with the final conformance gages specified in the B1.2 standard and final conformance within the specifications of the ASA B1.1 standard.

Gage Characteristics

Limit gages used in manufacturing checking may be of the same general design as thread plug and ring gages used in final conformance gaging. It is important, however, that thread plug and ring gages used in manufacturing checking have tolerances so applied as to be within the product limits of size, i.e., GO thread plugs with tolerance *plus*, HI thread plugs with tolerance *minus*, GO thread rings and GO setting plugs with tolerance *minus*, LO thread rings and LO setting plugs with tolerance *plus*. Although final conformance gages should be as close as practical to the extreme limits of size of the product threads, gages for manufacturing checking should be as far from those extremes as is practicable while still within X gage tolerance. When X pitch diameter tolerance is specified for setting plugs, it is recommended that W tolerances for lead and angle be specified.

A practice sometimes used is to check the pitch diameter of new gages as received, to assign for final conformance gaging those closest to the extreme sizes of the product thread, and to assign for manufacturing checking those farthest from the extreme limits of size of the product thread. This practice is intended to assure that product thread found to be dimensionally acceptable in manufacturing checking will most certainly be accepted by final conformance gages.

Gage Surveillance

Periodic surveillance of both final conformance and manufacturing gages will disclose when the manufacturing gages, due to wear, approach approximately the same size as those used as final conformance gages. At such time either of two courses of action is suggested: (1) transfer final conformance gages to the manufacturing gage application, and vice versa, or (2) transfer manufacturing gages to the final conformance application, and replace them with new gages from the manufacturing gage stock.

Perhaps the most difficult point to reconcile in such a program is that of deviations resulting from normal use. Starting threads of both plugs and rings bear the brunt of use when making an inspection. Wear is seldom uniformly distributed over the gaging length and the thread flanks, resulting in inaccuracies of flank angle and pitch diameter. It is important for the success of such a program that inspection and manufacturing personnel agree on the position for the pitch diameter check and the degree of taper which may be tolerated before that gage should be taken out of service. The HI/LO gaging practice which permits the minimum-material limit gages to assemble for their entire length, provided a definite drag is achieved on or before the third thread of entry, has alleviated appreciably the problem of worn end threads.

Gage Selection Factors

A number of other styles of limit thread gages are used in manufacturing checking for technical or economic reasons. Among these are caliper or snap gages using gaging elements of various configurations. Included are those using rolls, segments, serrated anvils, wires, probes, and ball points. Although all of these would accept perfect threads with little or no appreciable difference, they may react quite differently on threads having acceptable lead and flank angle deviations.

An additional problem, primarily stemming from economics, arises when relatively few parts with threads are involved and when neither limit nor indicating gages are available, and it is economically impracticable to procure them. Such situations are daily problems in model shops, experimental and research departments, toolrooms, and job shops. A discussion of some commonly used practices follows.

Optical projection instruments or mechanical gages of a general nature are frequently used, in such situations, for determining accuracy of thread angle, thread form, and linear or helical lead.

Numerical values for groove diameter may be determined by the three-wire method or, for LO minimum-material limit, by use of thread micrometers. The accuracy of the values is affected by the following factors:

1. Values obtained from three-wire measurements are influenced by deviation in geometry and pitch of product thread.
2. Product thread characteristics, e.g., cleanliness, surface texture, hardness.
3. Measuring force exerted over the wires.
4. Operator skill in handling parts, wires, and micrometer.

Values obtained with thread micrometers are influenced by the foregoing factors and by the accuracy of the cone and Vee contact elements. To make use of such values, as applicable to the maximum-material limit, i.e., functional diameter, the diameter equivalents of deviations in lead and angle must be taken into account.

The values may be used without change for use as a manufacturing check at minimum-material limit. However, these values may be more restrictive of pitch diameter limits of size than would be experienced with limit gages.

SCREW THREAD TERMINOLOGY

Screw thread terminology consists of four general groups:

1. Those relating to *types* of screw threads.
2. Those relating to *size* of mechanical parts in general.
3. Those relating to elements of both straight and taper screw threads.
4. Those relating only to taper screw threads.

The following definitions are limited to those directly associated with the gaging and measurement of screw threads. A more complete listing is contained in American Standard ASA B1.7-1965,[3] or in Handbook H-28-1957.[1]

Terms Relating to Types of Screw Threads

Screw threads, and the terms generally applied to designate their types, are defined as follows:

1. *Screw Thread.* A screw thread is a ridge, usually of uniform section and produced by forming a groove in the form of a helix on the external or internal surface of a cylinder, or in the form of a conical spiral on the external or internal surface of a cone or frustum of a cone. A screw thread formed on a cylinder is known as a straight or parallel thread, to distinguish it from a taper screw thread which is formed on a cone or frustum of a cone.

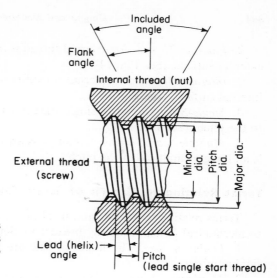

Fig. 14-1. Screw-thread terms relating to types and dimensions (single-start thread; lead equal to pitch).

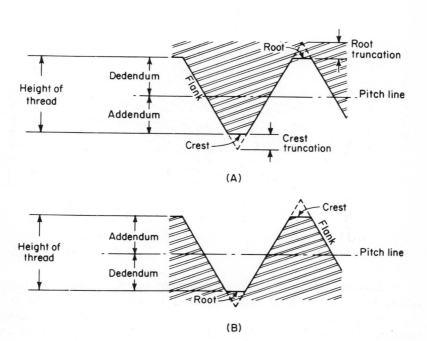

(A)

(B)

Fig. 14-2. Screw-thread terms relating to dimensions of internal and external screw threads: (A) internal thread; (B) external thread.

2. *External Thread.* An external thread is one on a cylindrical or conical external surface. (See Fig. 14-1.)

3. *Internal Thread.* An internal thread is one on a cylindrical or conical internal surface. (See Fig. 14-1.)

4. *Single-Start Thread.* A single-start thread is one having the lead equal to the pitch. (See Fig. 14-1.)

5. *Multiple-Start Thread.* A multiple-start thread is one in which the lead is an integral multiple of the pitch.

Terms Relating to Size Fit of Screw Threads

Terms relating to the size and fit of parts, which are generally applicable to mechanical parts, including threads, are defined as follows:

1. *Limits of Size.* The limits of size are the applicable maximum and minimum sizes.

2. *Maximum-Material Limit.* A maximum-material limit is that limit of size that provides the maximum amount of material for the part. Normally it is the maximum limit of size of an external dimension or the minimum limit of size of an internal dimension (see Fig. 14-3).

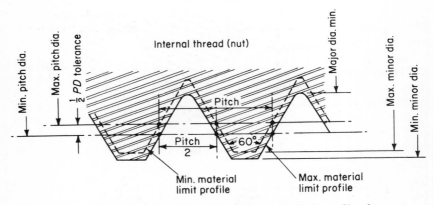

Fig. 14-3. Maximum and minimum material limit profiles for internal threads.

3. *Minimum-Material Limit.* A minimum-material limit is that limit of size that provides the minimum amount of material for the part. Normally it is the minimum limit of size of an external dimension or the maximum limit of size of an internal dimension. Examples of some exceptions are: an exterior corner radius where the maximum radius is the minimum-material limit and the minimum radius is the maximum-material limit.

Terms Relating to Dimensions of Screw Threads

Terms relating to dimensions of both straight and taper threads are defined as follows and are also shown in Figs. 14-1 and 14-2.

1. *Pitch.* The pitch of a thread having uniform spacing is the distance, measured parallel to its axis, between corresponding points on adjacent thread forms in the same axial plane and on the same side of the axis. The basic pitch is equal to the lead divided by the number of thread starts.

2. *Lead.* When a threaded part is rotated about its axis with respect to a fixed mating thread, the lead is the axial distance moved by the part in relation to the amount of angular rotation. The basic lead is commonly specified as the distance to be moved in one complete rotation. It is necessary to distinguish measurement of lead from measurement of pitch, as uniformity of pitch measurements does not assure uniformity of lead. Variations in either lead or pitch cause the functional diameter of thread to differ from the pitch diameter.

3. *Threads per Inch.* The number of threads per inch is the reciprocal of the pitch in inches.

4. *Included Angle.* The included angle of a thread (or angle of thread) is the angle between the flanks of the thread measured in an axial plane.

5. *Flank Angle.* The flank angles are the angles between the individual flanks and the perpendicular to the axis of the thread, measured in an axial plane. A flank angle of a symmetrical thread is commonly termed the half-angle of thread.

6. *Lead Angle.* On a straight thread, the lead angle is the angle made by the helix of the thread at the pitch line with a plane perpendicular to the axis. On a taper thread, the lead angle at a given axial position is the angle made by the conical spiral of the thread, with the plane perpendicular to the axis, at the pitch line.

7. *Helix Angle.* On a straight thread, the helix angle is the angle made by the helix of the thread at the pitch line with the axis. On a taper thread, the helix angle at a given axial position is the angle made by the conical spiral of the thread with the axis at the pitch line. The helix angle is the complement of the lead angle. (*Note:* The helix angle was formerly defined in accordance with the present definition of lead angle.)

8. *Height of Thread.* The height (or depth) of thread is the distance measured radially between the major and minor cylinders or cones, respectively. In American practice the height of thread is often expressed as a percentage of three-fourths of the height of the fundamental triangle.

9. *Addendum.* The addendum of an external thread is the radial distance between the major and pitch cylinders or cones, respectively. The addendum of an internal thread is the radial distance between the minor and pitch cylinders or cones, respectively.

10. *Dedendum.* The dedendum of an external thread is the radial distance between the pitch and minor cylinders or cones, respectively. The dedendum of an internal thread is the radial distance between the major and pitch cylinders or cones, respectively.

11. *Crest Truncation.* The crest truncation of a thread is the radial distance between the sharp crest (crest apex) and the cylinder or cone that would bound the crest.

12. *Root Truncation.* The root truncation of a thread is the radial distance between the sharp root (root apex) and the cylinder or cone that would bound the root.

13. *Major Diameter.* On a straight thread the major diameter is that of the major cylinder. On a taper thread the major diameter at a given position on the thread axis is that of the major cone at that position.

14. *Minor Diameter.* On a straight thread the minor diameter is that of the minor cylinder. On a taper thread the minor diameter at a given position on the thread axis is that of the minor cone at that position.

15. *Pitch Diameter.* On a straight thread the pitch diameter is the diameter of the pitch cylinder. On a taper thread, the pitch diameter at a given position on the thread axis is the diameter of the pitch cone at that position. On a single-start thread of perfect form and lead, it is also the length between intercepts of a line which is perpendicular to the thread axis and intersects thread flanks on opposite sides of the thread axis.

16. *Pitch Cylinder.* The pitch cylinder is one of such diameter and location of its axis that its surface would pass through a straight thread in such a manner as to make the widths of the thread ridge and the thread groove equal and, therefore, is located equidistantly between the sharp major and minor cylinders of a given thread form. On a theoretically perfect thread these widths are equal to one-half of the basic pitch.

17. *Functional (Virtual) Diameter.* The functional diameter of an external or internal thread is the pitch diameter of the enveloping thread of perfect pitch, lead, and flank angles, having full depth of engagement but clear at crests and roots, and of a specified length of engagement. It may be derived by adding to the pitch diameter in the case of an external thread, or subtracting from the pitch diameter in the case of an internal thread, the cumulative effects of deviations from specified profile, including variations in lead and flank angle over a specified length of engagement. The effects of taper, out-of-roundness, and surface defects may be positive or negative on either external or internal threads. (A perfect GO thread plug or ring gage, having a pitch diameter equal to that specified for the maximum-material limit and having clearance at crest and root, is the enveloping thread corresponding to that limit.)

STANDARD SPECIFICATIONS AND FORMULAS

Product Thread Specifications for Unified Screw Threads (60°)

Limits of Size. Conformance to the maximum-material limits of size is essential for interchangeable assembly. These limits are specified in terms of pitch diameter (Figs. 14-3 and 14-4). The *maximum*-material profiles (envelope) are established by the minimum pitch diameter limit of the internal thread and the maximum pitch diameter limit of the external thread. The *minimum*-material limit profiles are established by the maximum pitch diameter limit of the internal thread and the minimum pitch diameter limit of the external thread.

The degree of conformance to the minimum-material limits of size establishes the fit or the degree of looseness of the thread assembly.

In establishing the maximum- and minimum-material limits in terms of pitch diameter, the pitch and angle of the thread are considered basic or perfect. Since deviations in pitch and angle from this base are in the direction of maximum material, the full pitch diameter tolerance is not available unless the pitch and angle of the thread are perfect.

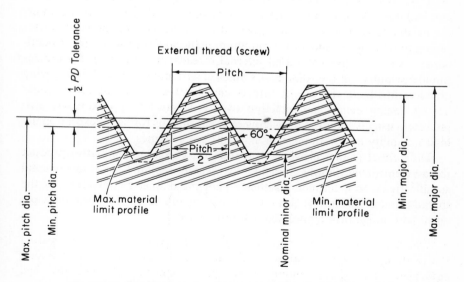

Fig. 14-4. Maximum and minimum material limit profiles for external threads.

With respect to the pitch diameter limits of size, it is intended that no portion of the complete thread be permitted to project beyond the envelope defined by the maximum-material limits on the one hand, or beyond that defined by the minimum-material limits on the other, and thus be outside of the tolerance zone. Also, it is intended that the diameter equivalent of the variation in any given element except pitch diameter should not exceed one-half of the pitch diameter tolerance. Deviations from specified size and profile include variations in lead, uniformity of helix, flank angle, taper, out-of-roundness, and surface defects.

The diameter equivalents of variations in lead, uniformity of helix, and flank angle are always in the direction toward maximum material; i.e., they increase the functional diameter of the external thread and decrease that of the internal thread. Thus, the maximum-material pitch diameter limits are a limitation of the functional diameter (effective size) and are so specified for all thread classes.[4]

Variations in taper and roundness of the pitch diameter, together with variations of the pitch diameter as a whole, may be in the direction of minimum material, and thus the minimum-material pitch diameter limit may be specified as a limitation of the pitch diameter as a single element.

Functional Diameter Gaging Practice. Functional diameter gaging practice (effective size), involving the use of thread-plug and ring-limit gages, is required for all maximum-material limits of size. This is to assure interchangeable assembly of mating threaded components. Functional diameter gaging practice is customary for minimum material limits of size for general-purpose external threads and all internal threads; it is the basis for dimensional acceptance in the ASA B1.1 standard. Minimum-material limit gaging practice, involving the use of thread snap limit gages or indicating gages having gaging elements contacting over a length of approximately two pitches, is usually required for gaging external threads for use in exceptionally high reliability applications such as aerospace activities.

Differential gaging provides a method for checking cumulative product thread-element deviations individually, where required by supplemental specifications, to determine whether or not the diameter equivalents of the thread-element deviations (lead and flank angle) exceed the allowable specified percentage of the pitch diameter tolerance.

Diameter Equivalent of Angle Deviation.[1] The general formula expressing the relation between deviation in the half-angle of thread and its diameter equivalent, that is, the amount of the pitch diameter tolerance absorbed by such a deviation, is

$$\cot \delta\alpha = \frac{5p}{4\delta E} \quad \text{or} \quad \delta E = 1.25p \tan \delta\alpha \tag{1}$$

Where, p = pitch

δE = pitch-diameter increment due to deviation in half-angle

α = basic half-angle of thread

$\delta\alpha$ = error in half-angle of thread.

The above formula applies to Unified threads based on a depth of thread engagement of $5h/8$.

Diameter Equivalent of Lead Deviations.[1] The formula expressing the relation between lead deviation between any two threads within the length of engagement and its diameter equivalent is as follows:

$$\delta E = 1.7321\delta p \tag{2}$$

Where, δE = pitch-diameter increment due to lead deviation

δp = the maximum pitch deviation between any two of the threads engaged.

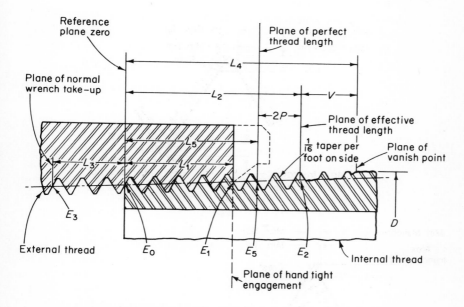

Fig. 14-5. Basic dimensions of taper pipe thread: (L_1) normal hand-tight engagement of external and internal threads; (L_2) length of effective thread of external thread; (L_3) wrench take-up length for internal thread; (L_4) overall length of external thread; (L_5) length of perfect threads for external thread; (E_0) pitch diameter at beginning of external thread; (E_1) pitch diameter at large end of internal thread; (E_2) pitch diameter of external thread at end of effective thread length; (E_3) pitch diameter at wrench take-up plane of internal thread; (E_5) pitch diameter at end of perfect threads of external thread; (V) vanish threads; (p) pitch of thread.[2]

The quantity δE is always added to the measured pitch diameter in the case of an external thread, and it is always subtracted in the case of an internal thread, regardless of the sign introduced by the lead deviation δp.

Product Thread Specifications for Taper Pipe Threads (60°)

Limits of Size. The limits of size of product taper pipe threads are controlled by gages. The various dimensions (Fig. 14-5) are given as basic, and the tolerance is stated in terms of one turn large or small from the basic dimensions. Proper control of the engagement of the assembled threaded joint is assured when the handtight (L_1 length) and effective thread lengths (L_3 length for internal thread and L_2 length for the external threads) are gaged to assure wrench take-up. Proper sealing of the threaded assembly (Fig. 14-6) is assured by controlling the truncation at the crest and root

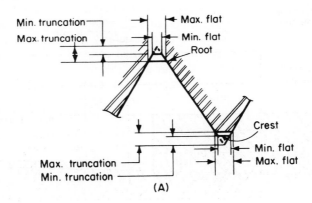

(A)

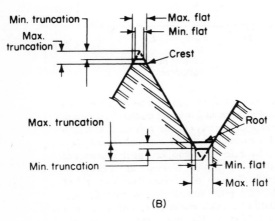

(B)

Fig. 14-6. Truncation of taper pipe threads: (A) internal thread; (B) external thread.

of the product thread, by limit gaging, or by optical projection. Truncation may be expressed in terms of thread height or equivalent width of flat.

Thread Elements. The tolerance limits for thread elements, such as taper, lead, and angle of product taper threads are stated in American Standard ASA B2.1-1960 and ASA B2.2-1965. These limits serve as a guide in controlling the tooling, and for conformance of product threads when required to supplement the plug and ring method of gaging.

Tolerances and Specifications for Straight Screw Thread Gages (60°)

Standard tolerances for thread plug and ring gages are of two classes: (1) *W* tolerances (Table 14-1) represent the highest commercial grade of accuracy, and are required particularly on setting plugs and master gages; (2) *X* tolerances (Table 14-2), which are greater than *W* tolerances, are usually applied to final conformance gages and manufacturing gages.

It is common practice to apply all gage tolerances within the extreme limits of size of the product thread, particularly at the maximum-material limit (GO gages), to ensure interchangeable assembly. The tolerances are sometimes applied outside of the product thread limits at the minimum-material limit (HI/LO gages, formerly NOT GO), to assure that usable product thread at the extreme limits of size is not rejected.

Tolerances on lead are usually specified as the allowable variation between any two threads over the length of the thread gage. Tolerances on lead embrace deviations in both pitch and helix, or total helical deviation.

Tolerance on angle is specified as flank angle or half-angle, to assure that the bisector of the included angle is perpendicular to the axis of the thread and within proper limits. The equivalent of the deviation from the true thread, such as convex or concave conditions, should not exceed the tolerance permitted on flank angle.

Tolerances on individual thread elements (lead, flank angle, and pitch diameter) are not cumulative, i.e., the tolerance on any one element may not be exceeded, even though the errors in the other two elements are smaller than the respective tolerances.

Tolerances and Specifications for Thread Elements of Taper Pipe Thread (60°) Gages (NPT)

Taper-thread plug and thread-ring gages should conform to the basic dimensions and be within the tolerances of the individual elements shown in Table 14-3. Master gages should conform to basic dimensions as accurately as possible, and should in no event exceed the tolerances shown in

TABLE 14-1. TOLERANCES FOR W "GO" AND "HI/LO"* THREAD GAGES

Threads per inch	Tolerance on lead†§		Tolerance on half angle of thread	Tolerance on major or minor diameters			Tolerance on pitch diameter				
	To and including ½ in. diam	Above ½ in. diam		To and including ½ in. diam	Above ½ in. to 4 in. diam	Above 4 in. diam	To and including ½ in. diam	Above ½ in. to 1½ in. diam	Above 1½ in. to 4 in. diam	Above 4 in. to 8 in. diam	Above 8 in. to 12 in. diam‡
	in.	in.	deg min ±	in.	in.	in.	in.	in.	in.	in.	in.
80	0.0001	0.00015	0 20	0.0003	0.0003		0.0001	0.00015			
72	0.0001	0.00015	0 20	0.0003	0.0003		0.0001	0.00015			
64	0.0001	0.00015	0 20	0.0003	0.0004		0.0001	0.00015			
56	0.0001	0.00015	0 20	0.0003	0.0004		0.0001	0.00015	0.0002		
48	0.0001	0.00015	0 18	0.0003	0.0004		0.0001	0.00015	0.0002	0.00025	
44	0.0001	0.00015	0 15	0.0003	0.0004		0.0001	0.00015	0.0002	0.00025	
40	0.0001	0.00015	0 15	0.0003	0.0004		0.0001	0.00015	0.0002	0.00025	
36	0.0001	0.00015	0 12	0.0003	0.0004		0.0001	0.00015	0.0002	0.00025	
32	0.0001	0.00015	0 12	0.0003	0.0005	0.0007	0.0001	0.00015	0.0002	0.00025	0.0003
28	0.00015	0.00015	0 8	0.0005	0.0005	0.0007	0.0001	0.00015	0.0002	0.00025	0.0003
27	0.00015	0.00015	0 8	0.0005	0.0005	0.0007	0.0001	0.00015	0.0002	0.00025	0.0003
24	0.00015	0.00015	0 8	0.0005	0.0005	0.0007	0.0001	0.00015	0.0002	0.00025	0.0003
20	0.00015	0.00015	0 8	0.0005	0.0005	0.0007	0.0001	0.00015	0.0002	0.00025	0.0003
18	0.00015	0.00015	0 8	0.0005	0.0005	0.0007	0.0001	0.00015	0.0002	0.00025	0.0003
16	0.00015	0.00015	0 8	0.0006	0.0006	0.0009	0.0001	0.0002	0.00025	0.0003	0.0004
14	0.0002	0.0002	0 6	0.0006	0.0006	0.0009	0.00015	0.0002	0.00025	0.0003	0.0004
13	0.0002	0.0002	0 6	0.0006	0.0006	0.0009	0.00015	0.0002	0.00025	0.0003	0.0004
12	0.0002	0.0002	0 6	0.0006	0.0006	0.0009	0.00015	0.0002	0.00025	0.0003	0.0004
11½	0.0002	0.0002	0 6	0.0006	0.0006	0.0009	0.00015	0.0002	0.00025	0.0003	0.0004
11	0.0002	0.0002	0 6	0.0006	0.0006	0.0009	0.00015	0.0002	0.00025	0.0003	0.0004

TABLE 14-1. (cont.)

Threads per inch	Tolerance on lead†§		Tolerance on half-angle of thread ±	Tolerance on major or minor diameters			Tolerance on pitch diameter				
	To and including ½ in. diam	Above ½ in. diam		To and including ½ in. diam	Above ½ in. to 4 in. diam	Above 4 in. diam	To and including ½ in. diam	Above ½ in. to 1½ in. diam	Above 1½ in. to 4 in. diam	Above 4 in. to 8 in. diam	Above 8 in. to 12 in. diam‡
	in.	*in.*	*deg min*	*in.*	*in.*	*in.*	*in.*	*in.*	*in.*	*in.*	*in.*
10		0.00025	0 6		0.0006	0.0009		0.0002	0.00025	0.0003	0.0004
9		0.00025	0 6		0.0007	0.0011		0.0002	0.00025	0.0003	0.0004
8		0.00025	0 5		0.0007	0.0011		0.0002	0.00025	0.0003	0.0004
7		0.0003	0 5		0.0007	0.0011		0.0002	0.00025	0.0003	0.0004
6		0.0003	0 5		0.0008	0.0013		0.0002	0.00025	0.0003	0.0004
5		0.0003	0 4		0.0008	0.0013			0.00025	0.0003	0.0004
4½		0.0003	0 4		0.0008	0.0013			0.00025	0.0003	0.0004
4		0.0003	0 4		0.0009	0.0015			0.00025	0.0003	0.0004

*Formerly called "not-go."

†Allowable variation in lead between any two threads not farther apart than the length of the standard gage.

‡Above 12 in. the tolerance is directly proportional to the tolerance in this column in the ratio of the diameter to 12 in.

§It has been customary in the past to specify tolerances on lead as plus or minus (±) values. Under the requirement above, the width of the tolerance zone is the nominal tolerance value specified regardless of sign. In view of the preceding, the tolerance symbols, plus or minus (±), should be removed in referencing lead to tolerances. The omission of the plus and minus does not change the total tolerance.

TABLE 14-2   TOLERANCES FOR X "GO" AND "HI/LO"* THREAD GAGES§

Threads per inch	Tolerance on lead†§	Tolerance on half angle of thread	Tolerance on major or minor diameters		Tolerance on pitch diameter			
			To and including 4 in. diam	Above 4 in. diam	To and including 1½ in. diam	Above 1½ to 4 in. diam	Above 4 to 8 in. diam	Above 8 to 12 in. diam‡
	in.	*deg min* ±	*in.*	*in.*	*in.*	*in.*	*in.*	*in.*
80	0.0002	0 30	0.0003		0.0002			
72	0.0002	0 30	0.0003		0.0002			
64	0.0002	0 30	0.0004		0.0002			
56	0.0002	0 30	0.0004		0.0002	0.0003		
48	0.0002	0 30	0.0004		0.0002	0.0003		
44	0.0002	0 20	0.0004		0.0002	0.0003		
40	0.0002	0 20	0.0004		0.0002	0.0003		
36	0.0002	0 20	0.0004		0.0002	0.0003		
32	0.0003	0 15	0.0005	0.0007	0.0003	0.0004	0.0005	0.0006
28	0.0003	0 15	0.0005	0.0007	0.0003	0.0004	0.0005	0.0006
27	0.0003	0 15	0.0005	0.0007	0.0003	0.0004	0.0005	0.0006
24	0.0003	0 15	0.0005	0.0007	0.0003	0.0004	0.0005	0.0006
20	0.0003	0 15	0.0005	0.0007	0.0003	0.0004	0.0005	0.0006
18	0.0003	0 10	0.0005	0.0007	0.0003	0.0004	0.0005	0.0006
16	0.0003	0 10	0.0006	0.0009	0.0003	0.0004	0.0006	0.0008
14	0.0003	0 10	0.0006	0.0009	0.0003	0.0004	0.0006	0.0008
13	0.0003	0 10	0.0006	0.0009	0.0003	0.0004	0.0006	0.0008
12	0.0003	0 10	0.0006	0.0009	0.0003	0.0004	0.0006	0.0008
11½	0.0003	0 10	0.0006	0.0009	0.0003	0.0004	0.0006	0.0008
11	0.0003	0 10	0.0006	0.0009	0.0003	0.0004	0.0006	0.0008
10	0.0003	0 10	0.0006	0.0009	0.0003	0.0004	0.0006	0.0008
9	0.0003	0 10	0.0007	0.0011	0.0003	0.0004	0.0006	0.0008
8	0.0004	0 5	0.0007	0.0011	0.0004	0.0005	0.0006	0.0008
7	0.0004	0 5	0.0007	0.0011	0.0004	0.0005	0.0006	0.0008
6	0.0004	0 5	0.0008	0.0013	0.0004	0.0005	0.0006	0.0008
5	0.0004	0 5	0.0008	0.0013		0.0005	0.0006	0.0008
4½	0.0004	0 5	0.0008	0.0013		0.0005	0.0006	0.0008
4	0.0004	0 5	0.0009	0.0015		0.0005	0.0006	0.0008

*Formerly called "not-go."

†Allowable variation in lead between any two threads not farther apart than the length of the standard gage.

‡Above 12 in. the tolerance is directly proportional to the tolerance in this column in the ratio of the diameter to 12 in.

§It has been customary in the past to specify tolerances on lead as plus or minus (±) values. Under the requirement above, the width of the tolerance zone is the nominal tolerance value specified regardless of sign. In view of the preceding, the tolerance symbols, plus or minus (±), should be removed in referencing lead to tolerances. The omission of the plus and minus does not change the total tolerance.

TABLE 14-3. TOLERANCES FOR AMERICAN STANDARD MASTER AND INSPECTION (MANUFACTURING) TAPER PIPE THREAD PLUG AND RING GAGES, NPT[5]

Nominal pipe size	Threads per inch	Tolerance on pitch diameter*	Tolerance on lead†§		Tolerance on half-angle‡		Tolerance on taper§‖		Tolerance on major diameter‡	Tolerance on minor diameter**	Total cumulative tolerances on pitch diameter		Standoff between plug and ring gages at gaging notch for dimensions at opposite extreme tolerance limits††
			Plugs	Rings	Plugs	Rings	Plugs	Rings	Plugs	Rings	Plugs	Rings	
in.		± in.	in.	in.	± min.	± min.	+ in.	− in.	− in.	+ in.	in.	in.	in.
1/16	27	0.0002	0.0002	0.0003	15	20	0.0003	0.0006	0.0004	0.0004	0.00080	0.00118	0.032
1/8	27	0.0002	0.0002	0.0003	15	20	0.0003	0.0006	0.0004	0.0004	0.00080	0.00118	0.032
1/4	18	0.0002	0.0002	0.0003	15	20	0.0004	0.0007	0.0006	0.0006	0.00092	0.00134	0.036
3/8	18	0.0002	0.0002	0.0003	15	20	0.0004	0.0007	0.0006	0.0006	0.00092	0.00134	0.036
1/2	14	0.0003	0.0002	0.0003	10	15	0.0006	0.0009	0.0010	0.0010	0.00097	0.00142	0.038
3/4	14	0.0003	0.0002	0.0003	10	15	0.0006	0.0009	0.0010	0.0010	0.00097	0.00142	0.038
1	11½	0.0003	0.0003	0.0004	10	15	0.0008	0.0012	0.0010	0.0010	0.00121	0.00170	0.047
1¼	11½	0.0003	0.0003	0.0004	10	15	0.0008	0.0012	0.0010	0.0010	0.00121	0.00170	0.047
1½	11½	0.0003	0.0003	0.0004	10	15	0.0008	0.0012	0.0010	0.0010	0.00121	0.00170	0.047
2	11½	0.0003	0.0003	0.0004	10	15	0.0008	0.0012	0.0010	0.0010	0.00121	0.00170	0.047
2½	8	0.0005	0.0004	0.0005	7	10	0.0010	0.0014	0.0016	0.0016	0.00158	0.00211	0.059
3	8	0.0005	0.0004	0.0005	7	10	0.0010	0.0014	0.0016	0.0016	0.00158	0.00211	0.059
3½	8	0.0005	0.0004	0.0005	7	10	0.0010	0.0014	0.0016	0.0016	0.00158	0.00211	0.059
4	8	0.0005	0.0004	0.0005	7	10	0.0010	0.0014	0.0016	0.0016	0.00158	0.00211	0.059
5	8	0.0005	0.0004	0.0005	7	10	0.0010	0.0014	0.0016	0.0016	0.00158	0.00211	0.059
6	8	0.0005	0.0004	0.0005	7	10	0.0010	0.0014	0.0016	0.0016	0.00158	0.00211	0.059
8	8	0.0005	0.0004	0.0005	7	10	0.0010	0.0014	0.0020	0.0020	0.00158	0.00211	0.059
10	8	0.0005	0.0004	0.0005	7	10	0.0010	0.0014	0.0020	0.0020	0.00158	0.00211	0.059
12	8	0.0005	0.0004	0.0005	7	10	0.0010	0.0014	0.0020	0.0020	0.00158	0.00211	0.059

TABLE 14-3. (cont.)

Nominal pipe size	Threads per inch	Tolerance on pitch diameter*	Tolerance on lead†§		Tolerance on half-angle‡		Tolerance on taper§||		Tolerance on major diameter‡	Tolerance on minor diameter**	Total cumulative tolerances on pitch diameter		Standoff between plug and ring gages at gaging notch for dimensions at opposite extreme tolerance limits††
			Plugs	Rings	Plugs	Rings	Plugs	Rings	Plugs	Rings	Plugs	Rings	
in.		*in.* ±	*in.*	*in.*	*min.* ±	*min.* ±	*in.* +	*in.* −	*in.* −	*in.* +	*in.*	*in.*	*in.*
14 OD	8	0.0008	0.0005	0.0006	7	10	0.0010	0.0014	0.0030	0.0030	0.00206	0.00271	0.076
16 OD	8	0.0008	0.0005	0.0006	7	10	0.0010	0.0014	0.0030	0.0030	0.00206	0.00271	0.076
18 OD	8	0.0008	0.0005	0.0006	7	10	0.0010	0.0014	0.0030	0.0030	0.00206	0.00271	0.076
20 OD	8	0.0008	0.0005	0.0006	7	10	0.0010	0.0014	0.0030	0.0030	0.00206	0.00271	0.076
24 OD	8	0.0008	0.0005	0.0006	7	10	0.0010	0.0014	0.0030	0.0030	0.00206	0.00271	0.076

*To be measured at the gaging notch of plug gage.

†Allowable variation in lead between any two threads in L_1 length of gage.

‡In solving for the correction in diameter for angle deviations, the average deviation in half-angle for the two sides of thread regardless of their signs should be taken.

§The lead and taper on plug and ring gages shall be measured along the pitch line, omitting the imperfect threads at each end.

\|\|Allowable variation in taper, in L_1 length of gage.

‡Tolerance on major diameter of plug gage at gaging notch.

**Tolerance on minor diameter of ring gage at large end.

††Maximum possible interchange standoff, any ring against any plug other than its master plug, may occur when taper deviations are zero and all other dimensions are at opposite extreme tolerance limits. Average standoff should be well within these maximum limits.

NOTE.—The large end of the ring gage shall be flush with the gaging notch of its master plug gage when assembled handtight within ±0.002 in. for sizes $\frac{1}{16}$ to 2 in., inclusive, within ±0.003 in. for sizes $2\frac{1}{2}$ to 12 in., inclusive, and within ±0.005 in. for sizes 14 in. and larger.

The tolerances for the length L_1 from small end to gaging notch of the plug gage shall be +0.000 and −0.001 for sizes $\frac{1}{16}$ to 2 in., inclusive, and +0.000 and −0.002 for sizes $2\frac{1}{2}$ in. and larger.

The tolerances for the over-all thread length L_2 of the plug gage shall be +0.005 and −0.000 for sizes $\frac{1}{16}$ in. to 2 in., inclusive, and +0.010 and −0.000 for sizes $2\frac{1}{2}$ in. and larger.

The tolerances for the thickness L_1 of the ring gage shall be +0.001 and −0.000 for sizes $\frac{1}{16}$ to 2 in., inclusive, and +0.002 and −0.000 for sizes $2\frac{1}{2}$ in. and larger.

TABLE 14-4. DIAMETER EQUIVALENT OF DEVIATION IN HALF
INCLUDED ANGLE FOR TOOLS AND GAGES*[5]

Deviation,† $\delta\alpha$	8 threads per inch	11½ threads per inch	14 threads per inch	18 threads per inch	27 threads per inch
min.	*in.*	*in.*	*in.*	*in.*	*in.*
1	0.00006	0.00004	0.00003	0.00002	0.00002
2	0.00011	0.00008	0.00006	0.00005	0.00003
3	0.00017	0.00012	0.00010	0.00007	0.00005
4	0.00022	0.00016	0.00013	0.00010	0.00007
5	0.00028	0.00019	0.00016	0.00012	0.00008
6	0.00034	0.00023	0.00019	0.00015	0.00010
7	0.00039	0.00027	0.00022	0.00017	0.00012
8	0.00045	0.00031	0.00026	0.00020	0.00013
9	0.00050	0.00035	0.00029	0.00022	0.00015
10	0.00056	0.00039	0.00032	0.00025	0.00017
11	0.00062	0.00043	0.00035	0.00027	0.00018
12	0.00067	0.00047	0.00038	0.00030	0.00020
13	0.00073	0.00051	0.00042	0.00032	0.00022
14	0.00078	0.00054	0.00045	0.00035	0.00023
15	0.00084	0.00058	0.00048	0.00037	0.00025
16	0.00089	0.00062	0.00051	0.00040	0.00027
17	0.00095	0.00066	0.00054	0.00042	0.00028
18	0.00101	0.00070	0.00058	0.00045	0.00030
19	0.00106	0.00074	0.00061	0.00047	0.00031
20	0.00112	0.00078	0.00064	0.00050	0.00033
21	0.00117	0.00082	0.00067	0.00052	0.00035
22	0.00123	0.00086	0.00070	0.00055	0.00036
23	0.00129	0.00089	0.00074	0.00057	0.00038
24	0.00134	0.00093	0.00077	0.00060	0.00040
25	0.00140	0.00097	0.00080	0.00062	0.00041
26	0.00145	0.00101	0.00083	0.00065	0.00043
27	0.00151	0.00105	0.00086	0.00067	0.00045
28	0.00157	0.00109	0.00089	0.00070	0.00046
29	0.00162	0.00113	0.00093	0.00072	0.00048
30	0.00168	0.00117	0.00096	0.00075	0.00050
45	0.00252	0.00175	0.00144	0.00112	0.00075
60	0.00336	0.00233	0.00192	0.00149	0.00099

*In solving for the diameter equivalent of angle deviations the average deviation in half-angle for the two sides of the thread regardless of their signs should be taken.

†Diameter equivalent $= 1.53812p \tan \delta\alpha$, where $\delta\alpha =$ deviation in half-angle of thread.

Table 14-3. Additionally, the master gages should be accompanied by a calibration report of all thread elements.

In calibrating master gages, it may be necessary to compute from measurement the decimal part of a turn that a gage varies from the basic dimension. The correction in diameter for angle and lead deviation is shown in Tables

TABLE 14-5. DIAMETER EQUIVALENT OF DEVIATION IN PITCH FOR TOOLS AND GAGES*[5]

Deviation, δp	0.00000	0.00001	0.00002	0.00003	0.00004	0.00005	0.00006	0.00007	0.00008	0.00009
in.	in.	in.	in.	in.	in.	in.	in.	in.	in.	in.
0.00000	0.00000	0.00002	0.00003	0.00005	0.00007	0.00009	0.00010	0.00012	0.00014	0.00016
0.00010	0.00017	0.00019	0.00021	0.00023	0.00024	0.00026	0.00028	0.00029	0.00031	0.00033
0.00020	0.00035	0.00036	0.00038	0.00040	0.00042	0.00043	0.00045	0.00047	0.00048	0·00050
0.00030	0.00052	0.00054	0.00055	0.00057	0.00059	0.00061	0.00062	0.00064	0.00066	0.00068
0.00040	0.00069	0.00071	0.00073	0.00074	0.00076	0.00078	0.00080	0.00081	0.00083	0.00085
0.00050	0.00087	0.00088	0.00090	0.00092	0.00094	0.00095	0.00097	0.00099	0.00100	0.00102
0.00060	0.00104	0.00106	0.00107	0.00109	0.00111	0.00113	0.00114	0.00116	0.00118	0.00120
0.00070	0.00121	0.00123	0.00125	0.00126	0.00128	0.00130	0.00132	0.00133	0.00135	0.00137
0.00080	0.00139	0.00140	0.00142	0.00144	0.00145	0.00147	0.00149	0.00151	0.00152	0.00154
0.00090	0.00156	0.00158	0.00159	0.00161	0.00163	0.00165	0.00166	0.00168	0.00170	0.00171
0.00100	0.00173	0.00175	0.00177	0.00178	0.00180	0.00182	0.00184	0.00185	0.00187	0.00189
0.00110	0.00191	0.00192	0.00194	0.00196	0.00197	0.00199	0.00201	0.00203	0.00204	0.00206
0.00120	0.00208	0.00210	0.00211	0.00213	0.00215	0.00217	0.00218	0.00220	0.00222	0.00223
0.00130	0.00225	0.00227	0.00229	0.00230	0.00232	0.00234	0.00236	0.00237	0.00239	0.00241
0.00140	0.00242	0.00244	0.00246	0.00248	0.00249	0.00251	0.00253	0.00255	0.00256	0.00258
0.00150	0.00260	0.00262	0.00263	0.00265	0.00267	0.00268	0.00270	0.00272	0.00274	0.00275
0.00160	0.00277	0.00279	0.00281	0.00282	0.00284	0.00286	0.00288	0.00289	0.00291	0.00293
0.00170	0.00294	0.00296	0.00298	0.00300	0.00301	0.00303	0.00305	0.00307	0.00308	0.00310
0.00180	0.00312	0.00313	0.00315	0.00317	0.00319	0.00320	0.00322	0.00324	0.00326	0.00327
0.00190	0.00329	0.00331	0.00333	0.00334	0.00336	0.00338	0.00339	0.00341	0.00343	0.00345
0.00200	0.00346	0.00348	0.00350	0.00352	0.00353	0.00355	0.00357	0.00359	0.00360	0.00362

*Diameter equivalent $= 1.732\delta p$, where $\delta p =$ deviation in pitch between any two threads.

14-4 and 14-5. These corrections are added to the pitch diameter of the external thread and are subtracted from the pitch diameter of the internal thread. The diameter equivalent for lead and angle deviations, plus the pitch diameter deviations multiplied by 16, equals the longitudinal variation from basic at the gaging notch. The longitudinal variation divided by the pitch equals the decimal part of a turn that the gage varies from basic at the gaging notch.

Formulas for Measurement of Pitch Diameter

General Formulas for Measurement of Pitch Diameter.[1] The general formula for determining the pitch diameter of any thread whose sides are symmetrical with respect to a line drawn through the vertex and perpendicular to the axis of the thread, in which the slight effect of lead angle is taken into account, is

$$E = M_w + \frac{\cot \alpha}{2n} - w[1 + (\operatorname{cosec}^2 \alpha + \cot^2 \alpha \tan^2 \lambda')^{1/2}] \qquad (3)$$

where E = pitch diam

M_w = measurement over wires (see "Measurement of Pitch Diameter")

α = half-angle of thread

n = number of threads per inch = $1/p$

w = mean diameter of wires

λ' = angle between axis of wire and plane perpendicular to axis of thread

This formula is a very close approximation, being based on certain assumptions regarding the positions of the points of contact between the wire and the thread.

Formula (3) can be converted to the following simplified form, which is particularly useful when measuring threads of large lead angle:

$$E = M_w + \frac{\cot \alpha}{2n} - w(1 + \operatorname{cosec} \alpha') \qquad (4)$$

where α' = the angle whose tangent = $\tan \alpha \cos \lambda'$.

When formula (3) is used, the usual practice is to expand the square root term as a series, retaining only the first and second terms, which gives the following:

$$E = M_w + \frac{\cot \alpha}{2n} - w\left(1 + \operatorname{cosec} \alpha + \frac{\tan^2 \lambda' \cos \alpha \cot \alpha}{2}\right) \qquad (5)$$

For large lead angles it is necessary to measure the wire angle λ', but for lead angles of 5° or less, if the "best-size" wire is used (see "Methods of Measuring and Using Wires"), this angle may be assumed to be equal to the lead angle of the thread at the pitch line, λ. The value of $\tan \lambda$, the tangent of the lead angle, is given by the formula

$$\tan \lambda = \frac{l}{3.1416E} = \frac{1}{3.1416NE} \tag{6}$$

where $l =$ lead
$\quad\quad N =$ number of turns per inch
$\quad\quad E =$ nominal pitch diameter of an approximation of the measured
$\quad\quad\quad$ pitch diameter

Formulas for Measurement of Pitch Diameter of Unified, American and American National Straight Threads.[1] For threads of the Unified, American, and American National coarse, fine, extra-fine, 8-, 12-, and 16-thread series, the term

$$\frac{w \tan^2 \lambda' \cos \alpha \cot \alpha}{2}$$

is neglected. This is done since its value is small, being in all cases less than 0.00015 in. for standard fastening screws when the best-size wire is used. Thus the above formula (5) takes the simplified form

$$E = M_w + \frac{\cot \alpha}{2n} - w(1 + \operatorname{cosec} \alpha) \tag{7}$$

The practice is permissible provided that it is uniformly followed. To maintain uniformity of practice, and thus avoid confusion, the National Bureau of Standards uses formula (7) for such threads. The Bureau also uses formula (7) for special 60° threads, except when the value of the term

$$\frac{w \tan^2 \lambda' \cos \alpha \cot \alpha}{2}$$

exceeds 0.000015 in., as in the case of multiple threads, or other threads having exceptionally large lead angles. For 60° threads this term exceeds 0.00015 in. when $NE \sqrt{n}$ is less than 17.1.

For a 60° thread of correct angle and thread form, formula (7) simplifies to

$$E = M_w + \frac{0.86603}{n} - 3w \tag{8}$$

For a given set of best-size wires

$$E = M_w - C \tag{9}$$

where $C = w(1 + \operatorname{cosec} \alpha) - \dfrac{\cot \alpha}{2n}$ \hfill (10)

The quantity C is a constant for a given thread angle and, when the wires are used for measuring threads of the pitch and angle for which they are the best size, the pitch diameter is obtained by the simple operation of subtracting this constant from the measurement taken over the wires. In fact, when best-size wires are used, this constant is changed very little by a moderate deviation or error in the angle of the thread. Consequently, the constants for the various sets of wires in use may be tabulated, thus saving a considerable amount of time in the inspection of gages. However, when wires of other than the best size are used, this constant changes appreciably with a deviation in the angle of the thread. (See "Methods of Measuring and Using Wires.")

Formulas for Measurement of Pitch Diameter of American Standard Taper Threads.[1] The general formula for a taper thread, corresponding to formula (5), is

$$E = M_w + \frac{\cot \alpha - \tan^2 \beta \tan \alpha}{2n} - w\left(1 + \operatorname{cosec} \alpha + \frac{\tan^2 \lambda' \cos \alpha \cot \alpha}{2}\right)$$

$$(11)$$

where E = pitch diameter
  M_w = measurement over wires
  β = half-angle of taper of thread
  n = number of threads per inch = $1/p$
  α = half-angle of thread
  w = mean diameter of wires
  λ' = wire angle.

The term

$$\frac{\cot \alpha - \tan^2 \beta \tan \alpha}{2n}$$

is the exact value of the depth of the fundamental triangle of a taper thread, which is less than that of the same-pitch thread cut on a cylinder. For steep-tapered thread gages, having an included taper larger than $\frac{3}{4}$ in. per ft, this more accurate term should be applied. For such a thread, which has a small lead angle, formula (11) takes the form

$$E = M_w + \frac{\cot \alpha - \tan^2 \beta \tan \alpha}{2n} - w(1 + \operatorname{cosec} \alpha) \qquad (12)$$

Otherwise, as for American Standard taper pipe threads having an included taper of $\frac{3}{4}$ in. per ft, the simplified formula (8)

$$E = M_w + \frac{0.86603}{n} - 3w$$

for 60° threads may be used. This simplified formula gives a value of E that is 0.00005 in. larger than that given by the above general formula (11) for the $2\frac{1}{2}$-8 American Standard taper pipe thread, the worst case in this thread series.

The pitch diameter at any other point along the thread, as at the gaging notch, is obtained by (1) multiplying the distance parallel to the axis of the thread, between this point and the point at which the measurement was taken, by the taper per inch, then (2) adding the product to or subtracting it from the measured pitch diameter, according to the direction in which the second point is located with respect to the first.

The formula for the pitch diameter of any taper thread plug gage, the threads of which are symmetrical with respect to a line perpendicular to the axis, then has the form corresponding to formula (7),

$$E = (M_w - w)\sec\beta + \frac{\cot\alpha}{2n} - w\cosec\,\alpha \tag{13}$$

in which $\beta =$ half-angle of taper of thread. Thus the pitch diameter of an American standard pipe-thread gage having correct angle (60°) and taper ($\frac{3}{4}$ in. per ft) is then given by the formula

$$E = 1.00049(M_w - w) + 0.86603p - 2w \tag{14}$$

THREAD GAGE MEASUREMENT

To assure accuracy in gaging, thread plug gages are controlled by accurate measuring methods, while thread ring gages are controlled by reference to appropriate thread setting plugs. The size of thread ring gages is determined by their fit on the setting plug as measured.

In measuring straight-thread plug gages the following elements are measured or checked: (1) major diameter, (2) pitch diameter, (3) root clearance, (4) lead, and (5) flank angle. On taper thread plug gages, in addition to the elements listed above, the taper of the pitch and the major diameter are checked, and also the length from the front end to the gaging notch.

As stated, the size of thread ring gages is determined by reference to their setting plugs. However, the form of internal threads may be checked by taking a cast of the thread form and, by use of optical projection, inspecting the flank angle and root clearance. Lead may also be checked in this manner, or on a lead testing machine.

Since the tolerances on gages are given to four decimal places in most instances, the equipment used in measuring should read to the fifth decimal places. Measurements should also be made under ideal environmental conditions at 68°F (20°C).

Measuring Pitch Diameter of Straight 60° Threads

The degree of accuracy to which the pitch diameter can be measured depends on the accuracy of the lead helix and form of the thread. As thread plug gages and thread setting plug gages have highly accurate threads, their pitch diameters may be measured to a high degree of accuracy by using the three-wire method of measurement as described below.

Small hardened steel wires (best-size wire) are placed in the thread groove, two on one side of the gage and one on the opposite side as shown in Fig. 14-7. The best size of wire to use is that which will contact the thread

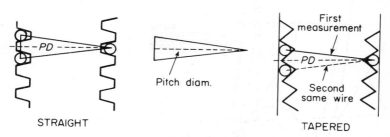

Fig. 14-7. Thread measurement by wire method (*Pratt and Whitney Co., Inc.*)

flanks halfway along their length, thereby contacting at the pitch line. (See Table 14-6.) The effect of angle errors is eliminated by the use of the best-size wire. However, when the best-size wire is not available, other sizes may be used. The computed value for the pitch diameter obtained from readings over wires will depend upon the accuracy of the measuring instrument used, the contact load, and the value of the diameter of the wires used in the computations.

Measuring Pitch Diameter of Taper 60° Threads

The pitch diameter of a taper thread plug gage is measured in a manner similar to that of a straight thread gage, except that definite positions at which the measurements are to be made must be located. A point at a known distance L from the front end of the gage is located by means of a combination of precision gage blocks and the cone point furnished as an accessory with these blocks, as shown in the inset in Fig. 14-8. The taper of a tapered thread plug gage makes it impractical to use the three-wire method when the gage is in a vertical position. Accordingly, the two-wire method is generally applicable to measuring pitch diameter of tapered thread plug gages.

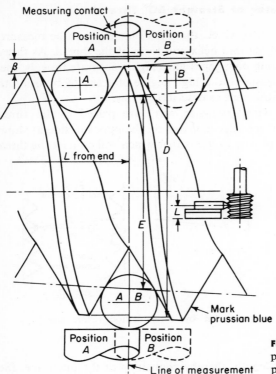

Fig. 14-8. Measurement of the pitch diameter of taper thread plug gages by the 2-wire method.[1]

The measurement is made with two wires, as shown in Fig. 14-8, one of which is placed in the thread to make contact at the same axial section of the thread groove as was touched by the cone point. This wire is designated the fixed wire. The second wire is placed in the thread groove on the opposite side of the gage, which is next above the fixed wire, and the measurement over the wires is made. The second wire is then placed in the thread space next below the fixed wire, and a second measurement is made. The average of these two measurements is M_w, the measurement over the wires at the position of the fixed wire [see formula (3)].

Three-Wire Method.[1] Depending on the measuring facilities available or other circumstances, it is sometimes more convenient to use three wires. In such cases, measurement is made in the usual manner, but care must be taken that the measuring contacts touch all three wires, as the line of measurement is not perpendicular to the axis of the screw when there is proper contact (see Fig. 14-9).

On account of this inclination, the measured distance between the axes of the wires must be multiplied by the secant of the half-angle of the taper of the thread.

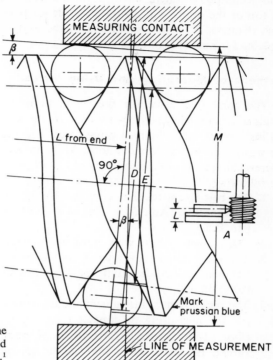

MEASURING CONTACT

β

L from end

90°

D E

M

β

L

A

Mark
prussian blue

LINE OF MEASUREMENT

Fig. 14-9. Measurement of the
pitch diameter of taper thread
plug gages by the 3-wire method.[1]

An adaption of the three-wire method is frequently used to reduce the
time required when the pitch diameter of a number of gages of the same
size is to be measured. Only light gages, up to about 2 in., can be measured
accurately by this method. The gage is supported on two wires placed several
threads apart, which are in turn supported on a taper thread testing fixture.
The third wire is placed in the threads at the top of the gage and measurement is made from the top of this wire to the bottom of the fixture with a
vertical comparator having a flat anvil, using a gage block combination
as the standard. The fixture consists of a block, the upper surface of which
is at an angle to the base plane equal to the nominal angle of taper of the
thread, 2β. Thus the element of the cone at the top of the thread gage is
made parallel to the base of the instrument. The direction of measurement
is not perpendicular to the axis of the gage but at an angle β from perpendicularity. A stop is provided at the thick end of the block with respect to
which the gage is positioned on the fixture. As the plane of the end of the
gage may not be perpendicular to the axis, a roll approximately equal to
the diameter of the gage should be inserted between the stop and the gage
to assure contact at the axis of the gage. For a given fixture and roll, a con-

stant is computed which, when subtracted from the measured distance from
the top of the upper wire to the base plane, gives M corresponding to the
pitch diameter E_0 at the small end of the gage. E_0 is then determined by
applying formula (13) or (14).

Methods of Measuring and Using Wires.[2]

The computed value for the pitch diameter of a screw thread gage
obtained from readings over wires depends upon the accuracy of the measuring instrument used, the measuring force, and the value of the diameter of
the wires used in the computations. Measurement of the pitch diameter of
a screw thread gage to an accuracy of 0.0001 in. requires strict adherence to
the following:

1. The best-size wires shall comply with the specifications listed for wires
   in Tentative American Standard ASA B1.2-19XX, Appendix B,
   par. B.8.[2]
2. The diameter of the wires must be known to within 0.000020 in.
3. The measurement over wires should be made with a measuring instrument which has flat, parallel contacts and reads directly to
   0.000010 in.
4. The measurement instrument should have a means for directly adjusting the measuring or contact force for the various values specified
   (8-oz, 1-1b, $2\frac{1}{2}$-1b). Corrections of pitch diameter measurements
   should be made when the measuring equipment or weight of the
   gage introduces deformations in measuring wires other than those
   for which compensation is provided.
5. The wires should be free to assume their positions in the thread
   grooves, without restraint. (The practice of holding wires in position
   with elastic bands can introduce errors in measurement.)
6. The measured value should be given to five decimal places to assure
   accurate values for pitch diameter measurement.
7. Measurements shall be standard at 68°F (20°C).

Wire Size. The size of wire which touches exactly at the midslope of
a perfect thread of a given pitch is the *best-size* wire for that pitch. Any size
wire, however, may be used which will permit the wires to rest on the flanks
of the thread and also project above the crest of the thread.

The depth at which a wire of a given diameter will rest in a thread groove
depends primarily on the pitch and included angle of the thread; secondarily,
it depends on the angle made by the helix at the point of contact of the wire
and the thread, with a plane perpendicular to the axis of the screw.

The best-size wire is that size which will touch at the midslope of a groove
cut around a cylinder perpendicular to the axis of the cylinder, and of the
same angle and depth as the thread of the given pitch. This is equivalent to

a thread of zero lead angle. The size of wire touching at the midslope, or *best-size* wire, is given by the formula

$$G = \frac{p}{2} \sec \alpha \qquad (15)$$

Where $G =$ diameter of wire
  $p =$ pitch
  $\alpha =$ half included angle of thread
For 60° threads, formula (15) reduces to

$$G = 0.57735p \qquad (16)$$

TABLE 14-6.   WIRE SIZES AND CONSTANTS, UNIFIED THREADS

Threads per inch, n	Pitch, $p = \dfrac{1}{n}$	$\dfrac{\text{Pitch}}{2}$, $\dfrac{p}{2} = \dfrac{1}{2n}$	Depth of V thread, $\dfrac{\cot 30°}{2n}$	Wire sizes*		
				Best, 0.577350p	Maximum, 1.010363p	Minimum, 0.505182p
	in.	*in.*	*in.*	*in.*	*in.*	*in.*
80	0.012500	0.00625	0.010825	0.00722	0.01263	0.00631
72	0.013889	0.00694	0.012028	0.00802	0.01403	0.00702
64	0.015625	0.00781	0.013532	0.00902	0.01579	0.00789
56	0.017857	0.00893	0.015465	0.01031	0.01804	0.00902
48	0.020833	0.01042	0.018042	0.01203	0.02105	0.01052
44	0.022727	0.01136	0.019682	0.01312	0.02296	0.01148
40	0.025000	0.01250	0.021651	0.01443	0.02526	0.01263
36	0.027778	0.01389	0.024056	0.01604	0.02807	0.01403
32	0.031250	0.01562	0.027063	0.01804	0.03157	0.01579
28	0.035714	0.01786	0.030929	0.02062	0.03608	0.01804
24	0.041667	0.02083	0.036084	0.02406	0.04210	0.02105
20	0.500000	0.02500	0.043301	0.02887	0.05052	0.02526
18	0.055556	0.02778	0.048113	0.03208	0.05613	0.02807
16	0.062500	0.03125	0.054127	0.03608	0.06315	0.03157
14	0.071429	0.03571	0.061859	0.04124	0.07217	0.03608
13	0.076923	0.03846	0.066617	0.04441	0.07772	0.03886
12	0.083333	0.04167	0.072169	0.04811	0.08420	0.04210
11	0.090909	0.04545	0.078730	0.05249	0.09185	0.04593
10	0.100000	0.05000	0.086603	0.05774	0.10104	0.05052
9	0.111111	0.05556	0.096225	0.06415	0.11226	0.05613
8	0.125000	0.00625	0.108253	0.07217	0.12630	0.06315
7	0.142857	0.07143	0.123718	0.08248	0.14434	0.07217
6	0.166667	0.08333	0.144338	0.09623	0.16839	0.08420
5	0.200000	0.10000	0.173205	0.11547	0.20207	0.10104
$4\frac{1}{2}$	0.222222	0.11111	0.192450	0.12830	0.22453	0.11226
4	0.250000	0.12500	0.216506	0.14434	0.25259	0.12630

*These wire sizes are based on zero lead angle. Also maximum and minimum sizes are based on a width of flat the crest equal to $\frac{1}{8} \times p$. The use of wires of either extreme size is to be avoided.

If it becomes necessary, on occasion, to measure pitch diameter by means of wires other than the best size, the following size limitations should govern: (1) the minimum size is limited to that which permits the wire to project above the crest of the thread, and (2) the maximum size is limited to that which permits the wire to rest on the flanks of the thread just below the crest, and not ride on the crest of the thread. The diameters of the best size, maximum and minimum, wires for Unified threads are shown in Table 14-6.

Measuring Force for Wire Measurements of 60° Threads. Measurement of the pitch diameter of a thread gage by the three-wire method is most conveniently made when force sufficient to properly align the wires and gage is applied to the wires by the measuring instrument. Since a wire touches a minute area on each thread flank, the deformation of the wire and thread will be sufficiently large to require some type of correction, and the measuring force must be limited to avoid permanent deformation of the wire and gage.

The maximum compressive stress at the points where a wire touches the thread flanks is high, and it increases to a point where permanent deformation may occur, especially for the small-diameter threads. It therefore becomes necessary to reduce the measuring force progressively as the sizes of threads decrease, as shown in the following:

Threads per inch	*Measuring force*
20 or less	$2\frac{1}{2}$ lb
over 20 but not over 40	1 lb
over 40 but not over 80	8 oz

Wire Specifications. The following standard specifications represent present practice relative to thread measuring wires.

Composition. The wires shall be accurately finished and hardened steel cylinders, the hardness of which shall not be less than that corresponding to a Knoop indentation number of 630. The surface shall not be rougher than the equivalent of 2 μin. AA (arithmetic average).

Construction. The working surface shall be at least 1 in. in length. The wire may be provided with suitable means of suspension.

Diameter of Wires. One set of wires shall consist of three wires which shall have the same diameter within 0.00001 in., and this common diameter shall be within 0.0001 in. of that corresponding to the best size for the number of threads per inch for which the wires are to be used. Wires shall be measured between a flat contact and a hardened and accurately finished cylinder having a surface roughness not over 2 μ in. AA. The measuring force shall be the same as used in the measurement of pitch diameter of a thread gage.

The cylinder diameters shall be as follows:

Threads per inch	*Cylinder (wire) diam, in.*
20 or less	0.750
over 20 but not over 40	0.750
over 40 but no over 80	0.125

Variation in Diameter. Variations in diameter along a wire (taper) over the $\frac{1}{2}$-in. interval at the center of its length shall not exceed 0.000010 in., as determined by measuring between a flat contact and a cylindrical contact.

Variations from true cylindrical contour of a wire (out-of-roundness) over its $\frac{1}{2}$-in. central interval shall not exceed 0.000010 in., as determined by measuring between a flat measuring contact and a well-finished 60-deg. V-groove.

Selection and Use of Measuring Equipment

An established practice to follow in selecting measuring equipment to check thread gages is to follow the one-tenth rule wherever practical. Since the tolerances for leads, helical deviation, pitch diameter, and major or minor diameters range from 0.0002 in. to 0.0005 in., gages should be measured using equipment with an accuracy of from 0.000020 in. to 0.000050 in. The measuring equipment or comparators, in turn, should be set or checked with reference standards—gage blocks which are calibrated and certified to an accuracy of approximately 0.000004 in. Surveillance of the equipment is essential, and, in particular, the condition of the gaging anvils or contacts must be checked periodically to assure continued accuracy.

Currently there is a broad array of available equipment. Way-type measuring machines and comparators are used to check the pitch and major and minor diameters of thread gages, while linear lead testers, helical deviation (drunkenness) checkers and helical path analyzers are available to check the various types of lead variations. Optical comparators and test tools are commonly used to check flank angles and thread form.

Wire Measurements Using Measuring Machine. The three-wire method is accepted as standard for the measurement of pitch diameter of straight 60° thread plug gages. Following are the principal steps:

1. The thread plug member (exclusive of the handle) must be positioned correctly into the measuring machine (Fig. 14-10). Except for the larger sizes, the thread plug is positioned on the elevating table in a vertical position as shown. Larger-size thread plugs may be positioned with the major diameter in contact with the elevating table. Thread plugs which are too large to rest on the major diameter can be adequately positioned with the face of the gage horizontal and supported on the elevating table with a small-diameter shaft. Prior to positioning the gage, it should be cleaned thoroughly.

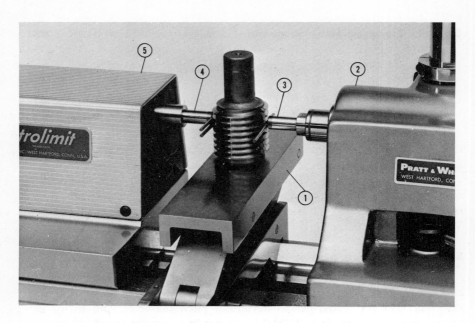

Fig. 14-10. Measurement of plug gage threads in a measuring machine: (1) elevating table, (2) headstock, (3) headstock anvil, (4) tailstock anvil, (5) tailstock. (*Pratt & Whitney Co., Inc.*)

2. The head stock should be adjusted to the proper dimension until the gaging anvils almost touch the major diameter, and the wires are slid into the proper position as shown in Fig. 14-7. The gaging anvils and the wires should be thoroughly cleaned.

3. Care should be exercised to ensure that each wire is in firm contact with both the thread flanks and the gaging anvils. This can be accomplished by tapping the gage lightly, and pushing or rotating each wire with the fingers prior to adjusting the measuring force. Care must be taken to assure that the wires adjust themselves in proper alignment with the threads. If the wires are placed in a vertical position, they should not touch the elevating table during the actual measurement.

4. Prior to taking a reading, the measuring force should be adjusted to suit the required threads per inch (see "Measuring Force for Wire Measurements").

5. Measurements should be taken around the circumference of the gage by rotating, and also at the front, center and back by adjusting the elevating table and repositioning the wires.

6. The maximum reading taken around the circumference of the gage should be recorded to five decimal places. Then the constant listed on the container for the wires should be subtracted from it. The result will be the measured pitch diameter. The major diameter can be measured directly after removing the wires.

The two-wire average method is usually applied for the measurement of pitch diameter of tapered 60° thread plug gages. In checking the pitch diameter it is general practice to take readings at two places on the gage: (1) close to the front end, and (2) at the gaging notch. By noting the distance between the two measurements, the taper of the thread may be computed. Following are the principal steps:

1. Prior to performing any measurements, the thread plug gage must be checked to assure that the front face is perpendicular with the axis of the gage, since the face is used as a reference surface in measuring.

2. Next, the length of the gage and the length to the gaging notch are checked. This can be accomplished by using a micrometer.

3. To determine the pitch diameter at the front end of the gage, the wire must be placed a known distance from the front end. This distance is approximately two pitches long, to permit measuring as close to the front end as practical and still leave space on the opposite side of the plug one-half pitch lower than the established height. This is accomplished by using a surface plate setup. A conical-point gage block accessory having an included angle equal to that of the thread (60°) is placed on the gage blocks and the thread plug is rotated until the conical point fits exactly into the thread groove and light is not visible between the point and thread flanks. The point is then marked, using prussian blue, directly above the place where contact was made. Next, the gage block stack is increased by an amount equal to, say, three pitches of thread, and another point which is in the vicinity of the gaging notch is ascertained and marked.

4. The thread plug gage member is then positioned in the holding fixture and placed on the elevating table. It should be placed between the anvils of the measuring machine, so that the location mark is directly in line with the anvils. Once this is done, the gage should not be rotated until all measurements have been made. One measuring wire is then placed under the locating mark at the front end (formerly occupied by conical gage point). The headstock is then adjusted to the proper dimension, the elevating table is positioned so that measuring anvils almost touch the major diameter, and the wire is aligned in proper position as shown in Fig. 14-11. Two readings over the wire are taken, one with a wire on the opposite side placed $D/2$ lower than the fixed wire, and the other with the wire placed $D/2$ higher than the fixed wire. The average of these two readings to five decimal places should be recorded, then the constant listed on the container for the wires is subtracted from it. The result will be the measured pitch diameter at the marked distance from the front face. (*Note:* Before a reading is taken, the measuring force should be adjusted to suit the required threads per inch.)

5. The same procedure is repeated at the other marked position of the thread. Two readings are recorded and averaged as before to determine the pitch diameter close to the gaging notch.

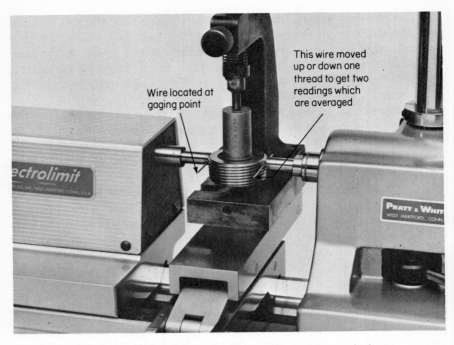

Fig. 14-11. Measurement of tapered plug gage threads in a measuring machine. (*Pratt & Whitney Co., Inc.*)

6. By computation, the pitch diameter at the front face and at the gaging notch can be determined, as well as the taper of the thread.

7. It should be noted that when mounting the tapered thread plug gage in a vertical position in a holding fixture, the three-wire method cannot be used.

8. The major diameter of a tapered thread plug can be measured on the measuring machine. This is accomplished by placing the thread gaging in the holding fixture as before. Rectangular gage blocks (0.100 in. approximately) are placed diametrically opposite over the thread crests. Rolls of known size are placed over the gage block and the measurement is then determined in a manner similar to measuring a plain tapered plug gage. The computation must, however, take into consideration the effect of the thickness of gage blocks as modified by the taper of the gage.

Use of Optical Comparators and Chart Gages. Optical gaging has four fields of usage: (1) measurement by movement, (2) measurement by comparison, (3) measurement of angles, and (4) measurement of contours by translation. Optical measurement of threads involves measurement by comparison, in which a magnified image of the thread form is compared

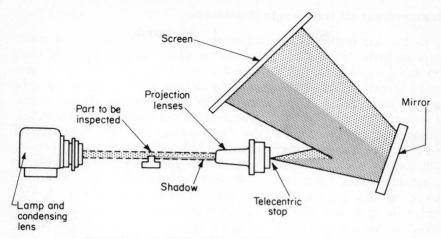

Fig. 14-12. Schematic illustration of an optical comparator. (*Jones & Lamson Machine Co.*)

with a chart-gage on the projector screen of an optical comparator. (See also Chapter 6.)

An optical comparator directs a concentrated parallel beam of light upon the part (gage) to be inspected (Fig. 14-12). The resulting shadow is magnified by a lens system and is projected onto a viewing screen by a mirror. The enlarged shadow-image can then be inspected and measured in comparison with a master chart or outline on the screen. To pass inspection, the shadow-outline of the object must correspond to the outline on the chart, or fall within predetermined tolerance limits on the chart.

An example of a tolerance-outline thread chart for Unified thread form is shown in Fig. 14-13.

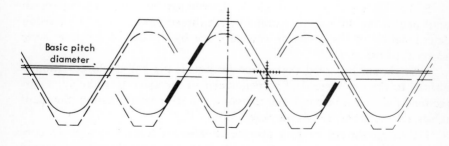

Fig. 14-13. Tolerance outline on thread chart-gage for 1/2–20 Unified National thread form, class 2A tolerance, at 62.5 X magnification. (Thread profile shown normal to axis: central tooth form compensated for helix.) (*Optical Gaging Products, Inc.*)

Measurement of Half-Angle Deviations

In the measurement of thread gages, optical comparators and chart gages are particularly useful in checking thread form, flank angle, and root clearances. Considering that the thread form when projected to the screen can be magnified to a high degree ($62\frac{1}{2}$X and 100X are common magnifications), deviations in thread form may be easily analyzed. Thread forms of thread ring gages, which are particulary difficult to measure, are checked by taking a cast of the thread form. The form can then be easily projected and deviations noted. Product external threads, particularly those designed with controlled root radii for high-strength application, lend themselves to optical inspection particularly well since the limits of the controlled root can be checked. The use of various staging fixtures and translating devices further increases the utility of optical projection in the measurement of threads to the extent that other features, such as lead, taper, length, diameter, and concentricity variations, can be analyzed and measured.

In the measurement of half-angle deviations of thread plug and thread setting plug gage, the following steps and precautionary measures are taken:

1. The thread plug is thoroughly cleaned and brushed free of all foreign particles, with particular attention given to thread flanks.

2. The thread gage is then mounted between centers, or in a V-block, and positioned on the work table.

3. It is then necessary to rotate the work table (or position the gage) through an angle equal to the helix angle of the thread under inspection. Unless this is done, the image of the thread form as projected will not be clear.

4. The work table is then adjusted to bring the thread form as projected in line with the screen chart. It is important that the gage be horizontal and parallel to the horizontal centerline on the screen. This is usually checked with reference to the major diameter of the thread plug gage.

5. The deviation in half-angle is determined by adjusting the screen until one of the 30° lines is parallel to the thread flank image. A precision determination of the deviation can be made by the use of a vernier scale adjacent to the screen.

6. It should be noted that, when projected, the half-angle deviation is normal to the axis instead of perpendicular to the axis. Accordingly, a correction factor must be employed to assure a precise determination. Standard tables are available for this purpose.

Half-angle deviations may also be checked by using test tools in conjunction with a light source and magnifying glass (see Fig. 14-14). The thread plug gage is placed between centers over the light source. The test tool having the required included angle is then pushed forward into the thread groove, shutting out the light. The tool and thread are then viewed through a jeweler's

Fig. 14-14. Basic equipment for measuring thread angle. (*Greenfield Tap & Die Div., United Greenfield Corp.*)

glass or microscope. Assuming that the test tool is basic (60°), a perfect thread angle would show a fine even line. If the thread angle has a plus deviation, a greater degree of light would show at the crest. If the thread angle has a minus deviation, a greater degree would show at the root. In using this method, the following precautionary measures are essential:

1. The gaging edge of the tool must be at the same height as the axis of the thread plug and perpendicular to it.

2. The pressure applied in inserting the test tool in the thread groove must be steady and not disturb the perpendicularity.

3. Both the gage and the test tool must be clean, and the tool free of burrs or nicks.

Measurement of Lead

Lead can be accurately measured by using the same basic equipment described previously for measuring thread angle (Fig. 14-15). The test point blocks are similar to gage blocks in appearance, with the apex of the angle accurately positioned from each side. Two such points are used and spaced apart by wringing gage blocks between them to give the proper distance between points which will be the equivalent of the number of pitches over which the lead is to be measured. The points are squared at the bottom so that the apex of the points are in the same plane.

The gage is placed between the centers. The test point stack is placed upon the platen and the points brought in contact with the flanks of the

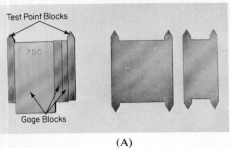

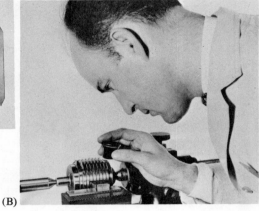

Fig. 14-15. Basic equipment for measuring thread lead. (*Green-field Tap & Die Div., United Greenfield Corp.*)   (B)

(A)

gage threads. When observed under magnification, the thread will have correct lead over the length being measured if the points shut out light on both thread flanks at both points. If light can be seen on the inside flanks at both ends, then the lead is "short." If light can be seen between the outside flanks and the test point at both ends, the lead is "long." To find exactly the amount of error, the gage block stack between the test points should be altered until light is shut out on both flanks at both points. The amount of change necessary in the block stack from the correct amount will be the deviation in lead over the length of engagement.

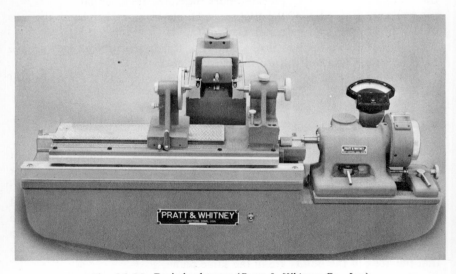

Fig. 14-16. Basic lead tester (*Pratt & Whitney Co., Inc.*)

Mechanical lead checking equipment can be grouped into three general categories: (1) linear lead checkers, (2) helical variation or drunkenness checkers, and (3) helical path analyzers.

The most widely used is the linear lead checker shown in Fig. 14-16. The principal units which comprise the instrument are: (1) A direct-reading headstock or measuring head from which the deviation in lead can be read directly to hundred-thousandths of an inch. The measuring head dividing screw, by means of hardened gaging anvils, actuates the (2) carriage which rides longitudinally on a ball slide and on which is mounted the (3) centers for holding the thread plug gage. Between the carriage and the measuring head is a rest support for four sizes of Hoke blocks, which are used to facilitate checking longer lengths of thread. Here the blocks contact a hardened carriage button and the measuring head dividing screw, so as to measure the distance that the carriage and mounted thread plug is moved in relation to the ball point in the thread locating head. The locating head with ball point (within the limit of maximum and minimum wire size for a given pitch) is mounted on a "V" ball slide on the bed.

The ball point is moved in and out of the thread grooves by the operator, but constant force is maintained automatically. A microammeter is conveniently located on the measuring head to show when the correct measuring point is reached. The operator reaches the correct measuring point by turning the dividing screw which, in turn, moves the work against the ball point until the pointer of the microammeter reaches the center of the scale. The reading is then read directly from one thread to another. The maximum lead deviation is at the point where there is the greatest plus deviation from basic added to the point where there is the greatest minus deviation. Readings for lead deviations are usually taken at six or seven random thread grooves throughout the length of the gage.

In checking lead at various pitches along the axis of the gage, do not take readings within one revolution of the thread. Within one pitch or revolution of a thread there is usually a waviness pattern simulating a sine curve, which is commonly called "drunkenness." Drunkenness checkers are available to check this particular feature. Usually the thread gage is mounted between centers, while two (one fixed and one movable) ball points engage the part 180° apart in the same thread groove. The movable ball is attached to an indicater mechanism which provides a reading indicative of drunkenness with reference to the fixed ball point.

To meticulously analyze the complete effect of lead deviation it is necessary that the total helical path of the thread be analyzed with reference to a true helix (see Fig. 14-17). Helical path analyzers, which analyze both the combined effects of linear lead and helical deviation or drunkenness, are available to measure the total deviation in helical path. Helical path analyzers

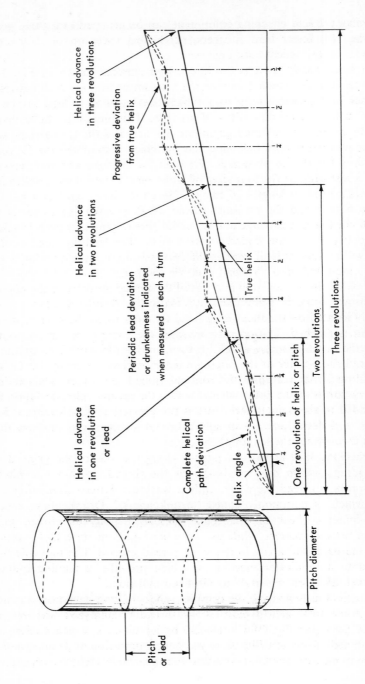

Fig. 14-17. Development of the helix (*Pratt & Whitney Co., Inc.*)

are equipped with a chart recorder which provides a trace of the actual helical path with reference to a true helix (see Fig. 5-37).

APPLICATION OF THREAD GAGES

Thread gages, by general types, serve the following functions:
1. GO thread gages check the maximum-material size, to assure inter-changeable (true) assembly. HI and LO thread gages check the minimum-material size.
2. GO and NOT GO plain cylindrical, snap, or indicating gages check the limits of size of the minor diameter of product internal threads and the major diameter of product external threads.
3. HI/LO gages having pitch diameter tolerances outside the product thread limits may be used to assure that usable product thread at the extreme limit of size (minimum-material limit) is not rejected, and also to avoid needless controversy in borderline cases.

Threaded and Plain Gages for Verification of Product Internal Threads

GO Thread Plug Gages. GO thread plug gages must enter the full threaded length of the product freely, without the application of significant torque which might tend to deform the product material. The GO thread plug gage is a cumulative check of all thread elements except the minor diameter.

HI Thread Plug Gages. HI thread plug gages may engage only the end threads when applied to the product internal thread. Threads are accepted when the HI thread plug gage is applied to the product internal thread if: (a) it does not enter, or (b) all complete product threads can be entered, provided that a *definite* drag from contact with the product material results on or before the third turn of entry. The gage should not be forced after the drag is definite.

GO and NOT GO Plain Plug Gages. GO and NOT GO plain plug gages for the minor diameter of product internal threads must completely enter the product internal thread to assure that the minor diameter does not exceed the maximum-material limit. NOT GO plain plug gages must not enter the product internal thread so as to provide adequate assurance that the minor diameter does not exceed the minimum-material limit.

Thread Setting Plug Gages.

GO and LO Truncated Setting Plugs. The W tolerance, truncated setting plugs are recommended for setting thread ring gages to and including 6.250-in. nominal size, and may be used for setting thread snap gages and indicating thread gages. Above 6.250-in. nominal size, the difference in feel between the full form and truncated sections, in setting thread ring gages, is insignificant, and the basic crest setting plug may be used.

GO and LO Basic Crest Setting Plugs. The W tolerance, basic crest setting plugs are frequently used for setting thread snap limit gages and thread indicating gages. They may also be used for setting large adjustable thread ring gages, especially those above 6.250-in. nominal size. When they are so used, it may be desirable to take a cast of the ring gage thread form to check the flank angle and profile.

GO and NOT GO Plain Plug Acceptance Check Gages for Checking Minor Diameter of Thread Ring Gages

The GO plain plug gage is made to the minimum minor diameter specified for the thread ring gage (GO or LO), while the NOT GO gage is made to maximum minor diameter specified for the thread ring gage (GO or LO). After the adjustable thread ring gages have been set to the applicable thread setting plugs, the GO and NOT GO plain plug acceptance check gages are applied to check the minor diameter of the ring gage to assure that it is within the specified limits. An alternate method for checking minor diameter of thread ring gages, where the minor diameter is larger than 0.375 in., is by the use of measuring equipment.

Threaded and Plain Ring, Snap, and Indicating Gages for Verification of Product External Thread

GO Thread Ring Gages. GO thread ring gages must be set to the applicable W tolerance setting plugs to assure that they are within specified limits. The product thread must completely and freely enter the GO thread ring gage for the entire length of the threaded portion, i.e., without the application of significant torque which might tend to deform the product material. The GO thread ring gage is a cumulative check of all thread elements except the major diameter.

LO Thread Ring Gages. LO thread ring gages must be set to the applicable W tolerance setting plugs. LO thread ring gages, when applied to the product external thread, may engage only the end threads, which may not be representative of the complete thread. Starting threads of LO thread rings are subject to greatest wear and, in combination with the incomplete product threads, permit further entry in the gages. This condition is augmented by the difficulty in detecting wear on the first and second threads, and the desire to achieve maximum utilization of the gage.

Unified Classes 1*A* and 2*A* product external threads are acceptable when the LO thread ring gage is applied to the product external thread if (a) it is not entered, or (b) all complete product threads can be entered, provided that a definite drag from contact with the product thread material results on or before the third turn of entry. The gage should not be forced after the drag is definite.

LO Thread Snap Limit Gages or Indicating Thread Gages. LO thread limit snap gages (or indicating thread gages) check Unified Class 3*A* product external thread LO minimum-material limit. The gages must be set to the applicable *W* tolerance setting plugs. The gage is then applied to the product thread at various points around the circumference, and over the entire length of complete product threads.

In applying the limit thread snap gage, threads are considered dimensionally acceptable when the gaging elements do not pass over the thread, or pass over the product thread with perceptible drag from contact with the product material or the gage. Indicating thread gages provide a numerical value for the product thread size. Product external threads are dimensionally acceptable when the value derived in applying the gage is not less than the specified minimum-material limit.

Check of Lead and Flank Angle of Product Thread. Two general methods are available for the inspection procedures of flank angle and lead of product thread:

1. The lead and flank angle of the product thread may be measured by means of such equipment as projection comparators, measuring microscopes, graduated cone points, lead-measuring machines, helix variation-measuring machines, thread flank-charting equipment, etc. Diameter equivalents of such deviations are calculated by applying appropriate formulas.

2. The differential between functional diameter and pitch diameter of the product thread is measured by means of indicating gages having gaging elements suitably designed to determine these diameters when set to applicable calibrated thread setting plugs. The differential so measured is the cumulative deviation in the thread elements, except pitch diameter. If it is a requirement of the design when the differential is greater than the specified percentage of pitch diameter tolerance for a single elements, it is necessary to make a further analysis to determine if the deviations of the thread elements (lead and flank angle) exceed the allowable percentage.

GO and NOT GO Plain Rings and Adjustable Snap Limit and Indicating Gages for Checking Major Diameter of Product External Thread.

The GO gage must completely receive or pass over the major diameter of the product external thread to assure that the major diameter does not exceed the maximum-material limit. The NOT GO gage must not pass over the major diameter of the product external thread to assure that the major diameter is not less than the minimum-material limit.

CERTIFICATION, CALIBRATION, AND RELIABILITY OF THREAD GAGES

Certification

Certification of a specific gage or lot of gages is made by a signed statement by a qualified laboratory or gage manufacturer, attesting that the gages have been checked and found to be within the applicable gage tolerances. Numerical values are not recorded on the certification. When gages are certified to the fourth decimal place, a laboratory should have the capability of measuring to the fifth decimal place.

Calibration

Calibration signifies the determination and recording of a precise numerical value for each essential dimension. Usually, the instrument or process used is identified and its reliability is made a part of the recording. All such reports are dated and signed, and frequently the specific area where readings were taken is identified. Calibration is usually confined to precision gage blocks, plugs, and rings which are used as masters or for setting purposes [see previous section on "Tolerances and Specifications for Thread Elements of Taper Pipe Thread (60°) Gages"].

Reliability

Reliability, as related to thread-gage metrology, reflects the degree to which the many involved factors are controlled. When making a precise determination of an accurate thread on a thread plug gage, for example, the specific condition of the gage, the accuracy of the instruments, and the care exercised in making the measurements will influence the reliability and accuracy.

REFERENCES

1. "Screw-Thread Standards for Federal Services," Handbook H-28 (1957), Part I, U.S. Dept. of Commerce, National Bureau of Standards, issued September 10, 1957.

2. "Gages and Gaging for Unified Screw Threads," Tentative American Standard ASA B1.2-19XX, American Standards Association.

3. "Nomenclature, Definitions, and Letter Symbols for Screw Threads," American Standard ASA B1.7-1965, American Standards Association, 1965.

4. "1963 Supplement to Screw-Thread Standards For Federal Services" (1963 Supplement to Handbook H-28), Parts I, II, and III, U.S. Dept. of Commerce, National Bureau of Standards, issued October 15, 1963.

5. "Screw-Thread Standards For Federal Services," Handbook H-28 (1957), Part II, U.S. Dept. of Commerce, National Bureau of Standards, issued November 16, 1959.

15

MEASUREMENT OF GEARS[*][†]

Much of the data in this chapter have been condensed from more detailed information that will appear in the "Measuring Methods and Practices Manual," planned to be released by the American Gear Manufacturers Association as a proposed Tentative Standard AGMA 239.01.

That manual recommends practices and measuring methods used to establish conformance with the tolerances listed in AGMA 390.02, "Gear Classification Manual." When specified, gear elements may be inspected by a number of alternate methods. The selection depends not only on the magnitude of the tolerance and the size of the gear, but also on procedure quantities, equipment available, and inspection costs. All gears are manufactured to

[*]By Casimir S. Kopec, Gear Metrology Laboratory, Institute for Basic Standards, National Bureau of Standards.

[†]Acknowledgment is made of valuable assistance in the preparation of this chapter from members of the AGMA Measurement Methods and Practices, the Master Gear, the Bevel Gearing, and the Worm Gearing Committees.

required accuracy by process control. For some quality classes, process control, rather than analytical inspection, is recomended to assure accuracy consistent with AGMA 390.02 Quality Numbers.

The "Gear Classification Manual" sets up a practical gear classification system for spur, helical, herringbone, bevel, and hypoid gears. It represents the broad experience of many gear manufacturers.

The gear-class system described here has become a language bridge for the gear designer, user, and manufacturer. In extremely simple terminology, gears are classified in terms of tolerances usually considered in manufacture and application. In addition, it lists the more common types of materials and heat treatments. The system allows extensions and revisions for future advances in the technology of gear manufacture. Special applications falling outside the broad range of the system are usually a subject for special consideration involving the designer, user, and manufacturer.

The data here presented cover only those practices and inspection methods which are recognized and accepted throughout the gear industry as being reliable. The methods described provide measurements which are accurate and repeatable to a degree compatible with the specified quality. Experienced personnel, using calibrated instruments in suitable surroundings, are required.

To correspond to industry practice, the information on spur, helical, herringbone, and bevel gears covers the range of fine-pitch gearing from 200 DP to 20 DP, up to 12-in. diam, and coarse-pitch gearing from 19.99 DP to 0.5 DP, up 200-in. diam. The separation by diametral pitches is generally recognized in the industry for the purpose of defining and distinguishing between fine and coarse pitches.

The gear industry now formalizes the long established concept of process control as a quality determinant and an inspection procedure. process control is the method by which gear accuracy is maintained through control of manufacturing equipment, methods, and processes.

When analytical inspection of gear elements is desired, the following data describe methods for measuring these tooth elements:

Runout

Pitch

Profile

Lead

Backlash

Tooth thickness

Composite method of gear inspection

Tolerance tables for the various quality levels of coarse-pitch and fine-pitch spur and helical, bevel, and hypoid gears are shown in AGMA Standard 390.02.[1]*

*Superior numbers indicate specific references listed at the end of this chapter.

RUNOUT

Runout is the total variation of the distance between a surface of revolution and a reference surface measured perpendicular to the surface of revolution. In order to be meaningful, the surface of revolution and the reference surface must be specified or identified. Typical specified runouts are radial and axial runouts.

Surface of revolution is a surface generated by revolving a line about an axis. Typical surfaces of revolution are cylinders, cones, planes, paraboloids, and hyperbolics.

Reference surface is the actual specified surface on which the variations from the surface of revolution are measured.

Runout tolerance is the total allowable runout. In the case of gear teeth, it is measured by a specified probe such as a cylinder, ball, cone, rack, or gear tooth. The measurement is made perpendicular to the surface of revolution. On bevel and hypoid gears, both axial and radial runout are included in one measurement.

Measuring Methods

Pin Check. Runout may be measured by indication over pins, balls, or other devices placed in successive tooth spaces.

Rolling Check. Runout may be measured by observing the center-distance or mounting variation between the gear to be tested and a gear of known accuracies. When the runout control is accomplished by rolling the test gear in tight mesh with one member on a movable center, which is spring- or weight-loaded, with a gear of known accuracy, and the total indicator reading is within the runout specification, the gear is acceptable. The total indicator reading of a rolling check includes tooth element errors in addition to runout.

Contact Pattern Check. Variations in runout may be observed by running the gears in a suitable test machine. The runout is characterized by periodic variation in sound during each revolution, and by the tooth bearing shifting progressively around the gear from heel to toe, and toe to heel.

There are no specified limits for this check. If runout is observed by this visual check, the actual amount should be determined by one of the previously mentioned methods. See Fig. 15-1A and B, "Tooth bearing patterns."

Runout of wormgears is often measured indirectly by using a testing fixture arranged with two fingers, one fixed and the other actuating a dial indicator, both of which are mounted on movable blocks with means to return the blocks always to the same position. The blocks holding the fingers are positioned approximately 180 deg apart, with the fingers making contact on the same set of profiles at the midface. A spring-tension device is desirable

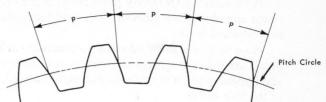

Fig. 15-1. Theoretical circular pitch.

to keep a definite uniform tension of the gear against the fixed finger. The difference between the highest and lowest indicator readings around the gear represents twice the runout with respect to the axis of rotation, or four times the eccentricity.

On small worms it is practical to measure runout by the projection method, in which a magnified shadow of the worm is compared with a template as the worm is rotated to successive positions.

On worms, the runout may vary appreciably across the face width, and consequently should be measured near both limits of the contact area. Appreciable difference in runout near the limits is an indication of wobble, which is more objectionable than uniform runout.

Wobble is likewise very objectionable on wormgears, and may best be detected in the test for area of contact.

PITCH, INDEX, AND TOOTH-TO-TOOTH SPACING

Pitch is the distance between corresponding points on equally spaced and adjacent teeth (Figs. 15-1 and 15-2).

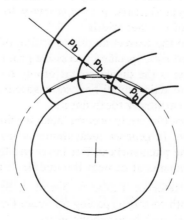

Fig. 15-2. Base pitch shown as a straight line measurement. Other pitch measurements are straight line, and may be measured at any corresponding points on adjacent tooth profiles.

Pitch variation (formerly pitch error) is the difference in the distance between equally spaced adjacent teeth and the measured distance between any two adjacent teeth.

Pitch tolerance is the allowable amount of variation. In general, measurements are made in a plane of rotation at or near the pitch surface. For bevel and hypoid gears, it is customary to make measurement at or near the middle of the face width.

Pitch range is the difference between the longest and the shortest measurements on the entire gear.

Pitch range tolerance is the allowable amount of pitch range. In general, measurements are made in a plane of rotation at or near the pitch surface.

Spacing variation (also tooth-to-tooth spacing) is the difference in measured spacing between corresponding sides of adjacent teeth (Fig. 15-3).

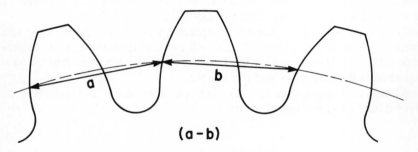

Fig. 15-3. Tooth-to-tooth spacing; a measurement of *three* adjacent teeth irrespective of an axis.

Spacing tolerance is the allowable amount of spacing variation. In general, measurements are made in a plane of rotation at or near the pitch surface. For bevel and hypoid gears, it is customary to make measurements at or near the middle of the face width.

Index refers to the correct angular position of teeth equally spaced about an axis established by a specified accessible proof surface (Fig. 15-4).

Index variation is the displacement of any tooth from its correct angular position about an axis established by a specified accessible proof surface and relative to an arbitrary tooth datum.

Index tolerance (formerly accumulated spacing) is the allowable amount of index variation. In general, measurements are made in the plane of rotation at or near the pitch surface. For bevel and hypoid gears, it is customary to make measurements at or near the middle of the face width.

Reference. Refer to Tables 5, 6 and 7, Section 3 of AGMA 390.02[1] for allowable tooth-to-tooth spacing tolerance (spacing variation) for coarse-pitch spur, helical, and herringbone gears.

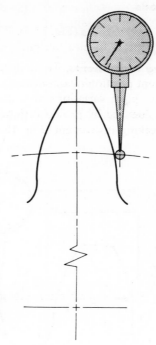

Fig. 15-4. Index (angular position); index is an angular measurement of a *single* tooth about an axis.

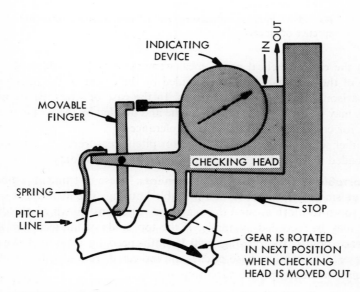

Fig. 15-5. Schematic arrangement of a pitch-measuring instrument.

Measuring Methods

Pitch checking instruments (Fig. 15-5). These, or dividing heads of suitable accuracy, can be used to measure pitch variations.

Pitch Measuring Instruments. These instruments employ a fixed finger and stop for consistent positioning on successive pairs of teeth, and a movable finger which displays pitch variations on a dial indicator or chart recorder. Readings will be influenced by profile variations and runout of the gear as mounted in the checking instrument (Fig. 15-6).

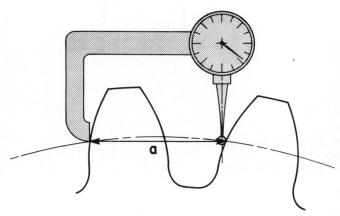

Fig. 15-6. Pitch is a measurement of *two* adjacent teeth irrespective of an axis.

In the case of helical gears, measurements may be made in the normal plane of the conjugate rack and divided by the cosine of the helix angle for comparison with standard tolerances. In the case of worm gears, measurements may be made in the normal plane and divided by the cosine of the lead angle for comparison with standard tolerances.

Either set of profiles may be used for pitch measurements, but preferably the loaded side, if the gear operates in one direction only.

Portable Pitch Measuring Instruments. These instruments embody the mechanism described above in a portable housing. The instrument is moved from tooth-to-tooth around the gear, and variations shown on the dial indicator may be recorded manually. If the top lands of the teeth are used for reference points, the readings will be influenced by runout of the outside diameter. If normal or base pitches are indicated, runout will not affect the readings; however, profile variations may.

Angular Positioning Devices. These devices include index heads, dividing places, optical polygons, theodolites, etc. They may also be used to determine spacing variations. Profile variation and runout may affect the readings, depending upon the device and method used.

One method involves a system where the gear is mounted coaxially on a spindle or table which can be very accurately indexed to the correct angular position for each tooth on a gear. After each index, a stylus is inserted into the space to contact the flank of the tooth at a fixed radial measuring position. Attached to the stylus is provided means to either visually observe or graphically record the error in position of the flank with reference to true angular position of index. It is important that the work spindle run true and

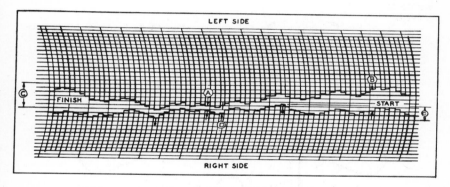

Fig. 15-7. Chart showing angular position measurements: (A) minimum space width, (B) maximum space width, (C) maximum index variation, (D) maximum pitch variation.

the part be located on its operating center line for accurate checking results.

The indexing, measuring, and recording of each side of the tooth can be done automatically, producing a chart (Fig. 15-7) to give a permanent record of the gear accuracy.

When both flanks of the gear tooth are checked and charted in this manner with parallel charts, they will indicate (a) pitch variation, (b) total index variation, and (c) space width variation.

PROFILE

Profile is that portion of the tooth flank between the specified form circle and the outside circle or start of tip chamfer. When the form circle is not specified, it should be that for a meshing rack. (See Fig. 15-8.)

Profile tolerance is the allowable deviation of the actual tooth form from

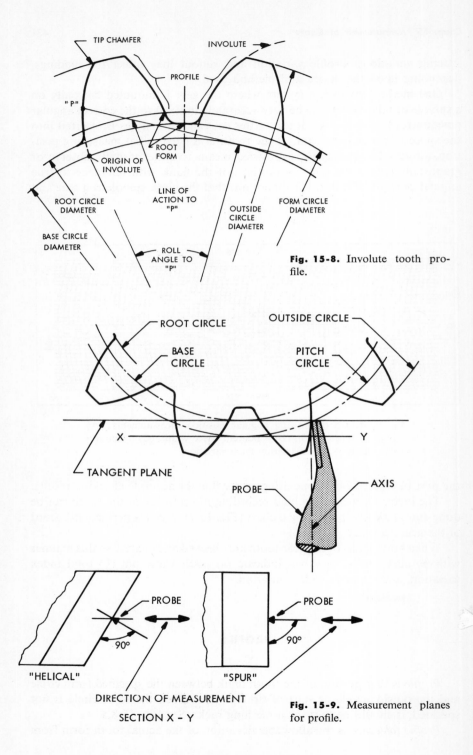

TIP CHAMFER

INVOLUTE

PROFILE

"P"

ORIGIN OF
INVOLUTE

ROOT
FORM

ROOT CIRCLE
DIAMETER

LINE OF
ACTION TO
"P"

OUTSIDE
CIRCLE
DIAMETER

FORM CIRCLE
DIAMETER

BASE CIRCLE
DIAMETER

ROLL
ANGLE TO
"P"

Fig. 15-8. Involute tooth profile.

ROOT CIRCLE

OUTSIDE CIRCLE

BASE
CIRCLE

PITCH
CIRCLE

X

Y

TANGENT PLANE

PROBE

AXIS

PROBE

PROBE

90°

90°

"HELICAL"

"SPUR"

DIRECTION OF MEASUREMENT

SECTION X - Y

Fig. 15-9. Measurement planes for profile.

the theoretical profile in the designed reference plane of rotation. For involute spur and helical gears, the reference plane is the plane of rotation. In cylindrical worms, the reference plane is sometimes the plane of rotation. In other cases, the axial section is taken as the reference plane. Tip relief and any portion of the tooth surface below the active profile is not to be considered.

Measuring Methods

Involute Profile Measuring Instruments. These instruments duplicate the generation of an involute curve of a base circle. A probe contacts the tooth profile to be measured, and registers any deviation from true involute on an indicator or recording device. (See Fig. 15-9.)

Analysis of Profile Charts. After mounting the gear to be inspected on a suitable arbor or holding fixture, the work is placed in the instrument and the probe is brought into contact with the tooth profile. To obtain the most accurate readings, it is essential that the probe be sharp, positioned accurately

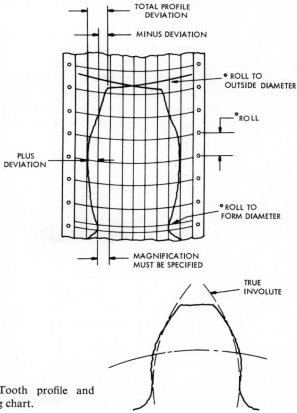

Fig. 15-10. Tooth profile and corresponding chart.

tangent to the base circle, and centered correctly on the origin of involute at zero degrees of roll (or at zero increment for machines so calibrated). As the gear is rotated in the instrument, the probe will detect any deviations from true involute on the gear profile. A profile with no deviations will be charted as a straight line. Excess material on the profile is considered a plus deviation, while insufficient material is considered a negative deviation.

Correct interpretation of a chart is dependent on the method used on the drawing to specify the required profile. (See Fig. 15-10 for a typical profile chart.)

In addition to inspecting tooth profiles in general, involute charts are extremely valuable for determining and controlling tip chamfers, undercut diameter, and involute crown.

Optional Profile Checking Procedures. Tooth contact, or bearing pattern (Fig. 15-11A) with a known or mating gear may also be used as an indication of profile accuracy. Although this method is not subject to numerical evaluation, it is an extremely accurate method for use on large bevel gears and large spur and helical gears. However, for results to be repeatable, the following conditions must be clearly defined:

1. Mounting accuracy or conditions for contact check.
2. Load applied during inspection.
3. Percent and location of contact area.

The above information refers primarily to spur and helical gearing. Profile checks, as such, are not usually taken on bevel and hypoid gears. That is, the profile is not measured in relation to an involute or other established form. Rather, it is measured in relation to the profile of its mate in a running or

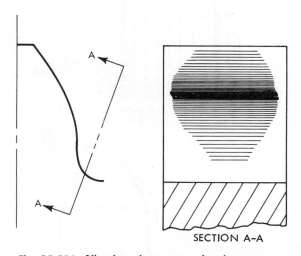

SECTION A-A

Fig. 15-11A. Visual tooth-contact or bearing pattern.

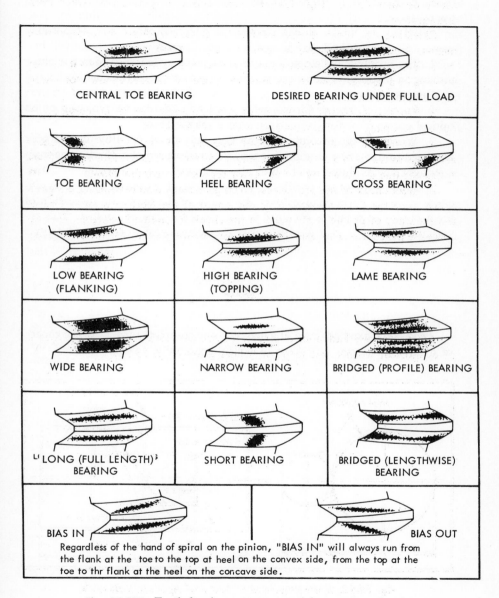

Fig. 15-11B. Tooth bearing patterns on pinion tooth or bevel gear. A left-hand pinion is used throughout. Patterns are representative of those on a right-hand pinion or a straight bevel pinion as well.

tooth contact check (Fig. 15-11B). The check is qualitative rather than quantitative.

Checking of worm thread profiles is generally done by comparative means. Several methods are in common use:

1. The profile may be determined from recording readings of an indicator moving in a straight line at the pressure angle of the thread and compared to a master reference.

2. Profiles of threads for worms of low lead angle can be projected on an optical comparator for comparison with a master form.

3. Worms of the involute helicoid type may be checked by an indicator arranged to travel in a straight line tangent to the base helix. Deviations from a straight line as shown by the indicator represent errors in profile.

A direct check of the profiles of worm gear teeth would be of little significance since the form changes over the length of the teeth. An indication of the accuracy of profile is obtained in the check for area of contact. This inspection process is also used to verify the accuracy of worm thread profile.

LEAD

Lead is the axial advance of a helix for one complete turn, as in the theads of cylindrical worms and teeth of helical gears (Fig. 15-12).

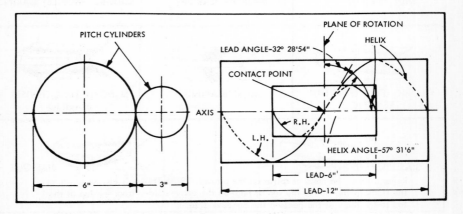

Fig. 15-12. Illustrating the terms *lead, lead angle,* and *helix angle.*

Lead tolerance as applied to spur, helical and herringbone gears, worm gears and racks is the allowable deviation across the face width of a tooth surface measured normal to the surface established by the specified lead and base cylinder.

Control of lead is necessary to insure adequate contact across the face width when gear and pinion are properly mounted with axes parallel and in the same plane.

Lead tolerance of a worm is expressed either as the total variation in lead for one convolution, or in the active length of the worm. In the latter case, it is assumed that the worm is long enough to extend the zones of contact in accordance with proper design.

Measuring Methods

Lead Checking Instruments. These instruments advance a probe along a tooth surface, parallel to the axis, while the gear rotates in a specified timed relation, based on the specified lead.

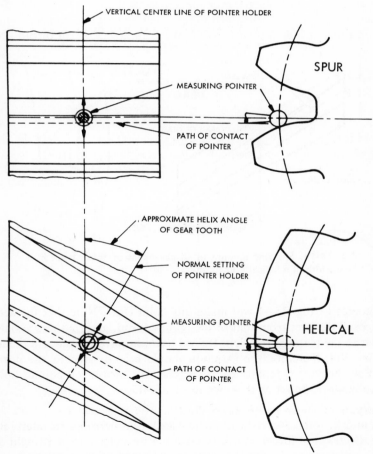

Fig. 15-13. Showing setting of pointer, relative to helix, for checking lead of external gear teeth.

In operation, the probe is positioned normal to the tooth surface near the pitch cylinder, although the radial position of the probe is not significant. (See Fig. 15-13.)

As the travel of the slide carrying the measuring pointer (Fig. 15-13) is parallel to the centers on which the work is held, it follows that the path traversed by the measuring pointer, along the tooth being checked, will always be parallel to the axis of the gear. In the case of a helical gear tooth, this means that as the slide is traversed and the work rotates, the measuring pointer *traces* a helix along the tooth in the vicinity of the pitch line. Therefore, any movement of the dial indicator needle represents an *up* and *down* movement of the measuring pointer, and the total amount of movement of the dial indicator needle over the distance measured indicates the amount of displacement of the gear tooth in the face width traversed.

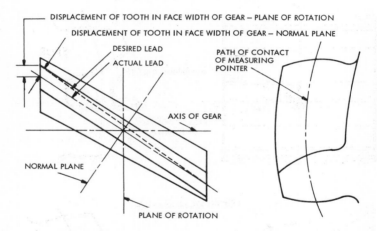

Fig. 15-14. Showing amount of displacement of tooth flank in face width of a helical gear tooth.

Reference to Fig. 15-14 will make this point clear. Note that the actual lead checked deviates from that of the required lead, and that this variation is greater in the plane of rotation. Helical teeth, however, contact in the normal plane and, therefore, the variation should be measured in the normal plane. For checking external helical surfaces, the measuring pointer holder should, therefore, be set as is shown in Fig. 15-13.

Analysis of Gear Tooth Lead Charts. The representative chart, Fig. 15-15A and B, will serve to illustrate how lead measurements are interpreted.

The electrical recorder converts an accurate helix into a straight line

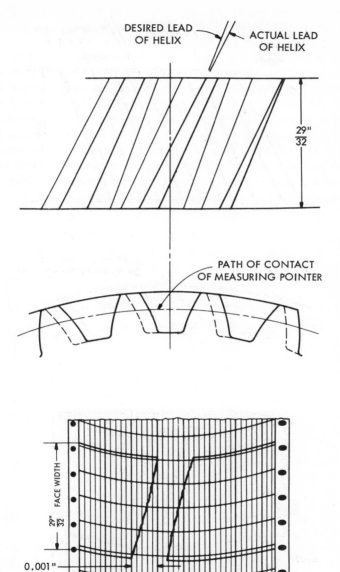

Fig. 15-15A. Chart of right-hand external helical gear teeth; short lead (−).

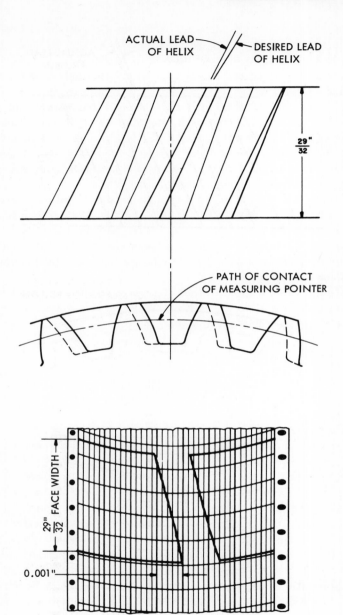

Fig. 15-15B. Chart of right-hand external helical gear teeth; long lead (+).

parallel to a datum line on the chart. Consequently, any deviation of the charted line from the datum line represents the amount of lead deviation at any point along the active face width being inspected.

If the gear being checked has right-hand external helical teeth, and the charted line deviates from the datum line in a minus direction, as is shown in Fig. 15-15A, then the actual lead is shorter than the desired lead. On the other hand, if the charted line deviates from the datum line in a plus direction, as in Fig. 15-15B, then the actual lead is longer than the desired lead.

Since the definitions for lead and helix angle show that, as the helix angle increases, the lead length shortens, a minus lead indicates an increase in helix angle, and a plus lead indicates a lesser helix angle.

Lead tolerance of a cylindrical worm may be measured by traversing an indicator along thread parallel to the axis while the worm rotates in a timed relation according to the specified lead. When the indicator is set in a direction normal to the helix, to avoid the side-cramping effect that might otherwise occur, the readings are converted to the axial direction by dividing by the cosine of the lead angle.

A difference from a specified lead in a worm may be acceptable if a corresponding difference is present in the worm gear. This should be given consideration in applying the lead tolerances.

BACKLASH

Backlash in gears is the play between mating tooth surfaces. For purposes of measurement and calculation, backlash is defined as the amount by which a tooth space exceeds the thickness of an engaging tooth. When not otherwise specified, numerical values of backlash are understood to be measured at the tightest point of mesh on the pitch circle, in a direction normal to the tooth surface when the gears are mounted in their specified position.

A tight mesh may result in objectionable gear sound, increased power losses, overheating, rupture of the lubricant film, overloaded bearings, and premature gear failure. Specifying unnecessarily close backlash tolerances will increase the cost of the gearing. However, it is recognized there are some gearing applications where a tight mesh (zero backlash) may be required.

See AGMA 390.02,[1] for detailed discussion of backlash and tolerances:

For coarse-pitch gears: pages 3-2, 3-3, 3-7.

For fine-pitch gears: pages 6-4, 6-5.

For bevel and hypoid gears: pages 9-3, 9-6, 9-7.

The following important factors must be considered in establishing back-

lash tolerances:
    Center distance.
    Parallelism of gear axes.
    Side runout or wobble.
    Tooth thickness tolerance.
    Pitch line runout tolerance.
    Profile tolerance.
    Pitch tolerance.
    Lead tolerance.
    Types of bearings and subsequent wear.
    Deflection under load.
    Gear tooth wear.
    Pitch line velocity.
    Lubrication requirements.
    Thermal expansion of gears and housing.

It is obvious from the above summary that the desired amount of back-lash is difficult to evaluate. It is, therefore, recommended that when a designer, user, or purchaser includes a reference to backlash in a gearing specification and drawing, consultation be arranged with the manufacturer.

Backlash in worms is commonly measured by holding the worm station-ary, and rocking the wormgear back and forth. The movement is registered by a dial indicator having its pointer or finger in a plane of rotation at or near the pitch diameter and in a direction parallel to a tangent to the pitch circle of the wormgear.

TOOTH THICKNESS OF SPUR, HELICAL, AND HERRINGBONE GEARS

Tooth thickness tolerances are to be interpreted as permissible variation of tooth thickness and are a method of controlling backlash.

Measuring Methods

Tooth thickness determination is essentially a measurement utilizing gear tooth calipers, micrometers, pins, balls, blocks, or master gears as speci-fied in the methods described below.

Method 1. Process Control.

Method 2. Vernier Gear-Tooth Caliper (Fig. 15-16). Theoretical settings of the gear-tooth caliper can be computed to any accuracy desired. Thickness

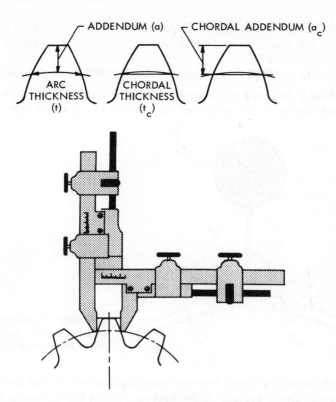

Fig. 15-16. Gear-tooth caliper, used in tooth-thickness inspection method No. 2.

may be measured at any convenient depth on the tooth, but it is usually computed and checked at the theoretical pitch circle.

Since the tooth caliper measures on a straight or chordal line, the distance t_c is slightly less than the distance along the arc of the pitch circle. This difference is frequently ignored; however, it becomes significant for coarse pitches and low number of teeth.

The theoretical addendum a is altered by enlargement or contraction of the gear or the pinion. It is directly affected by undersize or oversize of the blank, since the outside diameter is used as a point of reference in application of the caliper. Correction must always be made for taper and dimensional variation of the outside diameter of the gear blank. To set the chordal addendum a_c, and additional correction must be made for the height of the chord spanned by the tooth caliper. This correction is equal, for spur gears, to $t^2/4D$ and is always added to the theoretical addendum. For helical gears the correction is $(t_n \cos \psi)^2/4D$

where t = arc tooth thickness for spur gears in the transverse plane

$\quad t_n$ = arc tooth thickness in the normal plane of the reference rack

$\quad \psi$ = helix angle

$\quad D$ = diameter of gear at point of tooth thickness measurement

Method 3. Addendum Comparator. This instrument (Fig. 15-17) measures tooth thickness by comparing the gear addendum with that of a basic

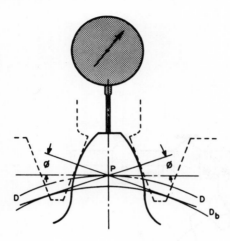

Fig. 15-17. Gear-tooth comparator, used in tooth-thickness inspection method No. 3.

rack. The comparator jaws have the same angle as the normal pressure angle of the tooth form of the gear to be checked. A steel block corresponding to a rack tooth of the proper diametral pitch is used to set the comparator jaws to the proper width. At this time, the dial indicator is set to read zero for the standard addendum. When a gear is checked, a thin tooth will project farther into the instrument and the dial indicator will read plus. Conversely, a thick tooth causes a minus reading. The change in tooth thickness may be computed by

$$\Delta t_n = 2 \times \text{comparator reading} \times \text{tan normal pressure angle}$$

Since the outside diameter is used as a reference point in application of the comparator, correction must be made for taper and dimensional variation of the diameter of the gear blank.

Method 4. Span Measurement. This method (Fig. 15-18) uses a vernier or plate micrometer to measure the distance over several teeth along a line tangent to the base cylinder. The distance measured is the sum of $n - 1$ base pitches (or normal base pitches for helical gears), plus the thickness of one tooth at the base cylinder. Measurements are not affected by outside diameter variations or by runout of the outside diameter. For method of computation, see AGMA Paper 239.01.[1]

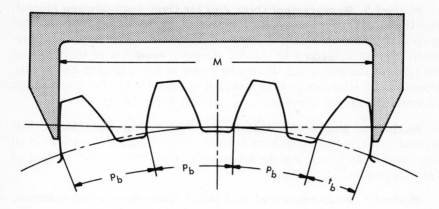

Fig. 15-18. Span-measurement tooth-thickness inspection method
No. 4.

Limitations.

1. Span measurement cannot be applied when a combination of high
   helix angle and narrow face width prevent the caliper from spanning a
   sufficient number of teeth.
2. Readings are influenced by errors in base pitch, tooth profile, and lead.
   Readings would be erroneous if attempted on a portion of profile which
   had been modified from true involute shape.

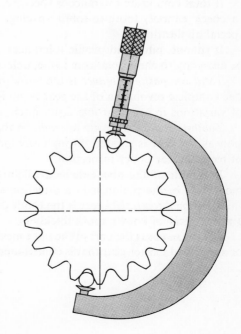

Fig. 15-19. Measurement over
pins, tooth-thickness inspection
method No. 5.

Method 5. Measurement Over Pins (or Over Rack-Shaped Blocks).
Pins (Fig. 15-19) afford an accurate method of measuring tooth thickness of
gears of any diameter within the capacity of available micrometers. Measurements are not influenced by outside diameter variations or by runout of
the OD. Measurements are affected by errors in tooth spacing and profile.
Formulas and tables are given in Standard AGMA 231.52[1]. For computation
of measurements for helical gears, see AGMA Paper 239.03.[1]

Method 6. Measurement of Center Distance at Tight Mesh. This
method measures functional tooth thickness, since it includes the effects of all
functional tooth errors. See the following section, "Composite Method of
Gear Inspection."

Method 7. Measurement of Backlash at Operating Center Distance.
This is a measure of functional tooth thickness of both pinion and gear combined. Center distance must be accurately determined and checked for parallelism and crossed axis. Backlash should be measured in at least four places
spaced around the gear at 90° intervals.

COMPOSITE METHOD OF GEAR INSPECTION

Composite action is the variation in center distance when a gear is rolled
in tight mesh (double flank contact) with a specified gear.

If total composite tolerance is specified, generally it will not be necessary
to check runout, tooth-to-tooth spacing, and profile, unless required for
special applications.

If runout, pitch and profile tolerances are specified, generally it will not
be necessary to check total composite, unless required for special applications.

Total composite tolerance is the allowance in center-distance variation in
one complete revolution of the gear being inspected. This includes the effects
of variations in active profile, lead, pitch, tooth thickness, and runout.

Tooth-to-tooth composite tolerance is the allowable center-distance variation as the gear is rotated through any increment of $360°/N$. ($N =$ number
of teeth in gear under inspection.)

For both of the above-defined tolerances, on bevel and hypoid gears,
movement of the pinion is in a direction at right angles to the pinion axis.

Functional tooth thickness is the tooth thickness as measured by means of
a master gear of known tooth thickness.

Testing radius is the part of the tight mesh center distance with a standard
or a specified master gear that is contributed by the work gear.

Measuring Methods

Process Control.

Composite Action. This section covers the double flank method of gear-rolling inspection, in which the gear to be inspected is mounted on a movable center, which is spring- or weight-loaded against a master gear, and the variations in center distance which occur as the gears are meshed together are recorded either on a chart or indicated by means of a dial indicator.

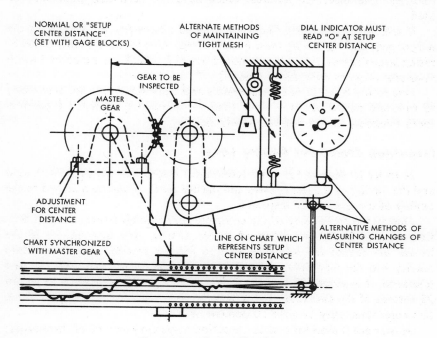

Fig. 15-20. Gear-rolling fixture.

Figure 15-20 shows a schematic diagram of a gear-rolling fixture. This is intended to show the kinematic requirements of the fixture, but it is not intended to imply that this is the only acceptable construction. Rather, it is to show the basic mechanical requirements for a fixture of the type required by the manual. The functions of the fixture are described in Section 6 of Appendix of AGMA Standard 239.01.[1]

The composite method is particularly applicable for the checking of worm gears. In checking a worm gear by this method, the master worm is made with threads thicker than standard to permit tight meshing with the gear at standard center distance.

Limitations of Composite Inspection Method

Practical considerations impose several limitations on this method of gear checking.

The tooth-to-tooth composite variation and the total composite tooth vatiation can be evaluated by means of master gears themselves, having smaller errors than those expected in the gears to be inspected. If only these two errors are to be evaluated, master gears having a relatively large tooth thickness tolerance, and fixtures, which have not been calibrated, may be used.

If the functional tooth thickness is to be measured, however, both the master gear and the fixture must be calibrated. Due to the difficulty of calibrating large fixtures, it is not common practice to check the functional tooth thickness of gears over 15-in. diam.

Due to the limitations of equipments and techniques, it is not customary to calibrate master gears of finer than 150 diametral pitch for functional tooth thickness by the methods shown herein.

Inspection Equipment Quality Level

In order to achieve the most ecohomical inspection, the procedure used and the quality of the test fixtures and master gears should be matched to the quality of the gears to be inspected.

Due to the complexity of the complete gear rolling fixture, it is not possible to specify absolute levels of fixture quality. Any inaccuracies in the fixture will reduce the tolerance allowed for the product gear. The fixture quality and the reliability of calibration must be compatible with the part tolerance. It is suggested that the fixture accuracy and calibration be within 25 percent of the part tolerance. When the part tolerance is extremely close, this percentage may become 50 percent or more.

Master gears used for composite action inspection may be of three types:

Type 1 is a master gear designed specifically to inspect the composite action of a gear or gears. It will always assure proper and complete inspection.

Type 2 is a standard "shelf item" master gear of known size and outside diameter; it may be used to check several different gears of a given pitch. Care must be taken to assure that acceptable gears are not being rejected because of an excessive depth of contact by an oversize outside diameter on the master gear. It is also possible to accept gears with a short depth of active profile, in the event the master gear has an undersize outside diameter.

Type 3 is a selected mating gear. It can be adjudged as to the degree of complete inspection by calculation and calibration.

Statistical Sampling Plan

Statistical sampling plans should be used where practical to further reduce inspection costs. Refer to MIL Standard 105.

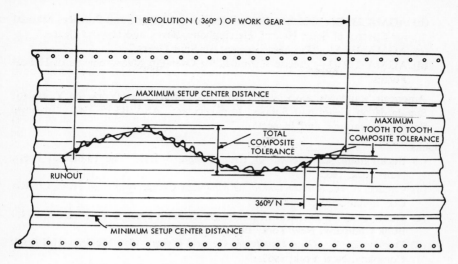

Fig. 15-21. Composite-action chart of a typical gear when run with a master gear on a gear-rolling fixture.

Interpretation of Charts

Figure 15-21 shows a composite action chart of a typical gear when run with a master gear on a gear-rolling fixture and illustrate composite tolerances.

Inspection of Splines

Involute splines can be measured to a large extent by the methods outlined for spur and helical gears. For detailed description of the design, specifications, and measurement of standard splines, see American Standard B5.15–1960,[2] or later revisions as they become available.

For detailed description of equipment required and methods used, see Appendix of AGMA 239.01.[1] For control of bevel and hypoid gears, see AGMA 330.01.

REFERENCES

Standards

1. American Gear Manufacturers Association, 1330 Massachusetts Ave., NW, Washington, D.C. 20005: Standards and Publications on Gear and Spline Measurement. In particular:
   (a) AGMA 390.02—September, 1964, "Gear Classification Manual."

(b) AGMA 239.01—October, 1963, "Measuring Methods and Practices Manual for Control of Spur, Helical, Herringbone, Bevel, and Hypoid Gears."

(c) AGMA 231.52—"Pin Measurement for Spur Gears."

(d) AGMA 239.03—"Precise Formulas for Over-Pin Measurements of Helical Forms."

2. American Standards Association, 10 E. 40th Street, New York, N. Y. 10016: Standards on Gears and Splines. In particular: ASA B5.15–1960, "Involute Splines, Serrations, and Inspection."

Books

(a) Buckingham, E., *Manual of Gear Design*, 3 vols., The Industrial Press, New York, 1935.

(b) Candee, A. H., *Introduction to the Kinematic Geometry of Gear Teeth*, Chilton Co., Philadelphia, 1961.

(c) Dudley, D. W., *Practical Gear Design*, General Electric Co., McGraw-Hill Book Company, New York, 1954.

(d) Dudley, D. W., *Gear Handbook*, General Electric Co., McGraw-Hill Book Company, New York, 1962.

(e) Fullmer, I. H., *Dimensional Metrology*, NBS Miscellaneous Publication No. 265, 1965. Subjects are classified and abstracted, also partially cross referenced. Sections 9 and 10 provide most complete information on publications and numerical tables for the measurement of gears, worms, screw threads, and splines.

(f) Grant, G. B., *A Treatise on Gear Wheels*, Philadelphia Gear Works, King of Prussia, Pa., 1899.

(g) Vogel, W. F., *Involutometry and Trigonometry*, Michigan Tool Co., Detroit, 1945.

16

THE MANAGEMENT OF INSPECTION

AND QUALITY CONTROL*

Early chapters of this book have developed the essential theory and principles underlying physical measurements. Other chapters have described the basic classes of measuring tools, gages, and instruments, with indications of their primary and efficient applications.

For effective use, this impressive array of data on the principles and tools of measurement needs to be tied together and utilized by sound operational management of the techniques used in inspection, quality control, and testing.

INSPECTION

From Craftsman to Segmented Skill

"Let one man make the parts for a mechanism, and another man assemble them, and you have the need for inspection," is a fair statement of the history of inspection.

*By Eugene V. Grumman, Chief Experimental Engineer, The Bullard Company.

In the not too distant past, man served an apprenticeship under signed agreement with an artisan or master craftsman. When his apprenticeship was completed, he became a journeyman and was then on his own to practice the art or trade in which he had become skilled.

Tools of the earlier days were simply an extension of man's hands which permitted him to do things which the hands alone could not do at all or else with great difficulty. During the construction of his wares, the craftsman was making continuous inspections with almost every move he made.

Man, with his ever-present curiosity and boundless energies, created simple devices to extend the skill and power of his hands further and further, finally resulting in simple machines such as the lathe, drill press, and planer. In so doing, he had now created the condition whereby other men could learn and become highly skilled in a segment of the art, hitherto known only to the master craftsman.

This, then, was the start of the Industrial Revolution, approximately 200 years ago, which has progressed at an ever increasing rate since the days of James Watt and Richard Arkwright. With this progression, the industrial worker, unfortunately, was getting further away from the end product. Rarely do the machine operators of today have the slightest conception of where or how the parts they are machining will fit into the end product.

It is this segmentation of broad skills that has created the need for examination of products in process to assure the manufacturer that the end product will meet the requirements. This in-process examination has been designated as inspection.

Definition of Inspection

Inspection is the art of critically examining parts in process, assembled subsystems, or complete end products with the aid of suitable standards and measuring devices which confirm or deny to the observer that the particular item under examination is within the specified limits of variability.

Inspection of parts, although generally done by a representative of the inspection department, was never intended in any way to relieve the machine operator or supervision of their responsibility for making a product within the limits of variability, but rather to check their effectiveness in the accomplishment of that task.

Specifying the Limits of Variability

Specifications are usually thought of as the sole prerogative of the product engineering division or department. This is because all products require some form of engineering, drafting, and layouts in the form of tracings, and also parts lists which spell out the requirements for all the parts and commercial items necessary to permit the end product to be assembled.

The development of specifications is affected by:

1. *Market:* customer needs, sales requirements.
2. *Management:* its desires, plans, goals and present products.
3. *Manufacturing:* its total capability to utilize the equipment available to produce to specifications at a profit.
4. *Methods:* the unique capability of the total organization to eliminate waste in materials, manpower, and money.
5. *Engineering:* its total ability to create, to analyze, and to design the simplest yet most effective mechanism which, regardless of stated price, makes this end product the most economic purchase for the customer.
6. *Manpower:* its creativeness, ingenuity, desires, goals, and skill. The environment under which it labors may be restrictive to the extent that the pace of the organization becomes that of a single individual or at least a limited few. On the other hand, it may be permissive and supply the needed encouragement and motivation to the extent that many people in the organization make major contributions to its progress and advancement.
7. *Money:* the financial wherewithal to do business.

While all of the foregoing affect the final specifications of a given product, the engineering department will invariably draw heavily on past experiences, experimentation, applied research, testing, consultation with commercial suppliers, direct contact with the customer, knowledge of manufacturing capability, advice from its own sales and service divisions and, in some cases, hiring consultants who are expert in a particular field.

Most engineering departments develop standards for metallurgical requirements, bearings, gears, shafts, oil grooves, securing devices, time standards, and a host of other items, all determined by the nature of their end product. Such standards are a vital part of the engineering function and are justly guarded as secret by most engineering departments. They are the results of long engineering experience, sometimes very costly mistakes, trends in customer standards, and trends in various engineering societies, as well as the myriad of standards set up by various state and federal agencies.

Final product specifications, then, are established by the engineering department. These specifications define the limits of variability which, if adhered to, will give satisfactory and reliable service for that class of product.

Communication of Specifications

All too often products are designed and put in process before a thorough understanding of what certain limits of variability may mean to the end product. Much effort is justified to channel this information to the lower levels of supervision and into the hands of the inspection department.

It is management's responsibility to apply the needed motivation to see that this is done in sufficient time to be effective. Usually this is brought about in scheduled meetings where those in attendance have preferably had some exposure to the product in question or are qualified to enter into a free interchange of ideas which will result in product improvement and further permit the transfer of information to subordinates.

Another technique is to hold non-scheduled meetings, usually run by engineering or other equivalent level of management, to explain the product to all concerned and to incorporate such suggestions as are appropriate to product improvement.

Still another technique, particularly in the small shop, is to foster close daily association of all department heads who transfer information and feedback to engineering, as well as management, such information as may be necessary for product improvement.

By far the best technique is to establish a design review task group, assigned by management and delegated certain responsibilities and authority to critically examine the design and specifications. In this process, the task group has the right to request specific action from engineering. Engineering must take some action, either standing pat with needed proof or making some changes to product design or limits of variability which the task group had reason to suspect. When the task group is satisfied that there are no further problems, it passes on the design as reviewed and so notifies the chief engineer.

A properly selected task group, given the necessary responsibility and supplied with the needed motivation from top management, should have no trouble in reducing new design difficulties in the order of 50 percent. Such a task group should spend not over one man-hour for each man-week spent on design and should consist of the following:

Chief Engineer.
Master Mechanic.
Director of Quality Assurance.
Service Manager.
Industrial Engineering Manager.
Superintendent of Fabrication.
Superintendent of Assembly and Erecting.

A major problem is with communications. It is essential not to let them remain oral, but rather to have them recorded wherever possible. While this may seem costly and unnecessary, written records become absentee communications and through them we are very often able to proceed without undue delay. Most delays are the results of people, not so much in what they did, but nearly always in what they failed to do.

The engineering department, through the creation and distribution of drawings, is probably the one department with nearly complete communications. Every blueprint is an engineering communication, assuming that it can be read. Management has in recent years resorted to "functional drafting." While now an accepted practice, there have been many instances where this left much to be desired. It is important to remember that a few hours of additional work in engineering, clearing up certain details, may save 10 to 100 times as many hours in the shop, aside from the loss due to parts being incorrectly made from scanty drawings.

The Nature of Dimensions

Dimensions are a part of the total specification assigned to parts designed by engineering. The dimensions given should be those which will assure that the part will be made only in one way, and exactly as intended by the designer.

In dimensioning a drawing, the designer should keep in mind the finished piece and its function in the assembly. The proper dimensions on a drawing are so given that it will never be necessary for a workman to calculate, scale, or assume any dimension in order to make a part, and no dimensions are given except those needed to produce or inspect the part.

Dimensions given between points or surfaces have a functional relationship to each other or control the location of other mating parts. These dimensions are the exact or theoretical sizes desired by the designer. There will always be some variation from the exact size because, in nature, there are no two items exactly alike, although it is sometimes difficult to determine the differences.

Exact sizes are not needed, since an assembly will function satisfactorily with some variation in part sizes. Also, exact sizes would be too expensive to produce. To inform the workman how much variation from exact size is permissible, the designer uses a tolerance or limit dimension technique. A tolerance is defined as the total permissible variation of size, or the difference between the limits of size. Limit dimensions are the maximum and minimum permissible dimensions.

Tolerances on dimensions are also used to shift the responsibility for exact size control from the judgment of the workman to the judgment of the engineer. One example is the fit between mating parts. The old method of indicating dimensions of two mating parts was to give the nominal dimensions of the two parts in common whole numbers and fractions and to indicate by note the kind of fit desired, that is, running fit, sliding fit, or force fit.

The American Standard ASA B4.1-1955,[1]* "Preferred Limits and Fits for Cylindrical Parts," defines terms applying to fits between plain cylindrical parts and makes recommendations on preferred sizes, allowances, tolerances,

*Superior numbers indicate specific references listed at the end of this chapter.

and fits for use wherever they are applicable. Limits are quoted for several classes of the following types of fit: running or sliding, locational clearance, transition, locational interference, and force or shrink.

Types of Tolerances. Tolerances are maximum permissible variations from specified design sizes. There are two types, unilateral and bilateral.

Unilateral tolerances allow variations in only one direction from the design size. They are used extensively for sizes of mating features of companion parts where a variation in one direction is more critical than in the other direction.

Bilateral tolerances allow variations in either direction from the design size. They are used on nonmating surfaces and on mating surfaces that are to be selected by size and mated with companion surfaces of selected size. In most cases, bilateral tolerances are of equal amount in both direction. In general, a bilateral tolerance of different amounts in opposite directions is evidence of either the wrong choice in the type of tolerance in the first place, or in the wrong choice of design size.

Engineering tolerances may broadly be divided into three groups: (1) size tolerances, (2) geometric tolerances, and (3) positional tolerances.

Size tolerances are assigned to dimensions such as length, diameter, and angle, in either unilateral or bilateral form.

Geometrical tolerances are used to control some geometrical characteristic of features. Typical geometric tolerances are straightness, flatness, parallelism, angularity, and perpendicularity. All of these may be specified independent or interdependent of the size tolerance.

Positional tolerances[2] provide an effective way of controlling the relative positions of mating features where interchangeability is a definite requirement. When applied to cylindrical features, the positional tolerances can be represented by a circular zone within which the actual center of the work must be confined. Normally, positional tolerance includes the permissible variations in the geometry of the feature as well, and is specified for the maximum material condition (MMC).

For special cases, geometric tolerances closer than would be permitted by the positional tolerance are specified. In another special case, the positional tolerance is specified regardless of feature size (RFS). This specification deprives inspection from using the "additional positional tolerance" concept.

Typical of tolerances applied by engineering for certain manufactured parts are:

± 0.010 in. for bolt holes.

± 0.001 in. for gear centers and dowel centers.

± 0.0002 in. for ball races.

$\begin{matrix} +0.0003 \\ -0.0000 \end{matrix}$ in. for mechanical seal hydraulic cylinders.

$\dfrac{+0.000100}{-0.000000}$ in. for mechanical seal in servo valve bores.

± 0.001 in. per foot for general machine alignment.

0.0005 in. per foot for squareness of finished parts.

$\pm 0°5'$ for angular spacings.

$\pm 0°2'2''$ for precise angular spacings.

Selection of Gaging Equipment

In the job shop, gage selection to measure the above-listed tolerances is generally left to gage control, shop supervision, and the machine operator. Where standard devices are unsuitable, special gages are designed by the tool engineering function and become a part of the tooling for the job in question.

In the mass producing industry it is often necessary to develop automated gaging equipment to keep up with the flow of parts. A simple comparison of man to machine should clear up the reasons why gaging must be built into automated production lines. The plus factor of both are required but not always compatible in a given mechanism.

Man	*Machine*
—Variable (biased); motor skills.	+Exact (precise); subject only to the physical laws of nature.
—Slow (multi-paced); hesitates; tires easily.	+Fast (isochronous); does not tire.
+Flexible (mobile); quick to re-program himself; can do a multitude of things.	—Invariant (fixed); cannot re-program itself; can perform only those things built into it.
+Wide capacity (can expand intelligence; has ability to learn)	—Small capacity (restricted intelligence; a moron)

In the event that special gage equipment has to be designed, it must have the approval of the foreman in the area where it is to be used, as well as final approval of the inspection department or quality control division. (See "Case History of Gage Development.")

What Gages Should Be Used?

Gages used correctly are the sensing means which feed back information about the product in process to the operator, from which he can take corrective action.

Gages must be simple and convenient to use. Attribute gages such as plug and ring gages are simple gages which give the operator a yes-no or accept-reject answer. Where the limits of variability are at a minimum, such devices are totally undesirable.

Regardless of the limits of variability, the variables type of measuring device is preferred. Dial indicators, micrometers, air gages, and dial bore gages are examples. By the use of variables measuring devices, the operator not only knows the limits of the "set course" but precisely where he is on that course. Variables measuring devices are preferred for the more important reason that much more information can be secured about the process through sampling fewer pieces.

As a general practice, the capability of the variables gage should be one-tenth of the tolerance (the limits of variability) permitted in the product being measured. This presents problems. Gage equipment used for measuring 0.0001-in. tolerances would necessarily have to be capable of accurately measuring to 10 millionths of an inch. While such equipment is available, it is expensive and does not for the most part stand the normal wear and tear of the measuring equipment ordinarily available to the machine operator.

When tolerances are less than 0.0005 in., it becomes necessary to look at many other aspects than gaging alone. A clean atmosphere and/or temperature control of the area becomes necessary. Better machining equipment is required, which automatically demands a new and better program of planned maintenance for such equipment. A gage laboratory must be installed (if not already available) with precise measuring equipment capable of measuring to 0.000,005 in. or less. New standards in master gage blocks will be required; these should be in the order of plus 0.000,002 in., minus 0.000,000 in. These masters will require closer surveillance, since gage blocks of the normal steel variety wear at the approximate rate of 0.000,001 in. for each 100 times they are wrung together.

In the case of work done for the government, all inspections of these masters must be traceable to the National Bureau of Standards and so certified. For safety, at least two sets of blocks will be required, one in service and the other out for certification. In all cases, blocks that are out for certification should require the replacement of any blocks not within the specified tolerance for that class of gage block.

The proper gage for measuring the item or product is determined by the degree of variability that engineering has designed into the product. The following are generally accepted limits:

1. All fractional dimensions over $\frac{1}{32}$ in.—steel rule.
2. All decimal dimensions less than $\frac{1}{32}$ in., but not less than 0.001 in—micrometer, vernier caliper or vernier height gage, plug gages, dial indicators, etc.

3. Decimal dimensions of 0.001 to 0.0001 in.—vernier micrometer, air gages, autocollimators, optical devices, electronic probes, gage blocks, dial indicators, etc.

4. Decimal dimensions less than 0.0001 in.—air gages, electronic gages, certain optical devices, digital readout devices, interferometers, light waves, etc.

Over many years of experience with all types of gaging, it is safe to say for decimal values of 0.00002 to 0.001 in., air gages have withstood the rigors of shop use (abuse included) with far less maintenance than other gages of comparable capability. Further consideration in favor of this type of gage is that it can usually be repaired by one skilled in the repair of the ordinary dial indicator. This is not true, as of this writing, with present electronic equipment.

Where contact measuring equipment is used for precision work, contact pressures are quite important. Gages are currently available which will respond accurately to contact pressures as low as 2 to 5 grams and are necessary for measuring such things as gage blocks, super precision guidance mechanisms, and the like.

Case Histories of Gage Development

Taper Socket Gage. In one case, taper sockets for Morse tapers were measured with conventional attribute gages. The normal practice was to blue up the gage, and the decision to accept or reject was based on one's interpretation of how the "light coating" of blue rubbed off. In this type of operation much depended on how the gage was inserted into the socket and how it was turned when inserted.

Even the best operators are apt to be deceived by tapered attribute gages, whether of the male or female type. Since losses from faulty inspection exceeded 10 percent of production, and were found in the customer's plant, there was cause for immediate action.

These steps were taken:

1. Specifications for the taper sockets were investigated. Handbooks did not agree on the exact values; engineering generally called for a taper by number.

2. All references to the size of the taper from handbooks, and the American Standards Association for such data, were checked.

3. All data on the attribute gage from the gage manufacturer was procured.

4. All information was presented to engineering to get agreement on specific diameters of each taper at the large end and at the small end, and these were related to the end face of the socket or drift slot.

5. The above was tabulated, then gaging equipment was checked out. Disagreement was found.

6. Attribute gage equipment on the market to do this job was investigated. Most gage manufacturers (at the time this problem was solved) offered angular measuring means only. A few mathematical checks indicated that this route was undesirable.

7. An air gage which incorporated these considerations was designed to the following criteria:

   (a) Both male and female tapers had to be measured. (Reference here to male gage only.)

   (b) It had to conform in all respects to our attribute gage.

   (c) Two separate and distinct sets of air jets were planned to measure specific diameters at the large end of the bore and at the small end of the bore, with separate gages for each set of jets. Dial graduations of 0.000,050 in. were agreed upon.

   (d) A dial indicator with graduations of 0.001 in. was to be used to permit accurate control of the position of the taper from some reference point.

   (e) Air jets were to be properly positioned to provide adequate approach range.

   (f) The gage had to be able to measure the work without requiring removal of the part being measured.

   (g) A master was designed for the gage, which allowed a slight tolerance so that the large end would be slightly under the specified size (approximately 0.0001 in.).

The gage resulting from the foregoing planning (Fig. 16-1) showed a $10,000 saving the first year for gage equipment that cost $8,000. Of greater interest, no further rejections occurred over an 11-year period.

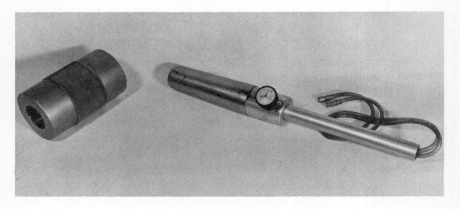

Fig. 16-1. Gage for inspecting taper sockets.

Ring Nut Gage. In another case, large ring nuts of approximately 26-in. pitch diameter were being individually fitted to a mating part. These nuts served a bearing function as well. Being individually fitted, they were not interchangeable in the field and caused a degree of hardship to replace them. The operation created a problem in manufacturing. The gage development considerations were as follows:

1. Investigation of attribute devices revealed the impracticality of such a cumbersome piece of gage equipment.
2. Commercial gage makers did not provide variables equipment in this range.
3. What was required of the gage?
   (a) It had to accurately measure the pitch diameter of a female thread of 26-in. PD, approximately one to one and one-half inches in length.
   (b) The gage had to be quickly and reliably set to size.
   (c) It had to be easily put into the workpiece and easily removed after the measurement was taken.
4. Since not available commercially, could some modification of existing equipment, either in-plant or available on the market, be utilized?
5. Beam gages were available to measure this diameter but, if equipped with thread segments, could measure at a specific point only and could not prove out-of-round conditions.
6. The final solution (Fig. 16-2): Thread rolls to work axially on a pintle as well as to revolve on the pintle were provided. In this way, measurement could be made at any point throughout 360°, and all measurements would be at 90° to the axis. The problem of setting was resolved

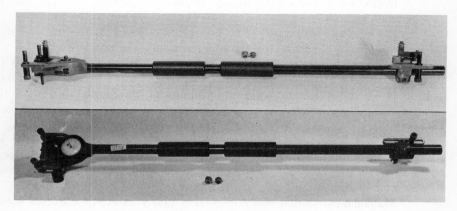

Fig. 16-2. Gage for inspecting ring nuts of 26-in. pitch diameter.

by making the OD of the thread rolls to a specific diameter in relation to the pitch diameter of the thread rolls. Then, by calculation, the gage was zeroed to a known dimension before each use.

The gain here is in interchangeability, and shortening of manufacturing time. Each ring nut is a gage and is now left with the mating part.

How Much Inspection Can Be Afforded?

The class of product being made and the competition the product is up against, will determine the extent of inspection required. It is doubtful if, on the average, over 15 percent of all products made by any given manufacturer receive complete and thorough inspection.

During periods of difficulty, management is prone to ask for 100 percent inspection of the product. Unfortunately, 100 percent inspection does not produce 100 percent results.[3] In general, 100 percent inspection at its very best is about 85 percent effective. The problem lies in many areas. One is that repetitive inspection is both fatiguing and monotonous. But principally, the problem rests in borderline conditions; the operator discards as many acceptable pieces as he accepts rejectable pieces. Strangely enough, automatic gaging equipment may function uncertainly in borderline conditions, and may sort components entirely differently on a second and third pass through the machine.

The problem, then, becomes one of establishing inspection safeguards which will operate on a low consumer risk. Quality control engineering can play an important part in establishing mathematical models for maximum protection.

Inspection systems vary widely by class of product but fall into six general categories:

1. *First-Piece Inspection.* The first piece is checked, for the operation being done, by the inspector, the supervisor, and the operator.

2. *Patrol Inspection.* This is an examination of parts in process at the machine. The finding of substandard material is cause to shut the machine down. Patrol inspection is the responsibility of supervision and, where this responsibility is carried out, a higher degree of quality of conformance is possible.

3. *Spot Inspection.* This is usually done at the completion of the job at the inspection area. It consists of taking samples from the lot and accepting or rejecting accordingly. Rejecting means the lot must be culled (sorted) to remove the substandard parts from the lot.

Management should study inspection policy carefully wherever culling is required at inspection, because it indicates clearly that the supervisor and the industrial worker are not living up to the standards, or that the equipment on which the job is being done is inadequate to produce the required quality. In either event, immediate remedial action is required. In the event that production still does not come up to the standards required, the responsibility for sorting the job should rest with manufacturing rather than inspection.

4. *Statistical Sampling.* The work done in this area during and since World War II has demonstrated that superior inspection and higher resultant product quality can be maintained. It is the responsibility of the quality control manager to select the most suitable sampling plan, to test it out, approve it, then see to it that all supervisors and inspectors who will use it, or come in contact with it, thoroughly understand its application and use.

5. *Toll Gate.* In this type of inspection, the product passes through several operations, then goes to an inspection area for evaluation of all work thus far completed. In general, this is too late and too costly to discover the defective work. Toll gate inspection has its greatest value as a final examination of the product going to stock.

6. *No Formal Inspection.* Where the skill of the machine operators is high and the interaction between supervisor and worker is good, no formal inspection may be necessary. This is not unusual in small shops. It should be the goal of all concerned to reach for this condition regardless of the size of the company.

There are several ways which can be established for the system of inspection. It may be necessary to use two or more depending on the nature of the product and the rate at which it is produced and used.

Gage Control Practice

Gage control is situated in that centralized area which is responsible for all measuring devices used throughout manufacturing. In this area only the very best practice can be tolerated, because many thousands of dollars of scrap can be produced if defective or poorly maintained and calibrated equipment is used to measure an item of product.

In general, gage control must be provided with and/or cover the following:

1. A clean, temperature-controlled area.
2. Racks for storage of precision devices between use.
3. A coding system to identify each individual item of measuring equipment.
4. Historical records which cover the frequency of inspection of all measuring equipment.
5. A system of control to permit issuance and return, as well as follow-up of delinquent gages that have remained in production beyond their normal cycle check period (Figs. 16-3 and 16-4).

THE BULLARD CO.
BRIDGEPORT, CONN.

TOOL & GAGE INSPECTION DELINQUENT REPORT — No. 1605

9-30-64
DATE

TO: Mr. Tom Brown — 131-B (DEPT.) — PROJECT

FROM: TOOL & GAGE INSPECTION — CRIB NO. G. R.

THE FOLLOWING EMPLOYEES HAVE FAILED TO RETURN THE INSTRUMENT AND/OR GAGES SPECIFIED BELOW:

EMPLOYEE	DEPT.	CLOCK NO.	SHIFT	DESCRIPTION	SERIAL NO.	DATE DUE
John Doe	131-B	3769	1	Micrometer	265003104	9/28

THE ABOVE MUST BE RETURNED IMMEDIATELY TO TOOL & GAGE INSPECTION CRIB FOR REINSPECTION

B5672 — George Best — TOOL AND GAGE INSPECTION FOREMAN

Fig. 16-3. Tool and gage delinquent report.

THE BULLARD CO.
BRIDGEPORT, CONN.

MEASURING INSTRUMENT & GAGE ORDER — No. 488655

131-B	8-28-64
DEPT. NO.	DATE
	265003104
PROJECT	SERIAL NO.
A 14	
BIN NO.	T NUMBER

QUANTITY	SIZE	DESCRIPTION
1	3"	Micrometer

B5673

ISSUED BY	CYCLE DATE	CRIB NO
G. B.	9/28/64	G. R.

SIGNED	SHIFT	CLOCK NO
John Doe	1	3769

RETURN THIS SLIP WITH INSTRUMENT OR GAGE

Fig. 16-4. Gage order form.

6. Provision for inspection, both visual and by calibration, of all returned gages from the production area.
7. Adequate area and manpower for repair of gages within the capability of the area, in particular, micrometers, dial indicators, and air gages.

8. Standardization of equipment including the maintenance of spare parts to facilitate immediate repair to the foregoing.

9. Where the area is not equipped, to return such devices to the original manufacturer for repair.

10. Development of data to show when it is no longer feasible to make further repairs to a given piece of measuring equipment and see that worn-out equipment is properly disposed of.

11. Development of, and adherence to a realistic budget.

12. A system of records that can show at a moment's notice where any given piece of gage equipment may be located.

13. From this area must be operated any and all mobile gage inspection equipment used for surveillance of outlying gage areas, tool cribs, experimental areas, etc.

14. Provision of a foolproof system so that all variables measuring devices are set under gage control supervision only.

15. Provision of protective boxes or other containers to protect all gages in transit within or between the manufacturing areas.

16. Provision for the checking and calibration of all superprecision devices used within the gage room only for surveillance of other measuring devices.

17. Gage control must act at all times to protect the measuring capability of the company. In this capacity it must insist, within the limits of company policy, that all measuring equipment used to measure the company's products be company owned or be subject to cycle checks to ensure that their capability will meet the measuring standards.

18. All purchases of precision measuring devices must originate or clear through gage control.

19. All new measuring devices must, upon receipt, be forwarded to gage control, and be thoroughly checked out before being issued to manufacturing and before payment.

20. Gage control must be capable of setting up and operating any piece of measuring equipment over which it maintains surveillance, as well as explaining its operation for proper use.

21. Gage control must provide storage for special instrumentation used by engineering, road service, research, and for experimental purposes.

22. Gage control records must show transfers of gage equipment from one crib to another or from one department to another.

23. Gage control must work closely with the personnel department and have all new employees register any precision measuring devices owned by them so that these can come under their surveillance until such time as the employee retires or severs connections with the company or removes such devices from the premises.

Gage Repair and Inspection Procedures

Men will, if properly instructed, follow specific procedures. When left alone they develop their own, thus in effect setting up multiple standards—a highly unsatisfactory condition.

The gage control area must, for most effective operation, have spelled-out procedures for repair, adjustment, wear allowances, and setting or calibration of certain gage equipment. A micrometer may be taken to illustrate the need for such procedures:

1. The micrometer is a precision measuring device.
2. It is subject to very frequent use.
3. To be of service it must be accurate throughout its measuring range.

To satisfy the above requirements, the micrometer must have:

1. Anvil and spindle faces parallel.
2. Minimum axial play in spindle.
3. Minimum radial play in spindle.
4. Correct alignment of zero on thimble with barrel graduations.

Micrometer manufacturers are somewhat reluctant to release the data for items 2 and 3 above. As a result of years of experience in the examination of both new micrometers and older ones in service, the following specifications were laid down for all micrometers being repaired:

1. Anvil and spindle faces must be lapped parallel.
2. Axial end play must be adjusted to a maximum of 0.001 in.
3. Radial play must not exceed 0.0015 in.
4. Zero on thimble must always split the line on the barrel when micrometer is being repaired.
5. Calibration must be within one graduation throughout its measuring range.

Besides micrometers, other types of measuring tools and equipment must be examined for their specific repair or maintenance requirements. A few are:

1. Ring Gages: What class to buy? When to consider them worn out?
2. Same as above for plug gages.
3. Gage blocks: At what point shall they be discarded? How often shall they be checked for calibration?
4. How should a height gage or other vernier device be checked out?
5. At what wear point shall test bars and bushings be discarded?
6. How often shall the calibration of dial indicators be checked? Should AGD Standards be adhered to, or should the checking procedure extend further?

Identification Codes for Measuring Equipment

Identification codes may be numerical, alphabetical, or an alphanumeric code. The best system for measuring equipment appears to be a straight numerical code consisting of nine digits. A code of this type provides for 1000 categories with 1000 items in each category, plus the added ability to give information on the size, range, or number of pieces in a set of gage blocks or V-blocks, etc. Thus, 1000 × 1000 or 1,000,000 items can be kept on record for immediate identification. The addition of one more digit would provide for 10 million items.

To set up such a system, first arrange all of the gage equipment now on hand in a clear alphabetical sequence. Review this list carefully and add in alphabetically some of the gage equipment that might possibly be purchased later, even though it might be five or more years before the purchase is made. Assign the first three numbers of the nine digit code to the final alphabetical list. Spread out the numbers, leaving at least half or more of the numbers in each group of 100 unassigned. This will allow for future unlisted equipment as well as permitting the utilization of the first and third digit alike when over 1000 items in any one name category become possible. Typical devices likely to fall in this category are dial indicators, micrometers, and the like.

The next step is to build range characteristics and number on hand into this code. Assume the number 265 is assigned to micrometers. The second set of three digits could define the range such as 002 would mean a 1-to 2-in. measuring capability. The third set of three digits such as 112 would indicate (if it is the last number issued) that there are 112 1-to 2-in. micrometers individually identifiable and under surveillance by gage control. The identifying number on the foregoing micrometer is 265002112.

Since, in a shop employing 1000 or more machine operators, there are probably over 1000 micrometers, the first three digits 285 might be kept open in the alphabetical listing for future expansion of micrometers. This association of similar numbers helps for quick identification.

Another good reason for a nine-digit code is that fewer mistakes are made in gage control since nine digits are required for complete identification of any particular item.

If any piece of gage equipment wears out or is damaged beyond repairs, re-use that code number for the replacement and note this in the records. In this manner the records will represent a perpetual inventory and will be current at any given time.

Except for the initial setup, this system has operated effectively for over ten years, maintaining surveillance over approximately 20,000 items with a loss estimated to be not in excess of 0.3 percent during that period. Before setting up any coding or identification system, it is important to reason it out thoroughly, since it will be quite costly and time consuming to start over or to have two or more systems in operation at any one time.

Methods of Marking. Haphazard gage marking is to be strictly avoided. Acid etching, vibro etching, strips of tape, metal discs, etc., rely on someone's ability to print or write and are often illegible. The use of metal stamps must be avoided because they will distort a precision device. By far the best method is mechanical engraving. The investment is modest and the service life of a small engraving machine is probably in excess of 25 years. Such a device should be kept in the gage control area and be a regular part of gage control service equipment.

QUALITY CONTROL

Definition of Quality Control

Quality control may be defined as the directed effort of all elements of a company toward competitive standards with minimum losses to the company. By this definition it is apparent that reporting to the company's chief executive officer is necessary to achieve the goal of "minimum losses to the company."

Dr. Juran, an eminent authority on quality control, has stated that Quality Control = Defect Prevention. This definition will be used later to illustrate responsibility as related to product quality.

Decision Making for Quality Control

The use of judgment alone, in decision making, is a qualitative procedure which all too often places unrealistic, unjustified reliance on experience and integrity. The use of facts alone is a quantitative procedure, and depends almost solely upon accuracy in research, measurements, and numerical analyses. Some combination of judgment and facts is necessary, and is employed by most skilled decision makers, since bias-free industrial data are not always available.

An abiding problem lies in the area of time because, when either the dollar value is high and/or the priority is high, the tendency is to use qualitative procedures without adjusting them to quantitative data which may be unavailable at the moment and might take considerable time to secure.

It is important to watch for staff and operators reactions to quality control decisions. People do not respond as readily to qualitative data as they do to quantitative data.

Regardless of how the decisions are made, they need to be followed up to test their validity; only in this way can one make better decisions in the future. Important points to remember about decisions are:[4]

Progress is built on decisions.

Decisions are forced by alternatives.

Alternatives provide facts.

Facts are acquired through research.

Research gives direction to change.

Changes involve thinking, planning, and making many little decisions before the final decision is reached.

Resistance to change is a normal human reaction; it requires anticipation and actions to minimize its effects.

Decisions reduce doubt.

Decisions involve risk.

Risk implies that there is a possibility of failure.

Failure implies the need for statistical evaluation so as to know the odds.

Decisions are conclusions.

The Acceptable Level of Avoidable Losses

At the start of a quality control program, it is not unusual to find that total losses to the company, attributable to poor quality control, equal or exceed 50 cents per hour for each direct hour applied to the product.

The losses sustained in manufacturing vary widely by the class of product manufactured. Considering the dollar loss due to scrap, rework, defective materials, and field service costs, and the costs of maintaining the records for these losses, quite often a very sizeable dollar value results. All too often, these losses are considered separately by management. When they are lumped together, management gets a new perspective and is the more disposed to take remedial action.

As to what constitutes an acceptable level for such losses, which we can well term avoidable losses, each company must set its own goals. If it is in a highly profitable or monopolistic position perhaps less emphasis will be placed on remedial actions than if it has to operate on a narrow margin of profit.

Pertinent data should be assembled to show all losses and recurring expenses related to the product *before* the start of any quality control program. Such historical data is of vital importance in determining the progress of a newly installed QC program. A quality program should not be instituted for better relations or for prestige alone. Rather, it should have inbuilt means of showing to management that it can pay its way.

Where Should Quality Control Report?

Theoretically, any new function should report at the lowest level at which it can effectively accomplish the goals set for the function. There are highly divergent ideas on where quality control should report. The following are likely areas: (1) manufacturing, (2) engineering, (3) sales, (4) industrial engineering, (5) president, (6) chairman of the board.

The most important matter that management must decide here is the degree of freedom of action it wishes to vest in quality control. Placing quality control under any one of the first four of the above reduces the status of quality control in the eyes of those who work in the department as well as in the eyes of the production worker. In reporting to these areas, there is a great tendency for quality control to be relegated to second importance, thereby making the true purpose and goals of quality control difficult, if not impossible, to attain.

By and large the best area for quality control to report is directly to the president or chief executive officer of the company. In this position, quality control acquires equal status with all other divisions and is in the best position to get action in all areas where, when, and as needed. QC reporting at this level will shorten the lines of communication to keep the president better informed, while simultaneously getting prompt action for quality improvement.

Quality Control Department Head Qualifications

A good quality control executive must be enthusiastic, versatile, ingenious, persistent, determined, and of the highest integrity. He must share his experiences with his subordinates if he expects to attain the goals that are possible under a well managed program. Above all, he must, to be effective, present an image that others would like to copy.

Functions Under Quality Control

Every management must decide on the areas it wishes to place under the manager of quality control. These will vary from company to company, but generally include: (1) inspection, (2) gage control, (3) salvage, (4) quality control engineering, (5) metallurgical laboratory, and (6) final product testing.

Study of Inspection Costs and Effectiveness

At the start of a QC program, two areas must be carefully studied with regard to the inspection function:
1. What is its cost of operation?
2. How effective is inspection in the existing environment in accomplishing its tasks?

The total cost of operating the inspection department must go beyond any tabulation of figures usually available through the cost department. Such items as the following must be studied in detail:
1. Wages and salaries.
2. Ratio of direct workers to inspectors by area.

3. Ratio of direct workers to supervisors by area.
4. Ratio of current dollar loss to inspector by area.
5. Ratio of current dollar loss to supervisors plus inspectors by area.
6. Evaluation of the capabilities of each inspector—background, experience, length of service.
7. A measure of each inspector's efficiency in terms of preventing a flow of defects.
8. A measure of the department's general health—absenteeism, first aid records, etc.
9. A review of job evaluation for all jobs.
10. Ratio of inspectors to the number of supervisors in inspection.
11. Complete review and examination of all paper work and records.
12. Ratio of the total cost of defects to inspection payroll.

Such a detailed study invariably points out certain strengths and weaknesses from which improvement can be made. Since inspection is an indirect function, it is often over-manned. Ratio delay studies can be of help in determining whether it is over-manned or not. If there are evident weaknesses in the inspection personnel, training programs can be established to overcome these deficiencies.

Inspection is, at best, a monotonous job. The efficiency of the inspector is related to the defects detected vs. the defects allowed to pass. Several checks along this line are necessary, taken at random periods, for proper evaluation of each inspector. The most important job here is to get to the root of all "cost origins," for only then can intelligent decisions for corrective action be reached. The second question, i.e., effectiveness of inspection, will require long-term study and evaluation. Principally, however, this study will deal with the following:

1. Gage equipment.
2. Location of inspection in relation to the production stream.
3. Degree of inspection supervision and its capability.
4. Degree of interest in and/or assistance given to inspection by manufacturing supervision.
5. Attitudes of the production workers.
6. Interactions of all these groups in relation to inspection.
7. Pressures applied by production to meet schedules.
8. Extent of paper work required of the inspector.
9. Limitations or lack of them on individual inspectors' authority to make a decision. Where is the line drawn?
10. To what extent does the inspection staff enter into the decisions to salvage defective work?
11. How is the salvage function handled?
12. Methods of inspection.

Routes to Quality Improvement

Statistical Quality Control. In general, the first exposure to quality control involves an extensive study of statistical techniques. The use of statistical methods to control quality are well proven and lend themselves readily to problem solving and process control. Where the flow is continuous or the lot size is sufficient, some form of statistical control is desirable. Job shop operation does not lend itself in all instances to statistical control and so other means must be relied upon to get the needed improvement in product quality.

The Practical Approach. It is estimated that 80 percent of total tonnage of all parts manufactured for all the various products made in this country are made in lots of 20 pieces or less. This indicates that very wide job shop manufacturing operations are in existence.

In this second route to quality improvement, a practical approach is strictly necessary. Careful studies in this area should solve such problems as follows:

1. Best gage to measure the part or parts in question.
2. Availability of such gage equipment.
3. Time required to procure the gage.
4. Whether a master is required with the gage.
5. Locations for gage cribs.
6. Training required to permit the machine operator to use the gage correctly.
7. The desirability of assigning certain gage equipment to specific machining operations on specific machines on a permanent basis.
8. Whether attribute or variable gaging equipment best satisfies the need for the quality level desired.
9. Extent to which the machine operator can be relied on to correctly measure the parts he makes and whether or not his integrity is such that he can be relied on to separate parts into accept or reject categories.
10. Mobility of such devices as surface plates which can be wheeled up to the machine to permit the operator to do a better job of surveillance of the parts he makes.
11. Extent that it is necessary for the operator to use certain graphic recording equipment normally in inspection areas such as pitch, center distance, involute, or lead gear checkers, or surface finish recorders.
12. Possible use of optical projection methods to assist the machine operator. This is of vital importance in cutter grinding areas. (One 30-in. optical projector with a toolroom grid chart has effectively eliminated four inspectors and has been in operation over ten years.)

13. Existence of charts and check lists which permit thorough evaluation of tests of subunits and complete assemblies.

14. Knowledge of the capabilities of machines producing each item of product.

15. Evaluation of the complete product, as ready to ship, in terms of machine capability studies.

16. Requirement to evaluate jigs and fixtures relating to the product. It is not unusual at the start of a program of tool cycle inspection to find that over 30 percent of the tools are defective and contribute to poor quality as a result.

17. Extent of inspection required at receiving and shipping.

18. The need to develop standards, either pictorial or physical, so that it is not necessary to rely on word of mouth or memory to reach decisions from time to time.

19. Extent of working closely with purchasing to get first-hand data on purchased items.

20. Speed of the existing system to advise quality control of engineering changes.

21. Flow and interchange of information and ideas in the prerelease period of new engineering designs.

Psychological Aspects of Quality Improvement. A third route to quality improvement is through a well grounded understanding and application of psychological principles. This is one area in industry that unfortunately gets extensive lip service and a minimum of application. Product quality is very closely correlated with integrity and morale. Quality usually improves as morale goes upward.

Morale in industry may be stated as "the worker's emotional reaction and adjustment to his work environment." Morale must be improved, if at all, right on the job. This means that all members of management must practice what they preach.

The means of motivating people fall into two categories. The first and easiest is by the use of "threat or fear." The use of threat is necessary under certain conditions, but its prolonged use will result in retaliation on the part of the industrial worker, to the detriment of product quality. The second means to motivating people is to appeal to their socio-psychological needs. Motivation comes from within an individual, which means that industrial supervision is responsible to handle each individual worker in a manner that awakens man's inner desires toward higher goals, in short, give the worker good reason for action.

The pressures of running a department and meeting production schedules is at times a frustrating experience for the best of supervisors. The big problem is not to let these frustrations rub off on the industrial worker, for he will do his best and extend himself further when he has confidence and belief in his supervisor and feels safe in his hands.

It is important that psychological factors be understood and carefully weighed by all quality control managers. The five basic human drives are for (1) survival, (2) security, (3) belonging, (4) self-esteem, and (5) self-improvement.

To get the best out of people, the last three of the stated basic five drives must be specially watched, in that changes about to be made must satisfy these three drives without creating anxiety or frustration and at the same time permitting improvement in the attitude of the industrial worker. The most important single thing that management can do to assist quality programs is to see to it that every man has a chance to grow.

Quality of Conformance—The Vital Concern

Three kinds of quality affect the final product quality. They are: (1) quality of decision, (2) quality of engineering, and (3) quality of conformance.

Conformance simply means that an end product is produced that meets, in all respects, the limits of variability established by engineering and stated in specifications.

Ability to produce to specifications is affected by:

1. *Facilities available:* the age and condition of the production equipment, the nature of planned maintenance programs and the amount of money management allots to such programs, material handling means and the rate of handling parts between operations safely, and the extent to which such parts are protected in transit from one operation to another or while in stores areas.

2. *Tools available:* the condition of jigs and fixtures, their availability when required, the degree of tools inspection to assure that they are correct and properly set before the next time used, and tools storage and handling facilities.

3. *Perishable tools:* The location of and service supplied by tool cribs, the extent of protection given to sharp edges such as on milling cutters and reamers, and the equipment available to keep these devices in A-1 condition. Cutter grinding is important to quality of conformance, for many quality problems have their origin right here. Quality control should concentrate on this area as a prime objective to assure manufacturing that cutting tools are correct for the required machining operations.

4. *Gage equipment:* availability and accuracy of measuring devices (covered previously).

5. *Process methods:* The nature of the routing of a particular part through the various machining centers determines the degree of quality we can expect in the finished part. Methods engineering may be restricted to some extent, based on information supplied by management, and hence

may under-tool for the product. Further, the time standards set may not be conducive to getting the production worker to do his best or even try to. Time standards become even more important under an incentive system.

6. *Morale:* The interaction between workers and between workers and supervisors is important. Caste systems may develop or favoritism may be shown by supervision, which in the eyes of the worker is just plain discrimination. The objective here is to develop and nourish favorable interactions which will boost morale and cultivate a healthy degree of intradepartmental competition.

7. *Housekeeping:* This has an effect on the quality of product. Even in the well-kept shop the little frustrations created by untidiness sometimes pyramid to impel the industrial worker to take on housekeeping chores unrelated to his job. Housekeeping chores beyond the machine or work bench take away production time and preferably should not be delegated to the industrial worker. Poor housekeeping is conducive to poor workmanship.

8. *Excessive overtime:* While this is desirable in the pay envelope, it does not increase man's efficiency. To the contrary, extensive studies have been made in the engineering drafting area and show that a fair rate of productivity during protracted overtime hours is about 50 percent of normal.[5]

9. *Inspection:* Speed of service and the fairness of decisions have a favorable effect on the worker's attitude and thus affect the quality of conformance.

10. *Tight schedules:* When delivery is shortened, added pressures develop on supervisors and workers. In an effort to produce the needs resulting from compressed schedules, the industrial worker gambles on getting substandard work through inspection. If the worker in the industrial situation can get away with making substandard materials, it should be questioned whether the man alone is at fault, or the system under which he works. Inspection effort must be increased during these periods.

11. *Stability of management:* The industrial worker is far more concerned about the machinations of the management hierarchy than management has reason to believe. "Push-pull" climates, resulting from power struggles or discord (or suspicion of either) at the top, create apathy and anxiety in the industrial worker and is not conducive to the highest quality of conformance. The worker will do his best in a stable atmosphere where it is evident to him that all levels of management are interested in him as a person and not just a number.

Where Conformance Responsibility Rests

Referring back to a statement by Juran, "controlled prevention" is specifically in the hands of the supervisor and the machine operator. The machine operator who measures each part is "sensing" the output of his machine, and has the responsibility to command a new output by feeding back this information by a simple adjustment to the machine. The alert supervisor will make sufficient in-process checks of the work being produced, regardless of other inspection efforts. It is assumed that he has been given by management full authority to command remedial action of the machine operator, so as to get the process back to producing the required quality of conformance.

Manufacturing is logically responsible for the quality produced. Failure on the part of management to pinpoint this responsibility with manufacturing and, instead, hold inspection responsible ultimately results in a degenerate inspection system. The quality of conformance cannot be inspected into a product.

Quality control's responsibility is to set up safeguards that can assure management that an absolute minimum of a known percent defective reaches stock or goes into the final product. Proper quality control methods also can predict with astonishing accuracy the degree of defectiveness that enters stock as being some percentage of tolerance beyond the normal limits of variability as specified by engineering, but which are nevertheless still acceptable to engineering.

Responsibilities of Quality Control Engineering

The aim of quality control engineering is defect prevention. While this is inherently a postmortem approach, its intent is to do such research as is necessary to reveal the cause of major losses exhibited by high cost concentrations. After determining the cause, it will make recommendations for correction. It is important that this function be guided from *quantitative* data and not by opinion, except where no other source of data exists.

Quality control is affected by all areas and all disciplines. It is important, therefore, that the statistical techniques developed, and used successfully by quality control engineering, be disseminated to other areas which can effectively use these same techniques.

This effort is chiefly concentrated in the fabrication and assembly areas. It is desirable that such a group be jointly directed by the superintendent of fabrication and the manager of quality control. In this way, the superintendent of fabrication is adequately informed of investigations in process and is in a position to cooperate and take remedial action as recommended. Better still, due to his association with the manufacturing problems, he may suggest action or bring out other areas for investigation.

In general, the number of quality control engineers should not exceed four per 1000 direct workers. To assure the company that the techniques will be passed on to other departments, it is desirable to have one-half of the group as permanent members reporting to the quality control department and the other one-half taken from shop supervision, industrial engineering, or machine repair departments. This latter group should remain a part of their home department, and after approximately one year in this work should return to the home department, where they can continue to use the knowledge gained and permit new selections to be made to perpetuate this important function.

The responsibility for training this group rests with the manager of quality control. Only the highest caliber of person possible should be selected for this important function because of the need to learn, develop, and use effective statistical methods. A properly guided quality control engineering group should have no difficulty in saving the company between two and three times its salary for each year they are in operation.

Areas of Operation. The quality control engineering group, while directing its efforts at high-loss areas in fabrication, should not be limited to this area alone. One area to which constant access is required is the salvage area. Observing the nature of rejected work should supply clues as to what departments are rejecting these materials. Further examination of such materials should reveal why they have been rejected.

It is desirable to make critical examinations of the reject records, compiling this in the form of Pareto Curve analysis. This will show: (1) what pieces have been rejected, (2) the frequency of rejection, (3) the dollar loss, (4) why a piece was rejected, (5) who rejected it, (6) where to concentrate improvement efforts.

A thorough analysis may require, among other approaches, machine capability studies, investigation of tools and fixtures, methods and time standards, measuring devices, and possibly the raw material situation.

The second major area of investigation is in the departments of subassembly, test, and final erection and assembly. If the company has a testing function under some other department head, it is quite likely that these areas will not require quality efforts embracing test procedures. On the other hand, if evidence exists that testing needs improvement, quality control engineering's close cooperation with the person responsible for this function should facilitate and accelerate corrective action.

What have been described here are primary quality control engineering functions. As time and needs develop, this group, under a well trained and aggressive quality control manager, may branch out into reliability studies and other advanced quality control techniques.

The Testing Function

Except for small shop operations and the in-line manufacturing operations which produce at a high volume, all manufactured components of an end product which is to be assembled commonly go to the stock room. At the proper time, production planning will release some or all of these components for subassembly and for erection or final assembly of the end product.

To assure proper operation of such an end product when erected, testing in some form is required of at least the major subassemblies and most certainly of the final assembled product. This is necessary for two reasons: (1) to assure management that the product conforms in all respects to the engineering specifications, and (2) to assure the sales department that the machine holds the tolerance which the customer has been guaranteed.

Gear Box Study. To indicate how much data need be known or determined, the following should be known before testing commences upon *a simple gear box:*

1. Input speed and rotation.
2. Output speeds and rotation.
3. Input horsepowers.
4. Output horsepower.
5. Either the torque or the end thrust expected at the output shaft.
6. Overload protection, whether internal or external.
7. Required lubrication and pressure for lubrication.
8. Acceptable noise levels of the gear train.
9. Expected temperature of operation.
10. Means of control of clutches and shifting of gears.
11. Means of interlocking and safety devices provided.
12. Nature of service, whether continuous or intermittent.
13. Anticipated rate of production.
14. Arrival date of first unit.

Having assembled such data, the next step is the decision for a suitable test stand. The arrival date and anticipated rate of production will supply clues as to what kind of a test stand is required. It is desirable from both a cost and time standpoint to utilize as is, or by suitable modification, the drive input mechanism which has been incorporated in the design of the machine that will contain the gear box. The gain here is manifold: (1) valuable tool design time is saved because the basic drive input is available, (2) only structural members are needed to hold the gear box, its drive, and the drive motor, and (3) the utilization of the basic drive input mechanism provides valuable data as to operation of the gear box over a period of time—in fact, it provides a life test of this mechanism.

Next, controls are needed which will simulate the normal machine controls, again, if possible, utilizing designed units to take advantage of the life test for that mechanism.

The final consideration is the instrumentation needed to measure accurately and record the performance data. In the case of the gear box, the following will be needed:

1. An ammeter or horsepower meter to provide data on what the input motor is doing.
2. A prony brake or dynamometer to establish output torque at any given speed.
3. Suitable hydraulic gages to check pressures of input and of lubrication.
4. Suitable graduate to collect overflow of oil from the gear box to determine rates of leakage.
5. Pyrometer to make checks of temperature at various locations.
6. Sound level meter to check ambient levels and changes due to operation of the gear box at different speeds and torque outputs.
7. Tachometer to check all output speeds.
8. An accumulated-time-run clock or $\frac{1}{10}$-hour recorder desirable, but not mandatory.
9. Check list which indicates required adjustments and points that must be checked, and in what sequence these are required.
10. Final record card, to be filled in completely by the inspector and signed by him when the unit has met all specifications. This should go to the manager of quality control for his examination and be maintained on record for future reference.

The test procedure should be spelled out by and approved by the manager of quality control, who is responsible to see that adequately trained and competent inspection personnel is available to handle the required testing. The decision to test is sometimes a difficult one. Occasionally, even the simplest of units may require testing due to field difficulties. Usually some simple error in the original engineering design will cause this to occur.

The goal behind all testing should be the proof that the subassembly meets the required performance specifications. It is important to keep good records and, after several satisfactory units have been checked, to start a sampling procedure where all units get a running test and those sampled are completely tested.

IMPORTANCE OF MACHINE TOOL ALIGNMENT

Final Alignment

Every machine tool, during the final erecting procedure, must meet certain limits of variability insofar as its alignment is concerned. The alignment of a machine tool to a critical extent determines the capability of the machine to produce adjacent sides square with one another. It also determines

Check table cross–slots for parallelism
with bed guiding way in 40 in.

Indicator mounted in bar and saddle
mounted along bed to check this reading

Extend bar 18 in. from face plate
and check bar for parallelism with
top of table — run saddle along bed
to make this check.

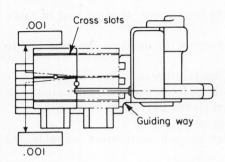

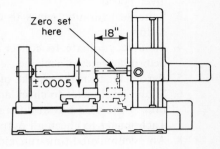

Extend bar 12 in. from face plate and
check runout of tapered hole in bar

Run machine at top speed for one
hour — extend bar 18 in. and check
for runout of spindle

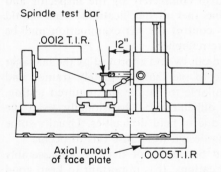

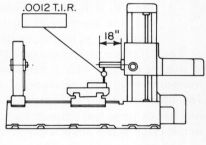

Fig. 16-5. Inspection operations for parallelism and runout on
horizontal boring machines.

work taper conditions, out-of-round conditions, and whether combinations
of pitch, yaw, and roll motions, which occur to some degree in every
machine moving member, will result in poor quality output from the machine.

During the early part of this century, Schlessinger[6] did extensive work
in developing machine tool alignment procedures. His work outlined in
detail permissible tolerances for almost every class of machine tool then
in use. Tolerance requirements for parts to be produced on present-day
machines are from $\frac{1}{10}$ to $\frac{1}{1000}$ of what they were in Schlessinger's time. This
imposes ever greater requirements of high quality in machine tool alignment
and capability. Again, quality control must here take a leading part in alignment procedures and proof of capability.

It is not within the intent or ability of this book to discuss this matter

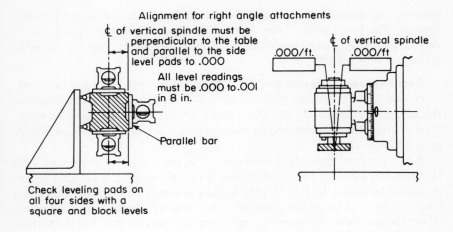

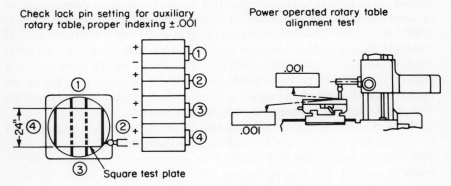

Fig. 16-6. Inspection operations for alignment on horizontal boring machines.

even in a condensed way. Just for a horizontal boring machine, one machine tool builder indicates 17 basic stages in erection alignment tests.[7] Figures 16-5 and 16-6 indicate only a few of many inspection operations for the same class of machine.

Testing of Integrated (Numerical Control) Systems

Numerical control of machine tools has developed at a phenomenal rate since the USAF research was concluded in 1950 at Massachusetts Institute of Technology. By all evidences, the use of N/C machine tools will continue to increase rapidly.

Because N/C machine tools are virtually integrated manufacturing systems, the testing of these machines becomes of vital concern to quality control. The investment is very heavy. The cost of parts scrapped due to defective operating commands can be prohibitive; fast testing and remedial action are imperative.

Test Engineer Orientation. The test engineer must know the basic machine tool and be familiar with the general functions and manipulations of the controls supplied by the N/C manufacturer. He does not, however, need to know the elements and circuitry in the "black box" whose commands he is about to test.

Since punched tape feeds information in the nature of command data to direct the machine for some specific terminal position, a suitable means is needed to assure us that it goes to that terminal point. Most numerical control units can be or are provided with "read-in" displays which indicate where the particular member is to go along a particular axis, but the display does not indicate that it arrived there. To know precisely that the member arrived at the correct address, some other form of measuring device, capable of close precision, is necessary. The device selected for read-out in the following stated case (random selection of input data) was a microline optical scale with the capability, through a vernier in the ocular, to read out terminal positions within plus or minus 0.0001 in. This device cut the measuring and recording time over previous methods nearly 80 percent. The use of the optical scale eliminated all manual settings and adjustments prior to reading and, for the first time, made only one reading possible.

Further, the microline scale had the capability of being remotely read by the test engineer through a closed-loop television system. This very desirable feature permits the test engineer to concentrate all attention at the machine control unit during testing. The monitor could be conveniently located at the machine control unit and all observed terminal points recorded rapidly.

Random Selection of Input Data. For a numerical control unit that is capable of operating to 0.0001 in., there are 10,000 potential stopping points per inch. For an axis having a 24-in. stroke, this means 240,000 discrete stopping points are possible. Assume it will take one-half minute per move to check out each command fed into the numerical control. For the 24 in.-stroke axis with 240,000 positions, checking requires in the order of 2000 man hours—an utterly impractical situation.

Using a statistical sampling plan for variables inspection, a sample size of 300 is sufficient to determine the status of the entire population of 240,000, provided these are randomly selected. Of importance to this system, therefore, was the generating of new random numbers for each machine tested.

Even though randomness is paramount, some liberties must be taken by the test engineer in preparing the test tape. In the case of this study, the choice went like this:

1. Stop at all inch points—a total of two stops from both directions.
2. Starting with the zero reference, repeat this approximately ten times during the test, and spread it throughout to get the effects of time-to-time changes.
3. Select an inch along the axis at random and explore this by 0.100-in. increments, again moving to these points in a random fashion.
4. Select another inch at random, a random 0.100-in. part thereof, and explore this by 0.010-in. increments.
5. Select another inch at random, a random 0.100-in. part and a random 0.010-in. part thereof, and explore this by 0.001-in. increments.
6. Select another inch at random, the 0.100-in. part, the 0.010-in. part, the 0.001-in. part, and explore this by 0.0001-in. increments.
7. Further checks can be made to get the variations in the feedback devices by selecting values that will cause them to stop every 90°.
8. If gears and racks are used, it may be desirable to take readings every 0.005-in. over at least two teeth to check the tooth form.

Recording the Data. Charts were provided which permitted the test engineer to plot all data at the time it was read for all the foregoing.

Analysis of Data. If a certain tolerance can be guaranteed from reference zero, it is a simple matter to draw in those boundary lines on the chart to determine acceptance or rejection of the total system performance.

By the above procedure, the machine control unit was checked for every digit of command that it was capable of issuing. With this sample of 300 size, the test engineer did not check all combinations of digital commands possible. But the results were well worth the effort, because a four-axis machine was checked out, not only for the command-position capability but for all auxiliary and manual functions as well, in a 40-hour week.

The success of such a system revolves around a well thought out procedure which should be spelled out in detail as part of the company's quality control manual. It also depends on the use of a line scale requiring no manual adjustment and from which one reading only can be obtained, the use of statistical data from variables rather than attribute tables, and the all-important *random selection* of the command data.

What the Future Holds

Since the introduction of quality control, many highly successful ideas have been developed. All of these have concentrated, by individual means and methods, on the reduction of losses to the company no matter where the source. In the future management must continue to concentrate on these losses, because even a momentary overlooking of them can bring about their reoccurrence. It also must concentrate on the development of as uncomplicated gage equipment as possible, and this equipment must be in the hands of the operator or in some way incorporated into the process to assure management that the quality of product is being maintained. Perhaps no other area is in such a favorable position as quality control, not only to *see* these needs but also to *develop* them.

The future will see a continued de-emphasis on the need for large inspection forces, as the new breed of management takes over and rightly insists on a *higher* standard of performance from both supervisors and machine operators.

The future will see greater effort made by management to give workers more responsibility for the end product, to give the worker a feeling of purpose and that all-important chance to grow.

For those products that are too large to come into the above testing category, the finished product will be transferred to newly created departments which will act as the customer in making a thorough evaluation to assure management that this product equals or exceeds the guaranteed performance. In the future too, there will be a continuous effort to improve human relations in all areas of the company as a means toward quality improvement. This is why: The mind of man continuously rejects what it does not understand, or what is in conflict with the individual's beliefs or goals.

REFERENCES

1. "Preferred Limits and Fits for Cylindrical Parts," American Standard ASA B4.1–1955, American Standards Association, New York.

2. Roth, Edward S., *Functional Gaging of Positionally Toleranced Parts*, American Society of Tool and Manufacturing Engineers, Dearborn, Michigan, 1964.

3. Kennedy, C. W., *Inspection and Gaging*, The Industrial Press, New York, 1951.

4. *Quality Assurance*, February, 1964.

5. Byrne Report,"" *Product Engineering*, June, 1957.

6. Schlessinger, George, *Accuracy in Machine Tools—How to Measure and Maintain It* (2nd ed.) Institute of Production Engrs., London, W1, England, 1941.

7. Grumman, E. V., "Metrology in Alignment of Machine Tools," paper presented at IEEE Machine Tools Industry Conference, October, 1963.

INDEX